D1178537

SONFLOWER

A Story of Love, Loss & Lyme.

ElizaBeth Moritz

Library of Congress Cataloguing-in-Publication Data
Available upon request

ISBN # 978-1-7353921-0-3

Cover and text concept and design collaborated by ElizaBeth and John Moritz.

Key words: Lyme suicide, tick borne illness, infectious disease, healthcare dilemmas, caregivers in crisis.

Dedication

Sonflower is dedicated
to those in the struggle of chronic pain
and mental health disturbance,
especially as a result of infectious disease,
and particularly as a result of tick borne illness.
You are loved. You are believed. You are not
alone. Your life matters.

Preface

This story had to be told. I suspect too many similar stories of such crisis often go untold. *Sonflower* is a tribute to my son, Zachary Moritz, and to our shared initial intention for telling this story as a team. Forever, I remain his champion. The telling of this story is also a tribute to the many lives and namesakes of tick borne trial and tribulation, both individuals and their loved ones impacted by infectious disease breakdown, crisis, and loss, instigated by the simplicity of a known or unknown random bite from the complexity of a bacterial laden tick. I champion your journey's significance and its story told.

The original premise for writing a shared accounting was the idea and agreement between mother and son of a collaborative intention. Our perspectives and experiences would be written and told from both the voice of my son Zachary, the suffering, struggling patient of Lyme and co-infection, and me, the observant and proactively involved caregiver parent and witness to all. We agreed our individual contributions and perspectives would offer valuable, insightful resource to those who are ill, to those who are loved ones of the ill, to those who treat and care for the ill, and perhaps even to those who are clueless and carefree about the tick borne chronically ill. Zach and I scoured available resources in 2014-2015, looking for personal stories of detail, especially in search of comparative specifics on psychiatric manifestation and any successful management strategies within tick borne disease long term wellness care. He needed to know if he could recover, if he would be able to live a quality life, if the recurring monsters in his head and the cycling manifestations throughout his body would ever die off or permanently quiet without his own assistance. Together, we held this project as a recovery attention and a pay it forward intention. He would aspire to rally, rise and recover from the many haunting symptoms of setback and shadow, fear and hopelessness, isolation and indifference. But that path in the roadway took a different turn. Our teamed mother and son commitment intention collapsed into a haze of grief and disillusioned direction. Grief healing consumed me, as pain and sorrow deepened.

While grief wakened and penetrated deep into the dark abyss of aching aftermath, the idea of telling this story, now my story to write and tell, lay in wait, possibly facing an end to its own short life in concept. But Zachary's farewell message, left behind for the family, referenced me as *'forever his champion'*. The three words resonated beyond an intended interpretation of our mother son relationship. His expression awakened in me an alternative authoring plan of action, and I considered an expanded perspective as to what a champion voice might message out from within our story. Telling the truth about the terror and trauma of our tragic tale felt necessary. It also felt necessary to shine a lasting light on Zachary, revealing his character and adult life bloom before infectious disease took him down. I was inspired to champion Zach but to also champion attention toward the bacterial impact including dark and disturbing psychiatric features among multiple symptoms and presentations of this illness. Overcoming the silencing weight and hush of suicide stigma, as well as my own grippingly protective stall and delay tactics subconsciously exercised throughout the years of this work, shielding myself from the anticipated exposure and vulnerability of such personal privacy invasion, I would wonder frequently and carefully, should our intimate story even risk being told? Could it be responsibly told, and even received, heard and held with tender compassion, while still delivering the daring and deliberate drama of truth in order to achieve greatest insight and significant impact for the reader? A nonfiction narrative demands truth to be told as uncompromised. Death would not be promoted or glorified in the telling of our truth, but nonetheless, truth is told as the story unfolds. Life and death co-exist within *Sonflower*. Metaphorically, life beginnings and endings are confronted throughout the chapter pages as one may grieve something that once was but no longer promises to be, or something in life never plays out as expected or intended. Life and death also collide within *Sonflower*, and the haunting question remains, could this confounded crisis have been avoided? In the telling of this story, perhaps precaution and prevention might prove the ultimate causes to champion. Without question, care advances must continue to be championed. I write in attempt to influence these priorities within.

In addition to writing a tribute homage to my son and his struggle, my intention is to also shed light on the shameless wounds afflicted toward the chronically ill, a community of sufferers so often neglected and minimized amidst their many grieved losses and shamed silent sufferings. I hope my story awakens and stirs those who remain unaffected and unaware, those who are still oblivious to the wellness seeking depth of despair for the chronically ill, especially tick borne illness infected individuals and what their families and loved ones endure. Continued research after Zach's death helped further my own deepening of personal empathy and understanding regarding the long standing history of these struggles. Record gathering from the many medical institutions and wellness seeking stopovers along our own journey helped clarify and specify what I came to understand as common occurrence of misunderstandings, misleads and even some mistakes that ultimately interfered with our loved one's diagnosis, treatment, and hoped for recovery plan. I became increasingly motivated to write, and within a year following his death, an extensive outline of memoir and advocacy narrative emerged. Choosing to tell our tick traumatizing tale, I pay thoughtful tribute to my son, our family foursome, and our enduring love in the process of revealing illness progression. The Lyme and the loss, the breakdowns and the bacteria, the conflicts and the co-infections, they are not all that represent us nor him. Zachary was and is a most beautiful being prior to and beyond his struggle and unfortunate demise. Like many in Lyme and tick borne disease struggle, he was a wandering warrior battling an unseen, unfamiliar enemy, seeking peace and prosperity until the war had its way and the soldier succumbed. I champion forever the gift that my son was and the gift that he forever is. We are a family of four, framed in our hearts forever. My story of love, loss, and Lyme is shared for your own lessons in life to champion.

As you read this book, I invite you into our very personal family reveal. It is my hope that you open yourself up to greater awareness, respect, and concern for any tick bite's bacterial infecting possibility, for the realities of insufficient current medical care pathways to effective diagnosis and treatment, and for the devastating potential toll that this disease's downplay, denial, and dismissal costs sick individuals and their caregiving families. I would also hope that you open yourself up to a greater compassion and consideration toward the challenges facing the chronically ill. After reading this book, I encourage you to ask yourself who you might know in a similar predicament, what you might do to stand up, protect and support that someone, when and where you might act and speak up with compassion, why you should especially practice and promote tick bite precaution and prevention, and then how you will personally carry *Sonflower* seeds forward. May the story of our loss enlighten you. May the love, life and lessons of our Zach's struggle inspire you to help save lives, assist in strengthening families and relationships, motivate improvement in medical practices, promote expansion of healing tools and strategies, and extend further a harvest of wellness wealth that might serve more realistic recovery hope and more promising possibility.

Thank you for your choice to journey through *Sonflower* with me. To all who are in Lyme and tick borne chronic illness battle, I see you, I hear you, I believe you, and I stand with you. You are not invisible to me. I hope this story will create visibility, establish credibility, and further necessary change.

YOU MATTER. Always.

Elizabeth Moritz

Sonflower.eim@gmail.com   November, 2020

Acknowledgements

I wish to acknowledge first and foremost my life partner, a loving loyalist, a steadfast supporter, a consistent cheerleader, a fantastic father, a helpful husband, a primary provider and a best all-around friend and companion, John Moritz. Together, we brought forth two precious beings into this world, privileged to witness their young adult bloom and to navigate a maturation of family through any number of life struggles and successes combined. We have lived, languished, laughed and loved. Together, we stood by our son and family in crisis and fought like hell. Our fabulous foursome of a family shattered itself into grief stricken remains. Together, we rebuild. Thank you for standing strong and steady amidst and beyond, for working with me to bring *Sonflower's* truth forward, for trusting in its public reveal, for encouraging and insisting in its significance, and for assisting me in most tasks related to research, creativity, composition and self-publication to provide a quality, memorable read. I am so much more with you by my side. Love you, man!

To my daughter Gabrielle, I love, admire and adore you. You expand my heart and my world. Thank you for returning to us from the shambles of such loss and pain, and investing with us in a family rebuild absent of such a dynamic physical presence, our happy go lucky, one of a kind, charismatic Zach. I honor and respect within the writing of this story, that your loss and experience is your own, defined in your own voice and shaped by your own relationship with your brother, only sibling and best friend. Your encouragement, acceptance, and perspective of my own voice and written choice are valued. Thank you.

To my dearest friends and family, of which there are many, thank you all profusely. You provided and continue to provide shelter and comfort during the unpredictable seasons and storms of our lingering sorrow and loss. Your light and love sustain me as our family rebuilds, rising up from the shadows into new and vibrant life. To my 'compass rose society' members acknowledged within, you each remain as deeply valued guides along a dark and unfamiliar trail filled with terror, trial, and trauma. To lean into your tender care and guidance when so lost and afraid, John and I are forever indebted.

Finally, to my beloved son, Zachary. I have told the story. Forever your champion, I am. Thank you for more joyful memories than sad, more laughter than tears, and for the many generous expressions of love from you in our shared lifetime. May the gift of *Sonflower* awaken questioning thought, broaden compassionate awareness, and stir responsible action. Grow the garden, harvest the crop, sow the seeds.

Contents

Part One

Action

SONFLOWER

Chapter 1: Tick Tock, Therapy Clock

Knockin' on Heaven's Door, Bob Dylan

Mercy Mercy Me, Marvin Gaye

Approaching the ten o'clock hour on Thursday, August 6, 2015, the morning therapy session had been serendipitous in its specific timing and context. The routinely scheduled time slot happened to follow a sleepless night and an early morning search for my son and for answers. She and I spoke entirely of Zach, which was not at all uncommon. Where was he? Why am I so afraid? Is he safe? This mother had been worry sipping on a crazy cocktail of uncertain circumstances for far too long, my fumbling faith and frightened fear so shaken and stirred, crafted crazy by a twist of Lyme. When the gentle, melodic harp string ringtone soothingly interrupted the elevated tension escalating within the belly of the room, clarity seemed plausible and comfort a possibility. It was a sobering thought following optimism drought. A few years' prior, the cellphone ringtone programming would have soulfully delivered a Marvin Gaye ballad, *Mercy Mercy Me.* A hauntingly melancholic sound, that tune's lyrical message and tonal resonance would have certainly been timely in our momentary moody blues. Things aren't what they used to be, and blue skies would promise what?

Glancing down to the purse on the floor next to the brown distressed leather chair, I wondered if it could be possible, in the harrowing heart of such a mystery moment, for angelic intervention to accompany that harp string halo. The smart phone ringtone was steadily ringing while blue sky possibility was barely still clinging. Surely, the ringtone would imply reassured explanation. Sadly, the phone call would impose realized expiration. Precisely at the moment of the session end, cascading strings softly serenaded. My longing eyes moved from purse to therapist to clock on the wall and back. A final flicker of faith flashed, flirting forward with optimism's half full glass in this most vulnerable of intersecting standstill. The visual voice of my body language begged for the best of outcomes; eyes wide, limbs tense, mind desperately pleading its final prayer. Here? Now. Answer? Answers. "It might be him!", I declared unconvincingly, yet subconsciously convinced. She and I had spent the 50minute session exploring the *what ifs*, which included conversation about where Zach might have been, what he might have been doing, and even what he may have already done. It seemed grace that I was in her care that day, in addition to the previous seven months, and profoundly so in that specific window of standstill time. We had invested in and worked weekly toward a deep understanding of our family crisis and the effect it was having on each family member. Working with me throughout the diagnostic and early treatment stages of my son's mysterious and then very evident illness, we had done some deep healing work together. If there was a safe place to enter into the sanctity of that phone call, it was here in her care. Here and now. Referring Eckart Tolle's book, '*The Power of Now*', early on in therapy, Donna had helped me recognize mindful truth in Tolle's message. This was something my son had tried to communicate and share with me when he was in a well mind. Everyone in our family had been working at managing our past premonitions and future fears around this awful awakening of tick borne disease, utilizing therapeutic care as one primary tool amidst a collection of explored tools to research and rationalize reason, to render a recovery. In the immediately impending freeze frame moment from this unexpected yet ever persistent phone call, we were certainly quite mindful of now.

Reaching down to take hold, I pushed an exhale up and out of my physical body, as if I needed to make space for what was to come. Our eyes locked, piercingly blue sets each, longingly holding much unspoken, yet much heard and understood. The sight of the familiar ten digits, the vocal sound so raw and vulnerable upon the push of the answering button, my husband spoke with an emotional tremble the words we hoped to not hear. I will never forget. "Oh Beth", he moaned with deep and dark presence of pain and sorrow. "He did it." Flat line, heart break, reality slap, stunned silent. The clock stopped. The appointment was finished. And so was our son. Just like that. John proceeded to gather momentary composure for the strength and clarity to speak further of the received police officer call, the message delivered of next step responsibilities, the assurance of his return home shortly from out of town. We would then fall further into each other's arms, each other's pain, each other's now. For both of us, there was deafening defeat in the weight and finality of the traumatic truth…. 'he did it'. A resoundingly dark emptiness draped my

2

soul, the room, our life. My mind raced. Bury our son? Inform our daughter! Power of now? What the fuck! Too many three word combinations paced and presented, none of which were as critical as those so vulnerably spoken next. "I love you". Our mutual goodbye in the shadow of our son's farewell terminated the call.

My crumpled body language, the tone and emotion of my voice, and the brevity of this captive moment implied what was yet unspoken to my therapist. A very clear picture flashed before us of our shared story, our shared hour, our shared seven months, and our shared journey sorting out the past two years together while in crisis. Donna and I would now forever share a sacred bond of devastating loss from the window pane perch of Zach's death, and the doorway frame curse of Zach's disease. What about the previous twenty-five amazing years of this beautiful blooming being and our former family life so rich and full with laughter, love, and light? Are they to be lost forever in the dark stain of this day? I sank down into the chair I had been sitting in for almost an hour every week for 35 weeks straight, and passed the lifeless baton to my therapeutic teammate in the run out of time relay of our here and now moment revealed. Utterly powerless, I was.

"He did it", I repeated, in a flat and listless tone, three more words so sadly spoken. Together, she and I full faced this fatal finish line. We had discussed the possibility. Two words came forth with contemptuous fury and force, in the exhaustive finale of this day's appointment, then dramatic disappointment. Fuck Lyme. FUCK LYME! There I sat, in the gentle, calming space of a skilled and nurturing professional, surrounded by images, colors, books, plants, and various cultural and spiritual artifacts, all intended to heal and promote healing. I repeated the unfathomable message of the morning, followed by the fathomable fucks in the moment. Help and healing were not in the cards that day. Recovery would shift now in altered direction and definition. Ongoing therapy would be necessary. No longer would Zach power be present. There would be no Zach past to heal, with no Zach future to hold. For the family foursome, wellness and wholeness greeted death instead. For the family threesome, wellness and wholeness needed life ahead. Grief would begin in the grind of the mind, the sorrow to tomorrow, and the toll on our soul, beginning right here, right now. Mercy, mercy me.

Part Two

Adolescence

Chapter 2: Hoop Dreams

Empire State Human, Human League

Move on Up, Curtis Mayfield

Often a young person or an adult who stands tall well above the average height of man or woman inevitably gets asked if they play basketball. This was a truth throughout my son Zachary's adolescent and young adult life, as his ever increasing height became a marker of identification and recognition for him. An intriguing thought to contemplate about that basketball question is just what the inquiry and its response might imply to the recipient. How does one receive that question, over and over and over again, which is commonly what occurs to the extraordinarily tall person? After all, it is likely a simple conversation starter, an acknowledgement of what meets the eye, a social gesture without hurt intention. Does the question unintentionally become a perceived measurement or justification of one's personal value or self-worth in the heart of that very tall individual? What if the individual's answer is no, does that somehow suggest a sense of 'less than' with regard to one's identity? Does an answer of no imply that this individual may have been a poor steward of this physical attribute they happened to be born with, or could it suggest a shortcoming physically or emotionally, like perhaps a lack of coordination or competitive orientation? The message/inquiry is delivered as stereotype and associative transference, and many of us have uttered the words with an innocent intention. On the receiving end, some may welcome the association, and others may dread it. Many can lay claim to some version of this truth through a physical attribute of some sort, observed and assessed in the public eye, positively or negatively, thus affecting one's soul shaping self. The height thing, it definitely shaped the soul of Zach. It heightened all.

Our son Zach wearied of hearing the question so often in early adolescence, seemingly defining him without the where withal or maturity yet to more fully define himself. At 14, he was a willowy 6'5", drawn to the possibility of becoming a football tight end contender rather than a soaring hoop loving defender. He was developing athleticism, but confidence he lacked. Thus, he resented the hoops association to his height for a long time in its narrow scope of defining personal value. Eventually, within a matter of years, he shifted from resentment to representation, and ultimately, he embraced the question as a social icebreaker, and a way of life for a 6'10" frame. How tall ARE you? Do YOU play basketball? The basketball question is likely just a conversation starter or an observational thought spoken out loud, but it can be a confusing message to a young person in the developmental stages of identity and self-consciousness. If the answer happens to be yes, the association to being a basketball player might then override any other significant character trait or identity development, not only in the eye of the public, but also in the heart of the individual. This is hardly a deeply traumatic childhood setback, but definitely a shape shifter to a soul searching for self. Zach was conflicted around the size marker, the height measure, the attention getter, and eventually he crafted a response to greet it with power and grace. Even though Zachary Moritz, by the age of 15 and at the height of 6' 8", finally felt he could answer the basketball question with a yes, he still resented the varied stereotypes around this athlete association that followed him his entire life. For Zach, and anyone of extreme height, there is no hiding from the glare and the inquiries around your size and eventually even the basketball association. Height is something very valued in our culture, as is sport, and yet, ask any above average sized individual, and they will share the challenges that accompany the glory. Comfort, oblivion, and fit come to mind.

Not only was our Zach a physically oversized child, teen, and adult, but as a young lad he was oversized with energy. He had a 'happy go lucky' charisma, made friends easily, and bubbled with affection and curiosity. As early as 3, he was jumping off the diving board in swim lessons. By the time he was 4 years of age, he was racing around the neighborhood cul de sac on his Viper bicycle, training wheels off and confidence high. Exuberant was the adjective his kindergarten teacher used to describe him, and she did not use it adoringly. She was annoyed and agitated by his busy nature, and big size. His physicality and adventurous spirit seemed to challenge many of his teachers, called attention to him in any group setting, and created spatial awkwardness in the small cubicles, desks, chairs, piles of overcoats and shoes cluttered along the doorway entries and exits of elementary year classrooms. This little big boy employed his oversized physicality by presenting with humor and energy that belied his tender emotional soul.

Like many youngsters, young adolescents, even young men who possess a high emotional quotient, the impact and influence of this trait can be buried under an outward display that creates a false and misleading impression. Zach had a sensitive soul and yet projected an aloof, carefree spirit from preschool days, throughout his middle school years, and even beyond. Within our family, Zachary was playfully loving and joyful with all of us, while especially tender, caring, and attentive toward his little sister. He was often eager to go and do. He made friends easily, as he emanated a certain magnetism early on that was as consistent throughout his life as was the larger than peer group measurement of size. An adventurous spirit, with a curious and sometimes risk taking edge, this young man needed an eye kept on him for safety and guidance. His size shadowed everything, and as much as many coveted this feature as he was older, it held an increasing truth that became something to recognize, manage and respect with every passing year. There would be no hiding place, no blending in, no makeup or clothing to cover up the reality of his oversized dimensions.

As Zach learned to embrace the physical attributes of his being, eventually, and ironically, success in sports, especially basketball, helped him to do so. Something happened that shifted his angst. It was not the egotistical notoriety that sport might offer, but rather the soul satisfaction of a found sense of belonging. In sport, especially in basketball as a young man, he found a community with which to belong and identify comfortably. He experienced acceptance and worth, and he deeply loved what he referred to as brotherhood. Later in years, belonging and brotherhood would be among life treasures he most valued, longed for, and sought after, until a time of crisis, when he could no longer embrace them as possibility. One of Zach's coping strategies to reduce the angst he often felt from the constant visual reactions to his size was to craft a redirect of the almost daily height question he knew to be followed shortly by the basketball question. He would engage people in a 'guess my height' game, almost always finding entertainment from the often outrageous guesses. At 16, he was 6'10", and doorways now became an exercise of twisting the neck to the side, ducking the head below the frame, and gliding the rest of the body on into the next space. It was hard for people to not take notice. "How tall are you?", strangers would feel compelled to ask, the words moving slowly out of their mouths accompanied by a look of amazement and an expression of awe oozing from their face. He would joke with us that maybe he should just wear a sign, so that he could carry

7

on with his life, avoid the routine, attempt to feel normal and less like a freak. When the question came, Zach had begun to anticipate the basketball follow up, so he would divert it by responding, "How tall do you think I am?". He reframed the exchange and created a ping pong rally of conversational banter as folks would offer up a guess and he would bounce back with a playful response. Ultimately, a point would be made by one or the other, if not both, and each would end up on the scoreboard. Game on. This became an intentional effort to expand someone's experience of him beyond the surface. He would challenge people playfully to perhaps even recognize the invasive and stereotypical (basketball question) nature of the moment. And he would resolve the angst that would previously stir in him around judgement, measure, assumption, competitive comparison. Zach wanted to be known for more than his external size or his athletic skill. Hoops did enter his world, however, and conquered his heart by the age of 15. There would be no avoidance of the question. Basketball became a defining direction and a doorway to new adventures. He would embrace the game, and the game would embrace him in return.

Early on during Zach's involvement with sports, and specifically basketball, he did not display any advanced skill set or overzealous dedication that would match the advancing pace of his growth. The 'happy go lucky' label and behavior continued to be projected through middle school. In his high school years, the growth spurts exploded, his coordination developed, and a new found confidence awakened. He joined an AAU program, an Amateur Athletic Union league team, known to be a development and exposure route for aspiring collegiate athletes. The sport, the game, the basketball question......all inspired in Zach a greater motivation toward the college pathway, despite at least one teacher assuring him he was not college material. Too silly, too distracted, too mischievous, too misdirected. Right? Wrong! It was an ironic message delivered to an intelligent young man not inspired by the traditional K-12 education system. He was a student who got by. And certainly, he delved into extra curricula beyond the academic and athletic, unbeknownst to his folks just how much at the time. High school highs, and weekend wiles. His wit and motivations were antagonistic to an underdeveloped academic intelligence and an ever stimulated emotional quotient attempting to hide its vulnerability. Meanwhile, the game and his developing skills and height shifted his focus and now framed his local claim to fame! College was on the mind. He focused with discipline on training, workouts, AAU competition, travel, and practices balanced amidst the traditional high school academic, athletic, and social demands and temptations. By end of sophomore year, recruiting letters arrived and conversations were begun about the hoop dream of playing collegiate basketball. What a privilege. Ask the question!

Zach thrived at this time of his life, as skill caught up to height, and doors opened while dreams took shape. Those of us as family members basked in the fullness of our young man's bloom, celebrating with gratitude, humility, and certainly pride, the idea that he could attend college on scholarship while playing the game he had developed a deep and passionate love for. We believed him capable of college work, and now he had the motivation to secure his requirements and pursue these emerging dreams. Recruitment. It becomes quite an ego check for the athlete and the family, to manage gratitude, humility, and practicality while being courted and wooed by several coaches and school programs to join their university family for the next 4 to 5 years as a student athlete. The recruiting process somewhat overwhelmed Zach, and equally overwhelmed us as parents. There were no peers in our immediate circle at that time who had navigated this path with experience and wisdom to share. It was new territory for him, for his family, for his coach, and for his broader community of support. It had been 30 years since both parents participated in collegiate athletics, and neither engaged in recruitment. His AAU community had experience and wisdom to draw from, but for reasons unclear to us, guidance and support for Zach's journey to collegiate basketball was not part of our particular paid for program experience. And certainly, we were inexperienced and ill-informed as to how to seek assistance from them, or even if we should. Regardless of these gaps, the developing hoop dreams were moving beyond hope, hard work, and aspiration. There were choices, and a decision would need to be made. The formerly dreaded question, 'Do YOU play basketball?', would now be the more specific question, 'WHERE do you play basketball?'

Our son chose a midsized, mildly successful Division I collegiate program and made a 5year commitment to his education and the opportunity to play basketball at the next level. There was a belief among coaches of an expected upside to his game and development, and he had achieved recognition as one of the top ten high school posts in the West in a year when the Lopez twins and Spencer Hawes, each future NBA talents, were in the mix. He chose a program located far enough from home to create space, but close enough for access and support. His coach of choice, who he seemed to feel welcomed by as 'Big Z', the desired recruit, but also as the responsible and nurturing young man, was someone Zach felt he could trust. We witnessed this perceived connection in our living room at the dining table when the coach suggested, "You might even babysit my sons!", upon learning that Zach had previously babysat a family of three boys. There was a family feel to the proposed relationship and for Zach, a sense of acceptance as a responsible and caring human being and not just another player pawn. Roll the dice. Was Coach a salesman throwing a pitch, or was he truly the man he represented himself as to Zach? The dice gets rolled, the numbers are revealed, and the game goes on regardless of your gamble. His school of choice had a football program with tremendous success and community support, and to Zach, this seemed indicative of what the basketball program could draw from. The athletic facilities, the campus, and the teammates' welcome further convinced Big Z to sign on. Go Broncos.

In the match up and fit of a collegiate program and its athlete recruits, there is a significant vulnerability factor to the commitment made. The dream can be lived out in 4-5 years of technicolor bliss, or the dream can become a nightmare quickly. There is plenty of range in between on the scheme of the dream! Neither aforementioned extreme would be the definition of Zach's journey, but there were definite unexpected wake ups and a fair share of rude awakenings to disrupt this orange and blue colored dream sequence. As a student athlete, there are privileges, opportunities, resources, and unique experiences beyond the typical college career. There are also injuries, playing time issues, academic imbalances and irregularities due to travel and competition schedules, social distractions, public engagements, and ego checks to name a few. All high school recruits are not college superstars, and yet most college recruits are typically high school superstars. Everyone's ego must be kept in check. All college coaches and programs are not as trustworthy and forthright as they might present themselves in your living room, and often the athletic and university priorities and decisions are not transparent to the athletes or their families. To be fair, coaches cannot predict accurately the outcome of their recruiting balance, injuries sustained by players, or player and position development, let alone personality conflicts. Despite having felt that he made a solid choice for himself in pursuit of the hoops dream, Zach had an unsatisfying match up and he worked hard to overcome even the elements of the story he did not understand or have control over. A student athlete on campus carries much expectation, demand, and balance of time and work, thought to be solid preparation for life after. One enters into the assignment with optimism, enthusiasm, and eager anticipation, not unlike a new job or career. Ideally, one endures as the journey unfolds and the flight path is navigated, avoiding any added negative weight on the mental health baggage scale for an additional cost of the journey. Zach endured injuries, setbacks, disappointments, coaching and teammate changes not unlike what perhaps most athletes experience. He also celebrated highlight moments, physical and emotional maturity, community engagement, social skill development, and the continued discipline and work ethic refinement that would serve him throughout his life.

Perhaps the more impactful challenges for Zach in these hoop years were the constant stirrings of emotional sensitivity and depth of feeling he held around perceived relationships, communication contradictions, and a growing awareness of athletes placating the resulting emotional and mental vulnerabilities from sport through various unhealthy and destructive pathways. He himself would cycle between participating in the use of recreational drugs and alcohol to soothe physical and emotional pain, followed by a choice to abstain from those impulses, exercising an intention toward yoga, cycling, art, music or movies as tools for alternative healing and distraction. We knew of the rampant abuse and use of alcohol, drugs, and sex by athletes on college campuses. He believed better alternatives could be presented to athletes than this self-destructive model. Within his own athletic community, he witnessed and experienced firsthand the physical, mental, and emotional torment that he felt could be better supported in a program through a deeper toolbox of repair. It intrigued him over the course of his 5 years how prevalent unhealthy abuses were, and how absent healthier alternatives were within the athletic system of support. This would resonate with him for a long time. Our son was no innocent when it came to occasional recreational drug use and alcohol excess, he would admit to us in the struggle and balance of choosing healthier and more effective alternatives to pain management. He also understood this to be a problem beyond just the athletes on campus, but the athletic community on campus was his tribe within the university village. The medicines available and accessible to the tribesmen called teammates were not actually healing the wounds of battle, just presumably soothing the pain.

As concerned parents, especially in times of injury setback, or simply seasonal cycles of deep dissatisfaction, we wondered if a therapist or counselor would be made available to athletes. Most coaches are not qualified, skilled or trained to assist these unpaid ambassadors of the university in emotional and mental therapeutic care. During a particularly low point in a second and then third unsatisfying season and player role, we spoke of exploring depression and the option to pursue support. We encouraged Zach to reach out to his coaches, people we assumed were mentors of these men beyond their coach player role. It seemed challenging to coordinate as parents from long distance a mental health provider on campus whom he could coordinate with around the demands of athletic travel, competition and practice, as well as academic rigor and routine. We would have stepped in to coordinate, but felt it best for him to do so, and he agreed. Perhaps the coaches could help. It seemed a logical starting point, that should feel safe and be respected. He chose to go to the head coach, which proved to be a mistake, but he then sought counsel in a trusted professor and a trusted assistant coach. While neither were trained in mental health care, he found listening, empathic, compassionate adults, and their support helped him tremendously. Post season bike rides along the river trail didn't hurt either. These influential years and impressionable experiences were conflicting, for he loved the sport and the brotherhood as he called it, and yet he resented the mind fucks, the misleads, and the mental swings participation at an organized level all too often generated.

Welcome to the privilege of being called "the full ride", and what a ride it is! Zachary thrived, he performed, he contributed, and he succeeded. He also struggled, he failed, he recovered, he overcame, and he completed. He ultimately blossomed as an athlete and became a very introspective and ever more so compassionate human being. He made friends easily within and without the athletic circle, and he developed a personal expression of creativity and artistry in the classroom and beyond. Writing poetry, designing tattoos, scripting future journalistic pieces, practicing yoga, attending art film, seeking and listening to all genres of musical expression, growing his hair long, short, and anywhere in between, Zachary Moritz, the basketball player, was discovering Zachary Moritz, the emerging man. With deliberation and great personal pride, he ambled up to the stage podium on that afternoon of May 2011, having personally earned his college degree and eager to claim his freedom plea. Zach stood tall as the basketball player, the budding humanitarian, the intellectual and creative artist he had become. Long hair swaying, holding dreams of still playing, he owned every day, week, and month of those five years. Going forth with a Communications degree in hand and a Journalism major to explore, he believed his basketball days were far from over. He was determined to play overseas, to travel the world, and to find a more peaceful pathway to his future. Now that the freedom of choice was back in his court, he would form a new hoops dream, and a new hoops vision. He loved this game, he loved his teammates, and he loved leaving this chapter.

Zachary Moritz
Creative writing
6/15/06

Don't stare at the tall people

Don't stare at the tall people, we don't appreciate it. Usually when I go to the store or even when I walk the halls at school I feel a thousand little eyes piercing my skin. Especially when a short person walks by, they have to move their neck up and stare. I used to think that people stared because I was ridiculously good looking. I just figured that all of those people staring at me were just undressing me with their eyes, However I now no that they are not. I hear them when they speak beneath their breath, "Wow that kid is tall".

Once again I'll say that you shouldn't stare at the tall people. Adults at least keep the little comments to themselves and they only stare for about 3 seconds. They at least have a little respect. Kids on the other hand, dear god they stare, point, jump, shout, and sometimes puke. It's great, sometimes they will stare so hard that they will start to back up and they will knock something over and make a scene. Walking in the mall is sometimes amusing also, people who usually would be tall (lets say about 6'5 or 6'6) get a sense of shock when I'll walk past them. Just last weekend a young lady named Brienne and I went to the mall and we counted a total of 21 people just in the Mervyns store that stared in awe.

The number one spot in the world where people stare at me is the airport. When ever I travel with any basketball team whether it would be rivers basketball team or ICP team we get stared at a lot. The airport is the number one area because people are just passing by and they usually stare and just keep on walking, I usually stare back. Well in ending my "I believe" paper I would just like to say don't stare at the tall people.

Insert 1 •   2006 June high school poem "Don't Stare at the Tall People"

14

Dear Mom + Dad,

As I am writing this Note to you two the first thing I want to do is tell you both that I love you. I love you both so much and I can't thank you enough for always supporting me in all of my different life experiances. I want to sincerly thank you both for getting me intrested in this sport that I have fallen in love with. Without the both of you to push me and convince me to shoot the ball I doubt I would have even taken to basketball. I also want you both to Know how much I notice and how grateful I am to have two parents who love me, care for me, and respect me the way you two do...

Dad – I want to thank you first for always pushing me and for always being there when I was down. All of your texts and voicemails show me just how much you care and love me.

Mom – I want to thank you for all of your post game hugs and all of the time and enery you have put into my athletics over the past years. From your numerous volenteer hours to your awesome scrapbooks. And even though I am not always up to talk after tuff losses or what not I can always count on you to cheer me up.

THANK YOU! LOVE, ZAZK

Insert 2 •   2006 High school graduation note to parents

Insert 3 • **2007 BSU basketball**

Insert 4 •   2008 Family holiday card

Insert 5 •   2007 Modest Mouse tattooed lyric

The Buff Mob by Zachary Moritz

Fickle, fleeing, fair weather faces
Witty, cheering, collective races
Screaming their statements with conviction
Demonstrating their distinctive diction
Bringing with them their best howl
Arguing adamantly every foul
This vicarious vice
Marketed to entice
Why can't people prioritize?
Why don't they wake up and realize?
Seats full with pairs of brainless eyes
Every loss leads to demise
Should I be truthful or tell more lies?
Would it pain them to sympathize?
Super human, super sized
Sitting in my mesh disguise
An expendable animal
An enigmatic individual
My genuine charisma is given
Faux fans forgiven
Win or tie
Get looked in the eye
Lose or quit
Treated like shit
Becoming bitter from too many quips
Blood, sweat and tears continue to drip
Opinions will always abound
I'll buy the next round
I'm fed up with this town
Try not to get down
Yet my face stays frowned
The buff-mob's unsound

Insert 6 •   2009 'The Buff Mob' poem

Happy Belated Birthday!

Sorry about the delay, I have no real excuse so I won't try to sell you on one. But Congrats on another year! I doubt your boobs hang low yet although my hope is you'll live long enough and they'll attain man-boob status. I Enjoyed our time at home together and even without backpacking our pong, cycling, and golf moments were grand. I know that this season you and mom will appreciate watching me thrive and fully enjoy the game of basketball again. I wouldn't of stuck it out without your encouragement and guidance. And I know you know that, so thank you Dad. Goodluck with Gabbys departure — I think it will benefit you all more so than it will pain you. I look forward to reflecting on this weird transitional year with you all over cocktails, sand, and sun in Hawaii. Do your boobs hang low?

Much love
— Zach

Insert 7 •   2010 Father's birthday message

Insert 8 •   **2011 BSU basketball**

Insert 9 • **2011 Mother's Day message**

Insert 10 •   2011 College graduation with parents at BSU

Chapter 3: ADHD

ADHD, Truslow
Teach Your Children Well, Crosby, Stills, Nash & Young

When Zach returned home in 2011, to his community of childhood and adolescent upbringing after living in a college environment for five years, it was a welcome reunion but also new territory for each of us to acclimate. The family dynamic had shifted when the foursome of mom, dad, sister and brother separated in 2006 following his high school graduation. Attention and focus in the home transitioned that year of 2006 to his sister's high school activities and the pursuit of post-secondary goals for our second child and only daughter. Weekend poker games and the high school hoops, highlights, headaches, and occasional high jinx, departed that year just as he did when college beckoned. Our household energies shifted more fully to best friend sleepovers, kitchen cooking and baking adventures, and female team parties with our daughter. Her social life and interests were smaller and more specific, while her drive and discipline in the classroom and on the volleyball court created a refreshingly broadening experience for us. When she graduated from high school in June of 2010, and moved to Seattle for college that fall, Zachary was finishing his fifth year, his senior year at college. This was the one year of both children attending college away from home. Exhale. We finally did.

John and I found ourselves witnessing amongst friends and associates not yet in this stage of parent life, about the newfound freedom and quiet of so called 'empty nesting'. It was more aptly experienced as 'parent resting'. We had arrived at this rest stop on the parenting journey, taken the exit ramp, and refreshed ourselves before continuing on down the never ending road of parental progression. Suddenly, weekly calendars opened up to time and choice, a welcome refreshment in this intermission break. Empty would not be any expectation long term for our life, family, or nest. For the anticipated fullness of future family life for us was a parental highway in route to all kinds of yet to be lived

24

out destination expectations, both individually and collectively as family members. Presumptive, it was. Health, safety, and belonging could be the names of the metaphoric towns we expected to continue to meander through on that 'life well lived' highway. John and I based this belief upon the lived thus far internal GPS guidance which we instinctively trusted and followed. We were as best we could, and as best we knew how, driving the highway of life under the influence of faith, hope and love, trusting in our direction and dreams, fueling ourselves with constant self-discovery.

There were detours and storms to weather on the parenting path, and certainly amidst the independence seeking wrath, but drive on we all would. We would meander from one exit ramp collegiate seasonal break to another, continuing to visit with and support each child within their university calendar, expecting to do the same throughout their post collegiate days. Given that there were fewer meals to cook, fewer events to attend, less cars, clothes, and characters to manage at home base in this particular life season, it had been a momentary household pause to reflect and refuel. John and I were grateful for the respite. We felt we had survived quite well raising up responsible, loving children, surviving adolescence, preparing them for independence, and giving them a solid foundation from which to launch. Privileged, it was, and certainly, we were. Naively, though, we felt certain that the hardest part of parenting was behind us. With open arms in the immediate window following college graduation, we embraced Zach's layover, as his post college rest stop and his fuel station for the road ahead. The window of time following college graduation that we shared with him was priceless, even in the head to head moments of young adult emergence for him, and adult mid-life submergence for us. He was eagerly planning and working to pursue his goal of playing overseas, and we were immersed still in the realities of paying for private education, tending to neglected home improvements, and holding a flame to the hoped for life we assumed would follow us. Each family member was more fully awakening to each other and to our personal selves, as we moved into and beyond the empty nest. Lessons were given and lessons were taken; each of us were teachers, and each of us students, engagingly enrolled in the university of life. Discovering and sharing old and current musical artists, expressing perspectives on religion and politics, sharing conversations about racial and gender experiences with outrage around a variety of social injustices, engaging in and exploring the arts, film, and any form of creative expression......these exchanges increased once Zach was in college and further deepened as both children developed independent thought and found their voice of expression. Our shared time was ripe thus rich with new challenges and occasional confrontations of disagreement or misunderstanding when thoughts, beliefs, and differences surfaced. Loyal love remained at the foundation of these exchanges, and thus the undercurrent of the family river seemed a healthy but sometimes turbulent eco system.

To the children becoming young adults, it was difficult and often challenging to address their shifting responsibilities and expectations around work schedules, financial management, household rules, health care protocols, and shared spaces. To the adults in the family, it was confusing and often uncharted waters, navigating the tumultuous transitions of our children through the rushing onset of their adulthood ocean tides of change. The tides would come in, and the tides would go out, for each of us. We would find agreement, and we would find disagreement. And so the tidal flow of family fold would often go. This 2011 spring/summer reunion at a significant time of transition in our son's life allowed us the opportunity to assist him in his initial launch beyond college graduation, but also to engage in some emotional healing from a subpar collegiate athletic experience. Out from under some dysfunction and psychological bullshit within an NCAA program and leadership team obliviously disrespectful to the toll on their token athletes, Zach was soon able to navigate his own ship and seek his own definition of treasure. There would be no college scholarship or education at risk now with which to be measured. The price had been paid, and the puppet parade and catering charade ended. Relationships that once mattered, mattered still. Wounds that once shattered, were still accessible at will. The horizon held new beginnings. Time appeared to now be on our side. For Zach had only been home for short spells of time during those collegiate years, a common feature of college athletic life, as it is for many who leave town to attend college. He would work camps and train most of the summer at the university. Basketball happens to be a sport that consumes the entire winter holiday season, as competition usually begins by early November and can last through mid-March. During his five years away, we would strive to create pockets of time for family together.

John and I were committed as supportive parents to giving and guiding, building and providing, mostly within our means and sometimes around the edge of those financial seams. There were occasions of overspending and unraveling, for travel, supplies, programs, or deadlines, but overall the family managed to work, love and play fairly well together. As Gabrielle and Zach found their way into early adulthood, the siblings developed a bond of mutual admiration, and a safe haven in each other for shared thoughts and feelings. The gift of these days and this season of time would be forever treasured. Among many occasions that summer of 2011, there were moments of 'getting to know you more as an adult son active in our life' type conversations with Zach. One in particular dominated shared thought and conversation. There was an emotional urgency in the offering. Our son introduced us to a book, a four letter name, and a confrontational diagnostic assertion followed by a serious suggestion that both parents give consideration for similar diagnosis! *Delivered from Distraction* by Edward Hallowell and John Ratey was the book, ADHD was the name, and Zach's announcement that he believed he should have been diagnosed with this particular disorder long ago was the claim. He readily expressed anger, frustration, and disappointment that he was bringing this conversation forward to us in the here and now rather than our own discovery and acknowledgement of such diagnosis during his childhood. Or better yet, he questioned, why hadn't teachers who ridiculed him or labeled him as underachieving along the educational pathway assisted him with diagnosis evaluation instead? He was genuinely upset the more he spoke, challenging the disappointing educational frustration narrative of his youthful past. It had been in a university psychology class that he learned of Attention Deficit Hyperactivity Disorder, so moved by the idea that this distractibility disorder might be his own truth that he left class early quite emotionally distraught. For him, the information felt revelatory and liberating, the idea that he was not lazy or stupid or any number of labels teachers or perhaps even coaches may have referred to him when he appeared to be underperforming, misunderstanding or simply not quite measuring up. His brain ordered differently. WOW! Your 22 years of age, behemoth of a man child opens himself up and lays his vulnerability and perceived reflection on the living room floor, daring you to pick it all up, hold it close, embrace it, and then even answer to it. John, Zach and I cannot help but feel a vast array of sadness, confusion, hurt, as well as a hunger for understanding and exchange. I begin to respond.

"Zachary, when you were in kindergarten as a 5year old, and you along with a few other boys and girls were perceived by your teacher to be busy bodies, she made a suggestion to us that you be evaluated for something called attention deficit," I began to share with him. "She even suggested your busyness could be fetal alcohol related which I found interestingly insulting given that alcohol was not consumed during pregnancy. Given that you were our first born, and we were parents who entered into the educational arena naively trusting in the teacher's expertise at that time, we immediately chose to meet with the school psychologist. He observed you and asked us specific questions regarding assessment of symptoms for ADHD." I continued my admission to this mission. "His outcome and our agreement was that you may be borderline but that you just did not meet enough of the measurable symptoms. He found you to be busy and squirrelly but able to focus for periods of time beyond a typical diagnosis. He did not see you as hyperactive but possibly distracted easily, and he believed your size to be a more frequent observable trait that called attention to you more readily." John and I had agreed with this school professional, and we based this upon not only this man's feedback, who happened to stand 6'6" tall and shared his own stories of being ostracized for size growing up, but also the research we sought to further understand. "Zach, we even asked the professionals if we should hold you back a year for maturity sake since you were a summer birthday and among the youngest in the class," we revealed further to our wounded one, certain we had shared this with him prior to this living room moment. "Definitely no", was the response of the psychologist. His belief was that height would cause that much more of an issue, as Zach was already significantly larger than his peers. Although the traditional education system held challenges for Zach along his K-12 path, we never had clear guidance or qualified evidence to suggest we should be treating our son for a distraction disorder, let alone hyperactivity. Unfortunately, many students and families were stigmatized around this newly named disorder in the early 90's, accurate or not, and our experience included educators who were eagerly suggesting medication without proper knowledge or qualification of necessity. Drug them, please, was the message many of us heard loud and clear.

Ironically, Dr. Hallowell's first book on this subject was printed in 1995, and I had purchased it that year with an eye for not only better assessing my son, but for holding conversation with other parents who were facing this concern. *Driven to Distraction* was the book title, and often I would devour it as a guiding resource. To learn of this author's newly published book was intriguing, but more importantly, I was struck more so on how deeply this conversation affected my son. It was painful to feel so out of touch with struggles that Zach carried within and beyond the years he resided in this home. Perhaps we missed something years ago, or perhaps there is better information on accurate diagnostics and helpful treatment strategies today that we were unaware of or mislead around. Perfect parenting.... what does that even look like? Parenting is hard, and certainly not perfect. We would listen, learn and love. But what about the claim that Mom and Dad may want to be screened! Could we hear this suggestion, listen and receive it, and even act on it as a gesture of respect and love to our son and ourselves? We had often joked about various traits we each had that could qualify us for a diagnosis of some disorder, but then we also were successfully functioning adults with many strengths and adaptations. I knew I was a daydreamer, and could wander in distraction influenced by colors, shapes, noises, words, expressions and any number of details the average person would not even notice or value as important or distracting in the full intake of any moment, conversation, or surrounding. I rather liked this about myself! John knew he would procrastinate or struggle with completion of tasks because he would often take on so many things at once and held the capacity to do so. He understood that organization was a challenge to him from a tidy physical space perspective but not from the perspective of his amazingly sharp and detailed mind. How does one legitimately qualify a diagnosis?

Hallowell says it himself in his follow up book, *Delivered from Distraction,* which Zach referred. He states, "*the diagnosis of ADHD is based not upon the presence of listed symptoms, which most people have now and then, but upon the intensity and duration*". The three of us took the survey questionnaire referred to in the book and found the results enlightening. At this point, John and I agreed, we would support our son's concerns and encourage him to see a psychologist of his choice for a more thorough assessment. If this has truly been a setback for him, it is important to set free any chains of limitation and thus move forward in life with a liberatingly fresh outlook and perspective. The experience of this confrontation and the resulting conversations revealed to us one more example of Zach's continued awakening to a developing sense of self, and his increasing ability to examine a variety of tools and resources for use in life. He seemed to more effectively embrace and confront personal challenges discovered through deep self-examination and growth opportunities. As we witnessed his maturation, we could also reconsider ourselves as students of such self-mastery. When our children begin to hold mirrors up to us, we are wise to not immediately look away and deny, but carefully reflect on possible truths that within may lie. Reading the book that he recommended enlightened us to a different way of looking at ADHD symptoms and traits. Hallowell calls it misleading to refer to a trait or a way of being in the world as a disorder. If the trait impairs their life in some way, he says, it is then considered a disorder and the pathology tends to predominantly be negative in orientation. How sad that in diagnosing something it has to be referred to as disordered. I cannot help but wonder if shame attaches to the label. The author also lists common gifts of those easily distracted to include originality, creativity, charisma, unusual sense of humor, and areas of intellectual brilliance, all of which are uplifting messages offered within his well-researched body of work. One can attach more positive and encouraging associations with these common ADHD traits, and perhaps struggle with or suffer less stigma. Are we disordered if diagnosed ADHD, or do we simply order differently? Well done, Hallowell and Ratey. Well done, Zach.

Our son scheduled an appointment with a local professional, shared his story, and walked out with a prescription of Adderall to use responsibly and to assess whether it would help him focus and stay on task. In addition, the doctor dispensed some advice for him about various life adaptations in trait management of this 'disorder'. It almost seemed as if the conversation itself and then meeting with a professional was cathartic enough to calm his angst and fears about whether he was or he wasn't. He had already done extensive reading and research on this topic and other topics relevant to self-awareness, which we had been learning was an unquenchable hunger he returned home from college with that we seldom witnessed in his high school days. He was eager to better himself, and to do so, he had to fully know and understand himself so as to more responsibly seek strategies toward improvement. In choosing to improve upon his life, he would adopt a mantra messaged in a favored lyric of Modest Mouse, "*Work a little harder, work another way.*" That mantra became his first tattoo in early college years, the first of several that would inspire him and offer an alternative form of creative self-expression.

Zach's summer of 2011 included travel to Maui for a family vacation in celebration of his graduation, training and competition with an International Basketball League franchise in town called the Vancouver Volcanoes, travel to Las Vegas and New Hampshire to participate in tryouts for agent affiliation and international league placement, and additional travel with the Volcanoes to Japan for competition and league relationship development. ADHD or not, there would be tremendous focus exercised. One might observe that Zach's life beyond college had opened up to exciting new direction and expanded possibilities. Interestingly enough, the Adderall seemed to not significantly impact a lasting change for Zach. This proved fortunate for it was not an allowable substance for athletes participating in the Japan trip. He continued to explore and apply different strategies of self-help for himself, shifting further toward a maturing personal awareness and acceptance, fueling a renewed confidence previously so challenged amidst the collage of collegiate athletic mind games. Amidst training, travelling for tryouts and competitions, and working miscellaneous landscaping jobs, Zach would continue to consume himself with pleasurable pastimes of music, books, drawing, and writing. When his father's birthday arrived in September 2011, he shared his wordplay of poetic prose.

Insert 11 •   2010 Idaho summer on the dock

Insert 12 •   2011 Vancouver Volcano IBL summer season

SONFLOWER

...FROM YOUR SMART-ASS KID!

Happy Dad Day!

Thanks for letting me back into your home and for continuing to back my dreams. I'll do my best to keep you proud. College was weird but our relationship seemed to progress. I look forward to young manhood and whatever wisdom you still have to offer me. As always, I can't and don't thank you enough, so thanks! Here's to Hawaii blowing Mexico away, Happy Father's Day.

Love, Zach

Insert 13 • 2011 Father's Day and birthday message with ADHD poem

34

ADHD@23

Attention deficit hyperactive disorder

Accepting design hunt discovery

Acknowledge dividing hampering defects

Aesthetics determine heartfelt desire

Authority deaf humorously defiant

Aggressive demanding hysteric derelicts

Abstracting details hinge detraction

Appropriate delusions halt development

Animosities detour human direction

Anxious depressions hatefully damage

Academic dyslexia heaps discouragement

Atypical decisions haunt dignity

Avoiding deities hath damned

Agnostic David Hume's determinism

Analytical dichotomies host doubt

Advanced depth heightens daring

Athletically deft handle dexterously

Assertive dreamers hope driven

Alcoholic drunk hungover days

Abashed distraught heavily dope

Accomplish deeds hoist drinks

Appreciative digest habitual drugs

Artist's destinies host dysfunction

Chapter 4: Z in Zamora

Spanish Caravan, The Doors
Alive and Well, Big Little Lions

As exciting as the two week August 2011 Japan tour with the Vancouver Volcano International Basketball League team was for Zach, upon return he learned from his acquired agent that a few opportunities to sign overseas were missed while he was out of the country. It was a reality check about attentiveness and readiness with the overseas contract options. The Japan trip seemed to hold possibility for potential contract options, and had been a thrilling opportunity for a young grad to partake in. His introduction to the overseas pursuit to play professionally was a new education, reminding us each of the college recruiting season. Many conversations are held, possible options are put forth, one weighs their options, if one has some. One may be courted, misled, strung along, and then maybe a mutually satisfying match up might occur, which actually sounds like a description for online dating! September and October of 2011 were months of continued training, the pursuit of overseas positions, and then the waiting and the wondering around mutual attraction. We all began to accept the idea that he may not get a placement this first fall season post-graduation. Zach began to organize around networking, exploring and applying for employment that might align with his Communications degree and Journalism major, in hopes of opening new doors and inspiring new direction. The phone call and letter writing campaign became his focus, the mindset shift was exercised, and the clothes shopping for hopeful interviews proved a distraction.

Within a week of this redirected effort, his agent called to offer a contract as a replacement player in Zamora, Spain. He was elated to get the call. Someone was headed home from an injury or a contract violation, thus creating a spot for another hungry replacement. Our son would play for Grupo Inec Queso Zamorano in Zamora, Spain, Club Baloncesto. It was a fourth tier team, but for Zach, it was the first step into the future of his dreams and goals. As parents, we were thrilled to see him so happy after

36

years of feeling uncertain about his choices and his direction. It felt as though he had accepted an internship semester to play basketball abroad on a grant! Food, shelter, transportation and a small stipend were all included in the contract, and other than the name spelling error on the flight ticket sent from Spain threatening to cause a missed flight, the details lined up. Father and son resolved the issue at the airport, right down to the wire with respect to flight departure, and embraced each other quickly in farewell, resulting in a harried and mixed emotion send off. Neither were practiced enough in carrying forward their high school Spanish lessons to fully voice the brave moment in the symbolic language of destination, but both were emotionally charged around the opportunity placed before Zach. This would be the pursuit personification of a personal goal, a hoops pathway to play beyond college when not an NBA draft caliber player. The moment presented a man to man, father to son, parent to child salute significance to separation and maturation. To scout camp, to school field trips and to plenty of sport camps, we delivered him into the hands of responsible chaperones and organizers. To AAU road trips, to college and even off to Japan, we assisted in the transition of care, planning and readiness for our young man. Each of these previous deliveries were groups by definition and had supervision of some sort that assured us as parents of safety in numbers and support from leadership. It was time, in this moment of airport delivery, that we relinquish the roles we had unconsciously adopted and acted out for the majority of this young man's life. Zach had nicknamed us 'Micro Manager Mom', and 'Dictator Dad', along the years of micro managing the family and its detailed life, dictating how and when time, money and resources are distributed and how some of our adult opinions and directions would hold a tone of dictatorship and dominion. There had been an affectionate yet honest reference by him to these labels over recent years, and we joked about how he could do a standup comic piece focused on these behaviors and the humorous side of adult/child severance and independence. Alone together, and not in the presence of our kids, John and I would often commiserate around the idea of the two becoming parents one day and then walking the walk of this challenging assignment called parenting. Privately, we felt sure brother and sister entertained shared stories and parent persecutions. Why wouldn't they? We remember our own personal persecutions of family growing up, and the various idiosyncrasies of our parents and family members. It felt all in good fun, even if it resonated certain truths that were not all laughable or prideful. The

37

airport delivery was a first official 'out from under' and off to the' wild blue yonder', for Zach and for us.

Zamora was the step into independence for Zach, 'Han Solo'. Zach pursued, coordinated, prepared for and then bravely stepped out into this new threshold. He later shared with us via Skype, about his eager awareness of an angst and fear blended simultaneously with anticipation and excitement as he rode the bus from the Madrid international airport to the smaller Spanish city of Zamora. Looking out at the landscape so foreign yet also so familiar, listening to the language and the people so foreign yet also so familiar, it had been a stirring experience. His destination city lay on the north bank of the Duero River, and he was struck by how often a river had defined the landscape of his life to date. Born on the edge of the Ohio River, raised in the surroundings of the Columbia River, cradled in the shadow of the Boise River, he now would be baptized new in the surroundings of Duero. He later described this time as the happiest year of his brief independent life. Fall of 2011 through spring of 2012 was not only a liberating personal time span in our son's adult emergence, but also a time of deep creative awakening for him. Zamora proved to be a time of great healing and release, as the hoops schedule did not have an academic component other than anything he might choose to study. His classroom was now the great expanse of this scenic community and its people, and he found himself to have a zealous appetite for learning, growing, and exploring. Zach created a unique and fresh artistic blog which he posted weekly, consisting of music, visual art, poems, drawing sketches, video clips, and various forms of writing pieces, author quotes, and originals. His family and friends absorbed his postings with eager anticipation, feeling as if we, too, were living the experience over there through his art and expression. Within this beautiful tapestry, he would weave threads of his new worldview and his expanding heart and soul through messages of hope, love, beauty, conflict, wonder, and roar. He would explore various elements and principles of art in forms of color, texture, perspective, rhythm and balance.

Zach so thrived in the freedom to be his creative artistic self, to meet locals of all ages and ethnicities, to interact with athletes from around the world, and to assess himself differently in this new environment provided by basketball. He seemed to begin to set free the haunting doubts and tender scars he carried in life as a young man influenced by negative measures within school systems and by unmet personal goals within basketball.

The reign in Spain did not fall mainly on the plain. It was anything but plain, and the kingdom's domain we referred to as 'Thrive'. While Zach was mastering the kingdom of Thrive, one of the crown jewels did not include a ticket home for that season's Christmas holiday. Given that he arrived in mid-November, to return home 6 weeks later was an unrealistic and impractical use of the club's time and money for this rookie American. Zachary arranged to travel and stay with teammates in Madrid when the team was given December holiday time off. At 23 years of age, somewhat worldly and wise, he faced known and unknown fears in this multi-cultural capital city, landing in a house full of Senegalese men, surrounded by foreign speaking, supersized athletes, and sensing ever more than before just how it might feel to be a minority among men. He thought he understood a version of the plight of minority measure by nature of his size differential, and then again increasingly through his friendships and relationships developed with men of color and cultural difference throughout his basketball travels and team affiliations. This experience abroad, he shared, was a wider lens of how big the world is and how vulnerable one can feel within it. He felt small and this was as foreign to him of a feeling as the country of Spain was to an all American white bread lad. He felt vulnerable; not by the powers of others over him but by the choice he had made to be courageously and curiously present in that pocket of time and place. He stepped out of his comfort zone, and again found brotherhood.

The season went well for Zach, given that he received honorable mention in the league, he had no significant injuries and he received sufficient playing time to prove his worth. That spring, his sister came to visit him after saving and planning for weeks, and she was able to see him play hoops with his Zamora team and witness his post collegiate bloom. They explored the art and food scene in Madrid together between competitions and practices, and built a stronger more relevant thread of family bond as sibling adults, each coming into their own personal understanding of themselves and each other. After chasing both athletes for ten intense years, John and I chose to wait a year to travel and witness Zach in his overseas environment. We felt it best to give a break from us as he ventured out and beyond, and to give ourselves a respite from the nonstop focus on the kids' lives. This was a decision we would come to regret, but could not know at the time. Both of us were deeply involved in our careers and work. With stories to tell, and new ideas on which to dwell, springtime soon brought Zamora Z back to our doorstep.

Insert 14 •   2011 Zamora Zach in uniform

THE ONE AND ONLY...
THE AMAZING...

WORLD'S GREATEST
MOM

MOM,

Unfortunitly I won't be with
you on your birthday this year.
I wish I was able to be back
for just one more week but I
can't. I miss you, alot. I realize that
more and more each time I come
home and spend time with you.
I want to thank you for all of
your support and advise lately.
And like always you managed to
make christmas special for me.
I love you and hope you have
a very Happy Birthday!!! I miss
you already!!

Love Zack

Insert 15   **2011 Mother's birthday message**

THE BURNING HOUSE

If your house was burning, what would you take with you?

It's a conflict between what's practical, valuable and sentimental. What you would take reflects your interests, background and priorities.

Think of it as an interview condensed into one question.

Name: Zach Moritz
Age: 23
Location: Zamora, Espana
Occupation: Expatriate-athlete

List:

- Backpack
- Work shoes
- Basketball
- Tape cutters
- Mac
- Ipod
- Headphones
- Journal
- Sanity sticks

- Lighter
- Passport
- Knife
- Thumb drive
- My current read
- Protection
- Map
- Water bottle

Insert 16 • 2012 'The Burning House' by Zach Moritz

Chapter 5: Hello TM, Farewell MUM

Transcendental Highway, Colin Hayes

Let It Be, The Beatles

Zachary arrived home from Spain that spring of 2012 with a man bun hairdo, a calm and confidence that was infectious, and a new found anxiety reducer in the practice and discipline of TM, Transcendental Meditation. His time away allowed him to look within, and explore personal transformation and peace. In his ongoing search for medication alternatives to quiet anxiety, reduce stress, and center himself around a more focused and intentional manner of living, he had discovered mindfulness and meditation. Upon arrival home, he chose to share with us his intention of seeking certified TM instruction. He had found a couple in Portland, Oregon, who were certified to instruct, and he was going to meet with them to learn more about the program of instruction. Wow…ok…. let's talk. This household was ignorant around this means of spiritual enlightenment, and thus there was a hesitant and wary reception. Strange, looking back now. Strange, after having been enlightened. What is transcendental meditation and how does it relate to our family beliefs and values, Mom questioned. Is it a religion, and how does it fit into a life of prayer and Godliness, I continued to ponder, expressing these uncomfortable unknowns then out loud to my son. I held an unspoken assumption that in this moment of time upon his return from a very Catholic Spain, that our Protestant beliefs and religious values continued to be rooted in similar belief systems. I thought his growing disillusion of our family's religious practices was more about our worship leadership style and various programming contradictions and conflicts, but it soon became evident I misunderstood.

The naive assumption I held in my mind was shaped by the parental hope and desire that faith, prayer, and practice (the way I knew it, the way we raised him!) would and should be sufficient enough for him as he moved through the challenges and celebrations of his life. What about this new idea and practice? Could I not listen and embrace that he might actually be seeking the very same things a churchgoing folk might seek but through an alternative loving and peaceful pathway? We who congregate in the name of religion can get pretty fixed in our worshipping ways and in our posture of prayers. Zach had affirmed some time ago a personal belief in a greater power, he was continuing to seek a purposeful and spiritually centered existence, and he was a consciously awake young man constantly seeking ways to manage emotion and share life lessons with others. Shouldn't these truths be enough example to allow myself to trust what he might bring forward for himself? What was my problem? Because, it was my problem, after all. For him, it was simply his solution. I hoped for him to have what I believed to be this rock solid foundation of faith in the church and system so familiar to our family. I hoped he would uphold the practiced rituals of promise for which he could lean into and trust the Christian Protestant walk and talk. I hoped he would believe that which I had leaned into personally, leaned my family into personally, and continued to lean into personally. I hoped our faith form and prayer practice to be one in the same. I hoped, I hoped, I hoped, I hoped! But he had increasingly been expressing disappointment and a lack of spiritual fulfillment from our familiar faith practices as early as college days, possibly even in adolescent years. He witnessed too many puzzling contradictions in message and action within the church system, and it confused him. In his formative years, he would volunteer that he didn't see or hear truth in the unconditional of an unconditional love, and he didn't sense the forgiveness in the forgiveness of sin. And judgement……. he found it to be ever present and everlasting. As an observer, and even on occasion as a recipient, the system and its contradictions confused his commitment and excused his lack of allegiance.

Oh, the humanity of it all! Perfect church, perfect worship, perfect faith, where does anyone find it? He gradually sought God's grace (my words), practiced world peace, and sought a Divine face independently out in the world and not within the walls of the church in which he was raised. He would speak to me of how he wanted to find a spiritual community that was more inclusive, more universal, and I was hopeful that he would. It had been difficult to accept and embrace his growing distance from the church and the organized religion within which we had raised him, but we also knew that each child needed to find their way and their own definition of spiritual practice. Baptized and confirmed in the Episcopal and Lutheran denominations of protestant Christianity, there had been intentional dedication to guiding his spiritual life. His rejection initially was received as a parental disappointment to discern that I/we may have personally failed in

44

nurturing the spiritual seed in this child of God. Hello ego. Let's make this about you and your life, when he is trying to make it about him and his own life. Listen and learn and love. How do you know that a spiritual seed has not been planted? Where is your own true faith, hope, and love measure? Zach's reception from me to his sincere TM interest was not what he hoped for, but likely what he anticipated. My insecure monsters from within included fear, uncertainty, control, and they reared their heads and slithered their tongues delivering a dose of rejection before I had even really attempted to understand. He and I became confrontational around the discussion of the program expense, the root of TM and how it was or was not like prayer or a religion substitute, and it all turned into a welcome mat at the front door of home flipped on its backside. My fears were driven by his ever increasing divide from the faith he was raised in, the rapidly approaching age of 26 at which time he would need to have his own insurance and enough monies to support himself, and a continued transferred association by me of his life choices to those of another family member I had feared he was emulating. I was unfair and reactive. He was fair and proactive. We sometimes were a combustible combination of passionate beliefs, each tending to hold our ground. We would argue about these differing positions, and eventually we would work our way to some common understanding and acceptance. I wanted to be heard, he wanted to be heard, no one was listening. Until we finally put our egos aside, accepted our differences and stopped pushing our own agendas, we then could find common ground. We loved each other, and this would not be denied. Conditions on faith choices and independent voices would have to be set free. Unconditional love.

I regret to this day how I received him at such a vulnerable and impressionable time of discerning his young adult way. He chose to share something personal and meaningful before he simply went ahead and enrolled. He was being respectful in that gesture and I didn't respect the truth in the risk he took to share when he knew there was conflicting ideology. He lay down the conditions and I held them up. In my own life, I carried forward a few unhealthy layers from my own upbringing around the subjects of money and religion, and I managed to transfer plenty of it onto his lap in these moments of exchanged ideals. Increasingly, it was important for me as a parent to sort out my own shit from his, and to recognize and manage accordingly what actually was legitimately our shared shit! Couldn't I trust him enough to balance the upbringing we had provided with the intentions he held around his choices? It was as if I had expected him to model exactly his parents' life choices and decisions, and thus somehow validate our lives and choices by his doing so. He was, after all, a loving, nonviolent individual, and a seeker of creative expression and logical reason. Understanding this, I should have been able to trust in him to find and create his own authentic life, validating him in so doing, and thus one another. Parents can pile that guilt and expectation shit directly onto our children's lives, often unknowingly, and sometimes subconsciously. Why wouldn't our child become offended? We plant the seeds of spirituality and then fertilize them with the intention to witness beautiful bloom. But then we clip off the buds in an egocentric conflict before even allowing them to reveal their gifts from within. Wilted. Suddenly, we become active members of that team of naysayers, judgmental religious folk, bully like coaches, and any other roadblock being that had influenced their young life in a conditional and dysfunctional manner. This was painful to work through, but it was growth, likely more for me than for him. Zach gifted me the book *Transcendence* by Norman Rosenthal that Mother's Day, and I entered into an awakening stage of my own around personal beliefs and wellbeing. Zach had a way of doing this for people. As he learned, he shared, and the wealth of knowledge and healing expanded. Many have shared with me the ways in which he would open their hearts and minds to new ways of thinking, new pathways to expanded enlightenment. The gift of this book and its resource became especially helpful to me further on down the parenting life road, aiding me in understanding and accepting my son's personal pursuits and interests. The expanded perspectives helped me personally feel less threatened within my own beliefs, and further expanded my scope of a faith based life. Thank you, son. I am forever grateful to the gifts both of my children offer me in the form of mind expanding concepts centered in love, peace, and healing.

Deep and meaningful discussions and debates were not the only emotionally charged moments that spring and summer of Zach's return. The summer pace of occasional workouts with the Portland Trailblazer rookies, independent training and hoops practice, the pursuit of the next overseas opportunity, the TM instruction enrollment, and the hustle to secure and fulfill any paying job that would accommodate the flexibility of this unique schedule, Zach was on a natural high, meditatively speaking! But then his only living grandparent died, transcending this life, on to the next. Mary Moritz, our one and only Slovakian Bubba, had just celebrated her 91st birthday, fell ill, and went home to her Lord. The devout Catholic had been a dedicated servant to her church and to many in the small community of Derry, Pennsylvania. Diminutive in stature, but expansive in footprint, she was a dominant thread in the tapestry of our extended family's lives. We all lived far apart, and yet Bubba gave great reason to gather. The family headed east to Pennsylvania to memorialize her life and to gather with family and friends we would typically see once every few years if not less. A family funeral will gift you with reconnection to your roots, and we took advantage of rotating housing placements and get to know you better time with relatives we saw so infrequently. To gather around the loss of a loved one who lived 91 years, it was sad, but we all knew the end of life was approaching for her. The gift you hope for in death is to share that farewell moment with your loved one before their spirit departs, as they transcend this life and enter the great beyond. Perhaps it is to be able to tell them one more time how much you loved them, how much they meant to you, how much they will be missed. John and I, along with other family, were gifted this time with mother Mary. We know that opportunity just simply is not always the gift you get. Zach posted a tribute on social media to his 'BaBa' in remembrance, and gave us another glimpse into the sentimental, emotive side of the big man. As his mother, I felt immense pride in the kind and loving man he consistently revealed himself to be, right alongside his willfulness and conviction frequently voiced around personal beliefs and pursuits. This was a deeply meaningful trip east for all of the Moritzs and upon arrival home, Zach was thrilled to secure his next opportunity to travel further east overseas to once again play professional basketball. With only six weeks left before departure to Copenhagen, Denmark, a road trip with high school friends was in the makings. Hello Wyoming, farewell to Spain, on to Denmark!

Play basketball professionally for as many years as I can
*Most desirable countries
- Norway
- Finland
- Sweden
- Switzerland
- Australia
- New Zealand
- The Netherlands
- Denmark
- Germany
- Spain
- France
- Greece
- Slovakia
- Czech Republic
- JAPAN

Establish myself as an expatriate

Write, "Stream of consciousness" novels
- Four book series on the lifestyle of a 6'10, attractive, ADHD, student-athlete
- 1) Sold on a Dream
- 2) Potential Personified
- 3) Athletic Atonement
- 4) Columbia River's High. School.

- Gypsy Uncle Book

* Do stand up comedy
* Acting

* Write poetry with illustrations (Shel Silverstein)

* Open up bar/concert venue with Saber

* Go back to school for psychology or creative writing.
        * Continue learned interests of
        * Philosophy
        * African American Studies
        * Anthropology
        * History
        * Literature

* Learn to play guitar

Insert 17 •   2012 Personal list of dreams and goals

I'm smiling and laughing through the tears but this is tougher than I
anticipated. I want more time. I want to watch you and Dad have one
more entertaining argument. I want one more batch of snicker doodles.
One more nut roll. One more serving of rump roast. Another story.
Another game of Scrabble. Another random conversation. Another
birthday card. Another hug from your 5 foot, 90 pound frame...
91 years is a long time and I'm grateful to have shared 24 of them.
No thank you could do your life's work justice. Your void will be a big
one for us to fill.

Bye bye Baba – I love you much.

Insert 18 •   2012 Bubba grandmother tribute

Chapter 6: Why-oming?

Nature Boy, Nat King Cole
On the Road Again, Willie Nelson

Why-oming? Why not? College athletics owned Zach's life for 5 years, and he was eager to make up for some freedoms lost. His first high school girlfriend had settled in with her boyfriend in Jackson, Wyoming, and a group of four 24year-old high school friends were ready to drive east, camp, and touch base with nature on the road trip to visit Lindsay. Zach's big green beast of a dated Ford Expedition, which in honor of this trip could symbolically be called 'Old Faithful', would hold the big athletic bodies and plenty of gear with extra leg room for 'Sasquatch' seated up front. The name was among many monikers shouted as insult and distraction by opponents throughout collegiate competition. John had enthusiastically introduced his son to backpacking and camping trips in Zach's middle school years through an outdoor ministry program at church. Together, the two of them over the course of six or seven years, amidst coed groups of mixed age and religious background, traversed the Wallowa Mountain Eagle Cap Wilderness trails. They hiked the Bowman trail to Steamboat Lake on two different trips, and participated in at least two other summer trips through familiar territory up into the Wallowa wilderness of equally beautiful trails and lakes. His father had methodically coached Zach on list making, preparedness, proper gear and then proper care of that gear. These trips had been occasions for the two of them to encounter more fully each other's personalities, the likenesses and differences, and to develop a deeper mutual respect of one another. Through this father son commitment to backpacking, we had acquired a solid collection of camping gear, and we had plenty of it to share for the boy's memory making road trip. Other than gas and food, these young men had a low cost, nature laden, male bonding adventure ahead of them.

The destination offered adventure as well as introduction. Zach cared deeply for his friend Lindsay, and I understood his sincere interest in meeting her potential life partner, witnessing their relationship up close and personal. In this stage of his life, he himself expressed a greater desire to find his own life partner, thus he paid close attention to couples and their symmetry, their balance. His father recalls his son asking him in that window of time about how we met as a couple, and how Dad knew that I was the one, the life partner to be. Zach was invested in defining his own life and understanding himself more fully to ready himself not only for a vocation, but for a strong, lifelong partnership as well. Both of our kids saw Mom and Dad as an odd pairing that seemed to have its own unique chemistry and balance, and we fascinated them when they speculated about life partnerships. His young romantic heart hoped to find that special someone, and he had recently opened himself up to a fellow athlete from his university four years younger, allowing himself to be vulnerably honest about his feelings for her, knowing full well that she was in a committed relationship that mattered to her. Timing and opportunity; their connection wasn't meant to be in that window of time. Carefree and available, he was on the road again.

Zach had always been drawn to the power and beauty of nature, as it served him well physically, spiritually, and mentally. Moving through and among the great outdoors wasn't like transporting oneself by means of train, plane or automobile, where size can create restriction and become a discomfort or limitation. In nature, one size fits all. One could rest an anxious spirit, quiet a busy mind, and exercise the body at whatever pace one wanted. The wide open road spoke to his adventurous spirit, and the camaraderie among friends of former youthful days would be treasured in this summer vacation to Wyoming wilderness. There was an unspoken anticipation that there likely would be less occasion for this type of freedom and old friendship camaraderie in the days, months, and years ahead. He expected that he was going to travel back to Europe, and likely he would find a way to stay overseas if at all possible. The road trip would symbolically be a farewell to these friends for quite some time. Zach travelled with his TM in tow, to quiet the noise of it all when energy and actions got to be too much like high school. The meditation was likely an interesting practice for his friends to witness. The typical comically driven, happy go lucky oriented youth Zach of yore had become so intentionally introspective with his more-worldly life perspective. Nevertheless, visiting Lindsay, sightseeing and experiencing the Grand Tetons and Yellowstone National Park, and then carelessly and clumsily whitewater rafting the river rapids, the summer held an adventure to remember for all of these friends. Their trip and travels ended on a high note, perhaps even literally AND figuratively, I don't know, but I might suspect. One shouldn't be naïve, after all. Pretty sure, I typically was. 'Old Faithful' returned them safely home, and Zach prepared to journey on to Copenhagen, Denmark. His agent had confirmed the opportunity, contracts were signed, and by mid-August, the next round of professional basketball was in place. The world seemed to open up its arms to Zach and extend exciting invitation. He eagerly grabbed hold and became bold, tenfold! Life continued to be pretty darn promising for Zach Moritz.

Chapter 7: SISU Season One

Copenhagen, Tina Dickow

Find Your Tribe, Big Little Lions

SISU Basketball in Copenhagen, Denmark, was the European club and destination in August of 2012 that Zach felt would suit him well for a first full season overseas. The contract was somewhat better financially this season, however, Copenhagen was a much more expensive city than Zamora, Spain. The contract appeared to be more specific and comprehensive, and the club was bigger in size and seemed financially sound. Travel, transportation, furnished housing, monthly salary, additional paid work, and Mom's favorite......health insurance and cost free arrangements for health related issues! Given the nature of an athlete's work, and the fact that a college athlete is so conditioned to having extensive medical resources available to them, it was too easy for an out of country athlete to take for granted the significance and value of solid health care coverage. Between the national talk of the Affordable Health Care Act in 2012, and the accident his father would have a month after Zach's departure for Copenhagen, this mother became a real mother about health care coverage! Young adults in transition to independence do not fully comprehend the significance of this concern typically. This is especially true if they are vibrant and healthy and have never experienced a health crisis in their short lives, nor seen the true billings of the costs and expenses. One major health setback can bury a family or an individual, and everyone knows that good health is paramount to leading an active and expansive quality of life.

Our son Zach was in Copenhagen, transitioning to a new basketball club, our daughter was beginning her junior year of college, and both John and I were in demanding full time jobs that September of 2012. We hoped to visit Zach over Christmas break this second professional season overseas, but it wasn't meant to be. John had a freak golf cart accident riding in the passenger seat at a work related event, and his leg was broken in two places below the knee. Our break proved to be no holiday after all, but Christmas would still arrive. Fall and winter season were demanding and exhausting for us while healing at the home front. We managed to connect overseas with Zach regularly through Skype, which proved to be a great dose of medicinal care. He loved his new coach and settled in to his role with the team successfully. Other than a housing challenge that never quite lived up to the contract promise until late into that season, he was over the moon. His sister travelled to visit him in early December, and once again, she observed him thriving on and off the court. They indulged themselves in the local arts and culture, scheduling their time around the basketball priorities. We loved how successfully these two were growing up, continuing to expand their solid sibling bond, while travelling the world and shaping worldly perspective. Zach would speak during our Skype sessions of the city's allure, the food, the cycling, the international clubs for nightlife, the women and their independence, the brotherhood of his teammates, and the friendship of his new coach. We could feel the vibration of a full heart and the warmth of a kindled fire burning bright. He felt he belonged there, and hoped he could find a way to stay. He felt valued, and he worked hard to further the development of his game and his contributions. There was an optimism and an enthusiasm we had so missed, for these strengths had cycled up and down throughout his collegiate days, each year holding a new disappointment or a new battle to overcome in proving worth and value. His zest for life fueled us as we focused at home on the healing of a broken leg and the management of demanding, stressful careers.

Another Christmas holiday season would return and the four of us gathered together at home once again, grateful for the opportunity to maintain family traditions and rally around loved ones. Striving and thriving continued to be the name of the flourishing game we each practiced in this life season, with laughter, music, and love the primary skills and drills engaged around work, wages, and wellness each and every week. We were all in a comfortable groove, with seemingly all the right moves, feeling like we didn't have much to prove, and our safe, centered spot was at home in the 'Couv'!

Insert 19 •   2012 Copenhagen Zach in uniform

Chapter 8: Pink Martini

Happy Birthday, Altered Images

Splendor in the Grass, Pink Martini

Anticipating our kids return from Denmark, and desperately needing a broken leg recovery salute as well as a holiday/year end momma birthday celebration, John and I would decide to search out a local musical performance that the four of us might enjoy while we were home together. Host of a New Year's Eve birthday, I was accustomed to requesting year after year at the very least a dinner and a movie with the family prior to any other New Year holiday commitments. It so happened that Portland Oregon's Pink Martini musical group often performed in Portland on New Year's Eve, and we were miraculously able to secure front row seats from an online booking! There seemed to be serendipitous work at hand here, as online bookings are typically hellish and hurried. These select seats would comfortably accommodate John's fragile leg recovery needs as well as Zach's 37" inseam and overall spatial sizing needs. And no doubt, front row would accommodate quite well the viewing capacity for all four of us. It would prove to be a Happy New Year night to remember.

Pink Martini is a musical group identifying itself as a 'little orchestra', performing music that crosses multiple genres such as classical, Latin, jazz, and classical pop, while drawing inspiration from all around the world. Their Facebook description in 2017 referred to themselves as a 'United Nations house band of 1962 meets Lawrence Welk on acid'! Hmmm. Whether the evening idea was appealing to the kids or not, the descriptor held some allure, so both were game to take in the experience and participate in Mom's birthday request. Ours was a family that typically appreciated and explored a broad collection of musical sounds, genres, and artists, often exchanging and introducing a gamut of musical artistry shared into our home playlists or added to one another's. Increasingly, our children broadened a modern day scope of musical exposure. On this occasion, however, the parents would broaden their scope, inviting them to enjoy the year end dress up, happy hour, dine out, New Year's Eve entertainment combination. Happy Birthday to me! The greatest gift was to be together.

This magical moment in time held such promise to an expectation of so many more possibilities of future celebration and gathering. These two young adult children arrived home that 2012 holiday season full of stories to tell of their time shared in Copenhagen, while John and I marveled at the playful camaraderie. Blessings were in abundance as we toasted broken leg healing, birthday, and Danish adventure, hoisting a pink martini at home in Vancouver, followed by a Pink Martini at the Schnitz in Portland. The family was healthy, vibrant, and standing in each other's corner as we all adapted to the shifting life transition of this family foursome's grown up definition and an ever evolving holiday gathering at home tradition. Personal growth, returned health, and relational symmetry gave rise to our gratitude and grace in this calendar season, as the new year outlook ahead appeared predictably prosperous. The year 2013 inaugurated us with a return flight overseas to SISU Denmark on New Year's Day for Zachary, a Bolt bus ride back to Seattle University for Gab shortly thereafter, and the continuation of Mom and Dad's careers at work from Vancouver, Washington. A mere two weeks into the new year, however, and inauguration held an entirely different meaning that we wouldn't come to understand until a full nine months later. Inauguration would not be a ceremony, but rather an initiation. We were in for one hell of a slow, simmering initiation in 2013.

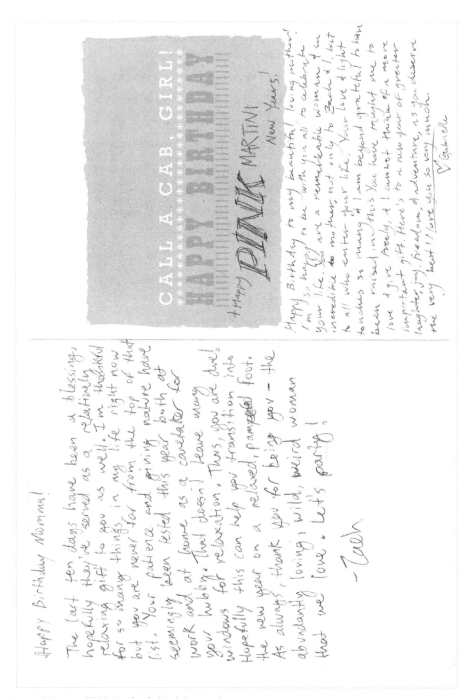

CALL A CAB, GIRL!
HAPPY BIRTHDAY

+ Happy PINK MARTINI New Year's!

Happy Birthday to my beautiful, loving mother! I'm so happy to be with you all to celebrate your life. You are a remarkable woman + an incredible mother, not only to Rachel + I, but to all who enter your life. Your love + light touches so many + I am beyond grateful to have been raised in this. You have taught me to love + give freely, + I cannot think of a more important gift. Here's to a new year of greater laughter, joy, freedom, + adventure, as you deserve the very best!! I love you so very much.

Gabrielle

Happy Birthday Momma!

The last ten days have been a blessing, hopefully they've served as a relatively relaxing gift to you as well. I'm thankful for so many things in my life right now but you are never far from the top of that list. Your patience and giving nature have seemingly been tested this year both at work and at home as a caretaker for you lately. That doesn't leave many windows for relaxation. Thus, you are due! Hopefully this can help you transition into the new year on a relaxed, pampered foot. As always, thank you for being MDV — the abundantly loving, wild, weird woman that we love. Let's party!

Caleb

Chapter 9: Carbuncle in Copenhagen?

Mystery Disease, MGMT

It's Alright Ma, Bob Dylan

Our pattern this particular basketball season in communicating with our son and watching him and his team play was to Skype weekly and catch the games on the internet. The weekend of January 18-19, 2013, the SISU team was to be on a road trip. When we looked for the game to watch late Sunday morning on the 20th of January, Zachary was not listed on the roster nor was he visibly with the team. We could not help but wonder about the situation and had previously planned to Skype at 10am that morning following the road trip, until we struggled with making an internet connection. John and I intended to explore this team absence mystery with Zach during that morning Skype, if only we could reach him. Anxiety began to rise up in the intuitive soul of the micromanaging Mom. Something was not right. To further fuel this angst, our daughter alerted us that the previous day her brother had spoken of a fever he was working through and a gross boil he had discovered on his arm. Keenly aware of Zach's increasing desire for us to not micro manage specifics nor dictate directions for his emerging adult life, Zach's intentional efforts to gain and manage the independence which he so valued, and Mom's trust in the health care clause within the player club contract, we could have reasoned ourselves to not worry. Still, I made the choice to write both coach and Zach to express concern and explore the little bit of information we gathered from his sister Gabby. Too many unknowns and uncertainties seemed to be missing from the full picture. And did that ever prove to be true, in time.

Mom email to coaches @ 12:58 pm USA time on Sunday afternoon, 1/20/2103:

Hello,

I am Zach Moritz's mother and we are concerned about our son's health and how to reach him. We learned that he had a fever and a boil last night, and we were to Skype with him today at 7pm

Copenhagen time, and then his sister was to Skype at 9pm Copenhagen time. We have not heard from him nor have we been able to connect via email. Did the fever cause him to be hospitalized? Your addresses were listed on the website so we have included all of you in hopes someone could let us know if he is ok. If any of you know how we could reach him or confirm that he is ok, it would put our minds at ease. Thank you so much.

Beth Moritz

Mom email to Zach @1:46pm USA time on 1/20/2013:

Zach,

Gabby told me about your boil and fever, and now I am concerned that you are not ok. I am realizing we have no way of contacting you to check on you other than through you only. Trying not to panic, but ever so concerned about your health and how we reach you. For future, we should have someone else we could reach at the club or something.

Much love, Mom

Zach's SISU head coach called, spoke to John, and agreed to check in with Zach. He emailed a phone # direct to Zach's residence @ 2:42pm USA time on 1/20/13.

Mom's email response to SISU coach @ 3:10pm USA time on 1/20/2013:

THANK YOU SO MUCH!!!! I am much relieved, as we here in the states always have media coverage about any and all things that can go wrong with health issues and after all, I am still a mama bear!!! Continued best wishes throughout the season, and thank you for the immediate feedback. It is helpful to have the phone number if we needed it! Zach will be embarrassed by my urgency. We just love him so!!!

Most grateful,

Beth Moritz

Zach email to Mom @ 6:22pm on 1/20/2013:

Good morning, our internet had not been working today but for whatever reason now at 3:20am it is up and running. I AM FINE. Fever gone, boil drained twice and seemingly on the mend. No worries about your paranoia. Your anxiety gets the best of you sometimes but it is much better to have a mother who cares too much opposed to the alternative. I'm glad you got ahold of coach and could calm yourself. Let us try to skype tomorrow, internet abiding. Let me know what works for you. Love ya!

Zach email to Dad @ 6:24pm on 1/20/ 2013:

All is well and I am on the mend. Internet wasn't working today so no Skype. Apparently mom or you got hold of coach and he in turn called me. Glad you could be informed. Boil is gross and the fever was brutal but gone now as I've drained the boil twice and am hopefully done doing so. Anyhow perhaps we Skype tomorrow. Love ya.

Mom email to Zach @ 12:43am on 1/21/ 2013:

Hey…. we three were pretty anxious when we could not reach you and we heard you had a fever. I, of course, acted on the fear while the other two anxiously awaited my knowledge of anything! I cannot help being a mama bear looking out for her cubs. Love you and I am home tomorrow for holiday as is Gabby. If your internet returns, we could try to Skype…. email when you can.

Hugs

Part Three

Awakenings

Chapter 10: Quest for Purpose

Changes, David Bowie

Live Your Life, Yuna

Following our January health scare, the remainder of the SISU season was without issue. Zach's father recovered from his broken leg injury, and so the two of us gave his leg strength a trial with a long weekend getaway to San Francisco in mid-February of 2013. John had physically gotten back up onto his feet and actively engaged in his job by January, but a weekend of walking San Fran would be a true test of stamina. The human body's ability to mend and heal continued to amaze us as his leg responded with full function and limited pain following successful surgery repair. Of course, the recovery was driven by the discipline and dedication of the patient John to do the rehab, the financial reliability of workers' compensation, and the circumstance of a treatable injury. Broken legs can heal. By the middle of March, we learned about Zach's hip pointer that wasn't healing which kept him from participating in the playoffs, and accelerated his April return flight home. He was pleased with the team's care and support for his injury, confident he would heal, and no other health flags were waved at this time. The January setback seemed to have quieted and resolved itself. Meanwhile, Zachary had continued his exploration of personal transformation and spiritual wholeness, sharing his latest intention about plans to engage in a rite of passage ceremony he had discovered through research. We were to be educated once again, by this new and unfamiliar spiritually transformative pursuit of our son. His email on February 28, 2013, was entitled

'Spiritual Summer'

Good evening,

As the regular season has ended and we prep for playoffs, my mind wanders toward the upcoming future. I have many plans and ambitions for this off season/summer, working a job, working toward financial independence, selling my car, travel, family/friend relaxation, etc.... One such thing that I know I will be doing however is taking a much needed rite of passage. Like the summer before I am seeking another means of spiritual wholeness that I hope you two can respect. Meditation has been a HUGE blessing for me and every time I go within myself I am gifted with more and more enlightening calmness and insight.

Maybe you can tell, but the last two years have been some of the happiest and most enriching years I've yet to have while pursuing basketball. And off the court, the combination of independence, privacy, maturation, and introspection that comes with my lifestyle has given me the ability to understand my complexities like never before. I look forward to having discussions about such discoveries, in person, with you both over the course of the summer.

But back to the meat of the message. After much research, consideration, countless conversation, and writing off the idea of attempting one of my own- I have decided to embark on a vision quest. Here is a link to the organization that I will be partaking in such endeavor with:

http://www.schooloflostborders.org/term/youth-programs

I just wanted to give a brief heads-up before I enroll and get asked monetary questions. It is extremely reasonable and I will be able to pay it all myself. The dates line up well for me considering this life I'm beginning to embrace. I can answer any questions you have that the site does not provide.

I love you two very much and hope you see that the things of this nature are equivalent to your faith life pursuits and price tags. I do not share in your faith or agree with many things associated with such. But I respect you and others that it works for. Meditation works for me and after much thought and deliberation with others, I am quite certain that this too will work for me. Thank you.

Unlike previous conversations and ideas brought forth that were foreign to us and to our own spiritual walk, we were much more gracious and receptive. It didn't hurt that Zach had taken such time to explain himself, and that we had begun the work some time ago in understanding this young man who left our home at 18, returned at 23, and very independently continued to work so hard at knowing and understanding himself more compassionately in the years since. John and I learned to do the research before allowing our instincts to pass judgement or to question his means to pursuing something significant and meaningful, all in the spirit of personal health and spiritual wholeness. We worked to understand more fully the purpose and intention that our son held, trusting in the forward movement of his vision rather than promoting our mainstream thinking or challenging his alternative ideas, as in moments of our recent past. We might have confronted that his baptism and confirmation were those spiritual rites of passage held in his life, intended to lay a spiritual wholeness foundation of Christian values and practice. But instead we practiced more listening than preaching, more acceptance than confrontation. He did not identify with the exercise and intent of these childhood practices, one having been performed on his behalf as an infant, and another in his adolescent years as is the typical Christian Protestant tradition. Accepting his perspective while holding our own at the time, we wondered if his beliefs would sufficiently support him at a spiritually vulnerable future point in time. For those rites of passage his parents and the church had dictated and defined as significant to his spiritual life were so convincingly full of promise and security! Zach made it quite clear, as an emerging young adult, that this quest rite of passage was an intentional choice of personal significance, made by himself and for himself, at an age and stage of deep awareness and readiness. He reminded us that the others had been done on his behalf, and I thought privately, but isn't it wise to cover all the bases of spiritual insurance?

Seeds of faith had been planted by the rites of passage which John and I had grown up to trust, accept, and practice. Rather than promote further our own agenda, we would choose to let go and let God, as the prayerful expression encouraged. I had begun to really wonder what that meant after all, 'to let God'. The letting go part, I understood, yet needed plenty of practice. The letting God part was confusing. Doesn't that imply we do nothing and God does all? How about let go and let godliness? God and godliness seemed very present in my son's intentions and direction of heart. There was no need for me to let or allow, other than to let go of my own fixated practice of narrowmindedness! I chose to lift and hold Zach's pursuits as Godly in nature and design, and to work toward more fully trusting in those mysteries unknown within each of our personal journey toward spiritual enlightenment. As parents, we could choose to reject our son in this rite of passage he brought forth, or we could embrace him, thereby opening our mind and heart to hold something new and expansive to our own faith picture. It was an easy enough embrace to make but a more complex intention to uphold and practice. Learning to put a voice to the choices of your children when they are different than your own can become a challenging exercise of patient, persistent and protective parenting. Best learned advice...... embrace and accept them, and allow them to teach and guide you. Find parallels. Love each other. Our job should not be to defend or define but to go forth and seek all that is divine. We all have room for enlightenment.

SONFLOWER

When Zach returned home late April, we received him with an expanded awareness and deeper acceptance to his personal goals and intentions. He secured work, he practiced his yoga and meditation, and he began to explore feasible arrangements and calendar time for his quest commitment. Having determined he could afford and would afford to enroll himself, he could not afford to neglect the details of preparation which held great significance for readiness at all levels, physically, mentally, and spiritually. The now rapidly approaching quest would include gathering with up to a dozen questers aged 16-25 from around the world in late July for approximately ten days. All would be seeking their own individual confirmation of entry into adulthood by choosing to fast in the wilderness alone and ask of themselves the critical questions, *who am I to be in the world and what do I have to offer as an adult?*. This seemed a brave and courageous commitment, an honorable and worthy quest. There would be preparation as a group, followed by three days of personal fast and self-reflection alone in the high desert of the Inyo Mountains in eastern California. Participants were to arrive equipped and prepared to camp, and to provide their own food for training and preparation days prior to the fast. Each would be asked to complete a fasting 'walkabout' for at least a 24hour window somewhere in nature but with the awareness of and access to available loved ones well prior to arriving for their official quest encounter. Upon gathering, questers would be encouraged to clarify and further develop their intentions for this chosen venture, in manner both written and spoken. Lovingly, and with guided mirroring, the listening and acknowledgement among the questing community would affirm each in their preparations before departing for the fast and again in the return from the mountain at closing ceremony after the fast. Among all the documentation and credible resources online that we as parents read about this endeavor, a familiar message within the material stirred association for us around some of the disappointments Zach had spoken of in his collegiate athletic days regarding youthful behavior and immaturity. He identified the behavior in himself with regard to alcohol and some recreational drug usage, and he witnessed it surrounding himself on such a broader scale within the community of athletes at varying levels of use and abuse. The message within this particular School of Lost Borders' rite of passage description that resonated with Zach's own experiences in collegiate athletics and college campus life was as follows:

.... *'Many modern societies have lost traditions that witness and honor this rite of passage (ie entry into adulthood). Without accepted ceremonies, adolescents may attempt to self-initiate into adulthood, using*

66

the symbols of 'maturity' that they see as the privilege of adults around them: alcohol, drugs, violence, sex. The result can be a confusing test of limits, feelings, and behavior from ecstasy to revolt to a dance with death. An alternative is to simply conform and accept the status quo – the search for an authentic self-knowing never takes place. An initiation ceremony in a wilderness setting provides a mirror for that deep self-exploration, a true test of oneself on many levels'.

While all of our research on rite of passage quests and on this program in particular quieted any wonder about Zach's newest pursuit, there were subtle yet noticeable shifts observed in his physical presentation during that 2013 summer at home. Specifically, we noticed an increased agitation that would reside close to the surface for him. He had also taken to cigarette smoking with a greater frequency to settle this frequent anxiety and state of agitation. Zach had begun to complain of back pain and joint pain, and his joints would noticeably crack when he climbed the stairway at home. We associated all of this to years of physical wear and tear on his body from training and competition. There had been no reason to fear or suspect something of greater significance. Yet. We knew he would indulge in some Copenhagen partying with the locals, and that cigarette smoking was a European high frequency behavior, as it was observed to also be so during the IBL team trip to Japan. Thus, these youthful explorations and practices did not seem that unusual in terms of suspicious behaviors or out of character choices. It was a curiosity, however, given that he was so oriented toward tools and pathways of wholeness and health. We also considered that perhaps some of the agitation was simply due to being home and under the roof of his parents, having had a taste of independence and freedom of choice. Consistently loving and respectful, Zach worked willingly with us around household boundaries and expectations. These subtle observations that summer were a curiosity to both parents, and we would return to ponder any significance to them more than once.

Zach invited us to attend the closing ceremonies for his life purpose seeking quest and we were grateful for the inclusion. His sister would be finishing her apartment lease and job in Seattle, returning home then to Vancouver during the month of August to prepare for her semester abroad in Barcelona, Spain, September through November. John and I therefore chose to attend the closing without her in attendance. As a couple, we gifted ourselves a front end vacation road trip traveling first south to the California northern coast, then across state and south again to destination Big Pine, California. In retrospect, we both wished that we would have coordinated the inclusion of his sister in joining us

SONFLOWER

for Zach's very meaningful rite of passage closing ceremony. Just another regret in the growing collection. Nonetheless, we all had a plan, and we each executed. Zach departed late July by plane, then by bus, then by foot to the campground in Big Pine. Gabby wrapped up her job and her lease and returned home to house sit and care for the family cat while preparing for Barcelona. John and Beth hit the road to Big Pine by way of Mendocino layover, and excitedly ventured into this new community of spiritual mentors, self-discovery, and community belonging for our son Zach. From SISU to Inyo, then Inyo to SISU, Zach entered and exited summer of 2013 coming off one mountain top after another, physically, mentally, and spiritually climbing to new heights and beyond. Who was he to be in the world? What would he have to offer as an adult?

Now, I bought this card weeks ago but after watching Jackass the other night, it might be twice as funny. Anyhow, congrats to your continuing success and gratification! It's much deserved. I suppose the only "raise" or "promotion" a father can receive is that of watching his kids come into their respective own. So again, I thank you for helping me come into my own and for supporting me toward the success of young manhood. It means alot to me that both you and Mom have taken interest in my latest pursuit toward self mastery. I look forward to shared time and reflection in the desert. I promise the NSA can't track this catnip and I know you'll enjoy in times of need – HAPPY DAD DAY!

...but I love you, man.

Happy Father's Day

- Zach

Insert 21 •   2013 Father's Day card message

69

Chapter 11: Awakening in Big Pine

Landslide, Fleetwood Mac

Fly Like an Eagle, The Steve Miller Band

On our northwestern tour of the great state of California, its scenic coastal routes just a day behind us, John and I found ourselves escorted into the eastern California landscape by a haze of soft gray, smoke filled air, driving east and then south down U.S. Route 395 that early August afternoon. Plumes of smoke the color of spent charcoal feathered the turquoise skyline above the terra cotta shades of the Sierra Nevada Mountains along the evergreen laced Yosemite ranges. Hendrix' *Purple Haze* should have been playing. The gripping visual was accompanied by the sensory stimulation of a burn smell so toasted that you could practically taste it in your mouth as it filtered its way through the ventilation system of the Nissan Armada. One more stunning California backdrop of natural landscape intersecting with the weather elements and we were driving right down into its storms, fires, and desert topography. We were awestruck by the beauty of the land's expansiveness, ever aware of the vulnerability we felt with respect to the power and mirth of this land mass called California. Excuse us as we kissed the sky. Humid summer storms flashed lightning, and when mixed with the high drought and abundance of kindling in the vast mountain ranges of the eastern Sierras to our right, and the collection of looming ranges to our left, fire was likely. A mere two weeks after the date of our drive through this area, one of California's biggest wildfires in the state's history to date, known as the Rim Fire, had ignited and flared out of control just north of where we were driving. We were awestruck amidst nature's mix of weather patterns on display as we drove along looking up and out toward the continuous rock wall formations bordered by blue skyline speckled in gray, cradling us on either side for miles. Marveling in the moment, we spoke of the complexity and vast beauty of it all, comparing the contrasts and complexities to our loved son, the young spiritual seeker we followed to California.

The date was Friday, August 2, 2013; this would be his third and final day fasting and searching deep within himself. Was he experiencing personal storm? Would lightning strike with fire and fury burning? As we drove along, we tried to imagine having the courage, the desire, the curiosity to explore such internal and external terrain. What drove him in pursuit of such passage? If we were witnessing fire, smoke, lightning, drought temperatures, and rain from the windshield of our safe, comfortable, temperature controlled luxury vehicle headed directly toward the Inyo Mountains, we reflected, what would he be experiencing while up on that mountain top? Without a doubt, we agreed, he was dramatically experiencing these external elements. But what was happening for him within? We would soon be privileged to know, and our own personal quest to stand alongside of our son's journey would continue. We spent that night in Bishop at a Best Western in the best little western hotel option nearest our final destination. Up early Saturday morning, we were eager to see our son, and witness the questers' return from the mountain fast, each preparing to personally share with family and leaders their mountain top experience. Along the dusty sage lined road taken from a turn off of Rt. 395 north of Death Valley territory, we drove onto the grounds slowly, our hearts beating with excitement and anticipation as we prepared to enter a physical space and sacred ceremony unfamiliar to our Midwestern roots. We pulled up to the small, narrow parking area in the Armada, a family vehicle treasured for its comfort and space that accommodated well the four long legged, above average sized family members of our clan. The serene, Eden like surrounding that greeted us upon entry into the complex was in contradiction to the bold invasiveness of our obtrusive machinery, navigating its way to a less conspicuous space on the parking lot gravel. We were a cruise line ship pulling into a creek side dock! I much prefer quieter less noticeable entrances. We were the big folks with the big son, pulling up in the big car, with the big comfy folding chairs to sit in small circle. No one spoke this message, nor implied it. Rather, this was the internal voice of insecurity finding volume amidst unfamiliar surroundings, expressing mocking desire to arrive less conspicuously and to sit silently observing on the sidelines.

We transitioned swiftly into the welcome and wisdom of the group, however, when the gathered guests and humble hosts advised us to raise and prop the front hood of the car while parked so as to minimize chances of a snake or rodent nestling up to the vehicle for shade and cover in the desert heat. Or was it actually the engine warmth attracting

71

them to a nesting spot? Either way, I had one thought. Creepy. The idea of a snake or rodent in or on my car was unsettling. I had worried for Zach about snakes on the fast, which irritated him to no end. OK. Hood lifted, no problem. Inexperienced were we with desert heat nesting, vision questing, sage smudging, council circle mirroring, or any of the other respectful and meaningful rituals and ceremonial elements soon introduced. These willing but still somewhat wary parents would look for shade from the August heat, warmth from the heart engine driving the event, and comfort from the calling of community. As we sat in circle, head and heart filled with intention to listen and love and learn, there was no judgement, and therefore, less fear. Welcome and inclusion prevailed. Self-conscious, I certainly felt; a little self-deprecation, I definitely dealt. But within the questioning quest's conclusive melt, it was self-actualization to which we all knelt. One could not be a part of this communal ceremony without personal and public enlightenment. Our time in southeastern California that weekend proved to be another transcendent experience introduced by and shared with our adventurous son, Zachary Charles. John and I were deeply touched by the participation, the people, the place, and the power. Divinity, in its many forms and faces, graced each of us throughout the experience. A challenge then remained as to how each, as questers, leaders, or guests, would integrate the divine practices and discovered purposefulness forward into our lives. The peaceful habitat we were surrounded by, the warm people we met and communed with, the generous spirit and hospitality of such sacred gathering and earth honoring ritual, along with the deeply personal truths that vibrated from each spoken word bravely shared, lovingly nursed any insecurities quiet. Letting go was practiced and rewarded.

With regard to embracing our son's faith journey and spiritual walk, we could now more fully comprehend his hunger, his pursuit, and his community defined. John and I were emotionally and physically present in this commitment for him, and equally so for each of the questers. All else encountered beyond these commitments would be a bonus. This was Zach's path we followed, after all, and he now had expanded a personal spiritual community base. God was ever present and honored in ceremony, as was His creation surrounding us. What we witnessed in the personal stories of these participants and friends, was an awakening of sorts that we all tend to seek in our lifetime here on earth. Stewardship of the land, of our bodies, minds and souls, of our gifts as a people of Divine creation, of relationships and compassion for our fellow man; these are universal tenets in all spiritually based messages and mantras. Leading a life with intention, and looking deep within to discover what that might look like, creating a footprint to transport your gifts out into the world and make honest use of them, as I heard these themes in the sacred conversations and personal messages shared, I would comfortably let go, let it be, let God. And I would more than ever, walk with my son's different and yet so similar spiritual pursuits, leaving fear and doubt in the past with regard to his choices and directional path. John and I were strengthened by this trip, and each of us had our own awakening to much about life, parenting, faith and trust. Full of gratitude at how spiritually awake and personally empowered our son had become, we recognized a life purpose and perspective taking shape that expanded beyond basketball, yet included the basketball community as one of many channels or vessels through which to serve. We witnessed his 'ah-hah' moment spoken out loud in the communal circle of trust, smudged pure, and held sacred by all present. We then were blessed with a written replica. Within a week of this life changing event for our son, he wrote his friends and family the following message.

Friends and family,

As those of you within in this email know, I partook in a rite of passage this past month and subjected myself to a ceremonial fast. I did this with 10 others, aged 16-25, from all over the world and from various walks of life. The School of Lost Borders is the organization whom directed us and it all took place in and around the Inyo National Forest.

It was many things for me. Some of it was centered on purging my past but the majority of it was about affirming my future. Vulnerability was and remains at the forefront of its power. I am still very much in the wake of it all and thus am not entirely comfortable talking about it. Especially not through a keyboard and computer screen.

I'm guarded for a multitude of reasons, however I want to thank you all for your genuine curiosities and support prior to and after its happening. I've felt respected by you all and want to reciprocate and mirror some of that respect back. Some of you were there for parts of the ceremony, some of you have experienced similar undertakings and perhaps some of you will pursue something similar in the future.

This letter that I've decided to share, was one I wrote for myself in the midst of my fasting. It just sort of happened in a sporadic, stream of consciousness, organic manner and was later puzzle pieced together in a more coherent way. It's a small piece of what the ceremony was for me, but an important one none the less. I only ask you to be mindful of who you share it with and how you discuss this topic. Perhaps on future occasions, if you remain curious, we can have further discussions regarding my time in the wilderness. For now, this feels like a fitting start at sharing...

"At 25, I've already made peace with much and severed with many. I see a piece of my past self in all of you and the parallels between us are comforting. Within my journey I've managed to do everything wrong, yet still succeed, and I've likewise done everything right, yet still found failure. At this exact crossroad I am beaming with a newfound balance between my past and future. I thank you all for your inspirations and contributions.

In many ways, severance first entered my life at 15. It was then that I initially came into some of my power. I was taken in by the subculture of the elite, amateur basketball circuit. It served as a second family; an abundance of diverse brothers, father figures with varying approaches, freedom, travel, excitement and competition. It was my first inkling of perceived manhood and I felt genuinely fulfilled. I finally found a place where I belonged, where I fit and where I was satisfied. Another stage of severance occurred at 18. When I left my home, my parents, my friends and many other comforts behind for the new state and culture of Idaho. The challenge of top tier collegiate competition and simultaneous schooling seemed like an affirmation of manhood. But of course between then and now, many more instances of severance occurred. The confirming of spirituality and the pent up disappointment with the faith life my family had raised me in. The confrontation between us of such confirming. The entire firing of my dysfunctional coaching staff and the subsequent hiring of the new. University graduation and the satisfaction/severance that came with leaving the academic structure behind. All these things and probably more. But, I found none of these things truly meaningful at the time, nor do I now in retrospect.

Ultimately, I wasn't ready at 15 to responsibly accept and embrace my powers. I was just along for the ride. From 15-20, I fought my gifts and frankly, fucked up. Then from 20-25, I've consciously tried to right my wrongs, to make up for lost time and to try to heal. So it is at 25, I find myself here to reclaim some of what I lost in child and young manhood, but also to affirm that I am indeed an adult. Without doubt, I feel right where I need to be for this ceremony.

I find myself feeling not quite among the youth fasters and just the same, not among our mentors or council either. I am on my own, somewhere in the middle of it all and it almost feels as if I am a balancing beam between us all. This insight came to me in a most peculiar way. By the route of a beautiful and mysterious creature, one I'd never seen before. It wasn't a butterfly, it wasn't a moth, and it wasn't really a hummingbird. But instead it was some radical combination of them all. And that is how I feel within this community; like some beautiful, mysterious, radical and perhaps previously unseen combination of you all. And I must say, it not only feels odd, but in some strange way I feel simultaneously humbled and empowered by it.

I know that I am a man. And I now realize that I've been a man for the better part of the last five years. I came here a man and I will leave here a man, but I will leave as a man who is in complete control of his powers, and I will leave as a man who has complete awareness of his weaknesses. There is no need for me to make mention of them all, but one of the more important aspects of my power is my strength. My physical strength but moreso the strength of my spirit. I have been blessed and burdened by them but I understand now that the gifts of my athleticism, my stature and my soul were not meant for me to waste. Furthermore, I have no right to decide when I should give up my gifts, for it would only be selfish of me to do so prematurely. Inevitably, pieces of my power will fade. When the end of my physical power comes, it will be decided by something larger than me and ultimately out of my control. Until that day, I vow to respect my powers as my responsibility. I know that they are useless unless they are shared. I vow to no longer be afraid of my strengths or weaknesses but to embrace them both through the confidence of self-knowledge. Now that I've seen the worst, both in myself and in others, I can become my best.

When I say that I came here already a man, I feel I speak the truth. However, I came only as half the man that I am capable of being. Many things motivated me to partake in this ceremony. Finding my purpose was not initially or necessarily among them. I came here seeking selfish answers. I am most grateful though for the tremendous peace I've found here. Yes, my selfish prayers have been answered, but also I have been gifted the clarity of my balanced purpose. I believe that purpose is to thrive. To thrive on the basketball court to the best of my capabilities, but more importantly to help others like me thrive. To help heal my community of athletes and to contribute to the evolution of sport in society.

SONFLOWER

I've always been a natural leader. Gifted with qualities that both influence and inspire. These last five years I'd began to embrace those powers. However, something was missing. That something was purpose; for what is a man if he only has power? It is the balance that I've attained here that I am most grateful for. That is, the merging of my powers with the direction of my purpose. I sit among you all in peace. Knowing that I deserve this sacred union. I deserve my power and I deserve my purpose. I have earned them both. I deserve to forgive myself, to be forgiven and to forgive others. I deserve the clarity given to me in this sacred place and I bask in the mutual respect felt between us. I've been rejuvenated by the lightning, changed by the wind, cleansed by the rain, warmed by the sun, inspired by the stars, humbled by myself and nourished by our earth. I too deserve to commune. To share candid conversation with the Raven, to find kindred spiritedness with the jackrabbit, and to feel inspiration from the speed and grace of the hummingbird. I deserved to bathe with the transformative frogs and to float with the reborn butterflies. It is and always has been that through nature we become at peace with our own.

With great lightness also comes great darkness. It was between the sun and the moon, at the apex of the valley, where I first found balance here. The perspective of my being. The organic nature of this ceremony. The reflection of 25, fully lived years. This sensation of balance continues to come to me now in ever so soothing waves. Equilibrium; two equal yet opposite entities, calming and holding me still. In this place and within me, I sought peace. I feel I have found what I deserved. Again, I thank you all."

Chapter 12: SISU Season Two

Under Pressure, Queen with David Bowie

SISU, Josh Garrels

SISU......(noun) *Extraordinary determination, courage, and resoluteness in the face of extreme adversity. An action mindset which enables individuals to reach beyond their present limitations, take action against all odds and transform barriers into frontiers. An integral element of Finnish culture and also a universal capacity, which we all share.*

The emotional high with which the three of us left the quest closing ceremony was short lived. Meaningful hugs and tender farewells framed our departure from the lush, hummingbird laden, pond glistening, quiet oasis of a utopia called Three Creeks. We pulled the 'cruise ship out of the dock' one last time and began the 2day drive home to Vancouver, Washington. The blissful picture within the frame of our utopian farewell was not to last long, for within a half hour of our road trip home, Zach was saying hello to great aggravation from lower back pain and knee pain, particularly in the right knee, in addition to overall body discomfort. He was obviously agitated, and we wondered if he might be dehydrated or hungry, or if it was simply frustration from the shift so suddenly back into 'real world'. John and I couldn't help but feel confused and slightly concerned by the conflicting energy and enthusiasm shift so quickly upon us. The pure physical pain for which he was complaining interfered with the pure peaceful gain of which he had been attaining. Was there a rhyme or a reason? We wondered if his pain was present all along, and if the euphoria of the event and its valued work simply masked the discomfort that his body was presenting with throughout the quest. Had he been quiet about this possibility, only to open up about it in the car? We had observed him sit with difficulty around the circle cross legged, supporting his back with a yoga prop, but we were feeling some of that discomfort ourselves. It didn't seem unusual.

SONFLOWER

The group had hiked often, camped on dry hard ground, eaten light and even fasted three days, and yet we know they hydrated often and mandatorily. Furthermore, Zach was an extremely fit athlete, accustomed to running up and down basketball courts for hours at a time. He came in as a physically and mentally prepared quester, although it would not be unusual that an event like this could weary the mind, body and soul coming down from the mountaintop, literally and figuratively. The agitation seemed a startling and unexpected conclusion to the quest. To minimize the discomfort and the challenge of the immediate situation, we tried to accommodate as many stops, seat adjustments, and size 16 feet extended fully into the face of the lucky driver, feet or foot resting on the center console to enable leg pain relief as needed. We reduced extra noise, conversation, and stimulation overload, imagining it to be difficult for him to transition back in to such a noisy, busy, overstimulating world. In the immediate 24 hours following faith retreats which John and I had participated in over the years, we would try to take a day off immediately following the gift of that retreat experience, or at least minimize the work stress of the next day so as to not immediately lose the peace and serenity received while in retreat. Transition is important to respect, and this one was happening in the back seat of a car driving home. Zach would face another significant transition a week from our arrival home. His plan was to return for a second season in Copenhagen and build upon what he initiated in 2012. He found a club, a coach, a community that felt like his place to call home. His flight was booked, and his mind, body and soul steered toward SISU. TM would be helpful about now. What all awakened in Big Pine? From the road, we called our local physicians and arranged for an exam prior to Zach's flight to Copenhagen, for reassurance and review. It was hard to imagine that in a week he would be able to sit on a long flight and resume high level training and competition if his knee had greater concern, and if the pain he spoke of on this return trip continued. The pain subsided significantly upon return home and the knee diagnosed as a mild strain from the hiking. With no recognizable concerns that would prohibit him moving forward with his return commitment to SISU, the aforementioned noun, and SISU, the aforementioned club, he flew to Copenhagen and eagerly began his second season. Accompanying his game, he brought his awakened and purposeful leadership goals to share with this growing community of brotherhood overseas.

His immediate emails communicated a more satisfying living situation, with a Dane veteran of the club for a roommate, and an apartment more in the hub of the city's sweet spots. Following a first year living arrangement challenge that Zach made sure to address with the club after his first season, he was relieved to have an improved home base in season two shared with a great teammate. Written to us in a voice of confidence on Tuesday, August 20, 2013, Zach shares:

I am exploring taking Danish lessons and once my paperwork and worker permits are finalized, I plan on enrolling in the free courses that the government provides......I have no doubt I made the right choice in returning here.

Zach had envisioned Copenhagen as his future home. Eager to support and encourage our son with his renewed focus, I wrote long and newsy updates in weekly emails that year. I had chosen to leave a profession that was negatively impacting my own health the end of the previous school year, and thus I had greater space and time this particular fall season of 2013 to tend each family member, myself, and our home life. I was grateful yet unaware how necessary my availability would soon enough prove to be. His sister once again visited her brother overseas, a trip quite feasible due to her internship site of Barcelona, Spain. Her trip was less of a physical adventure exploring the sights together and more of an emotional support undertaking once fully understanding Zach's plight. His knee pain lingered and thus restricted him; efforts to heal were not successful. Something was beginning to unravel. Our daughter, often a beacon of light within the family, would have occasion such as this particular visit where she could offer some insight around a Zach circumstance. She tried to be optimistic for him amidst the disappointing reality of the situation. When we Skyped both of them together in Denmark, there seemed a distinct hurdle in front of Zach that she was clearly working at helping him clear just by the mere presence of her calm and caring influence. We were grateful she was with him, and we expressed our eager desire to join him sometime this season in the Copenhagen environment. But Zach's knee pain dragged on, and despite steady attempts to balance rest, competition, practice, and rehabilitative care, there was clearly something else interfering with his healing. Increasingly, he was with pain and limitation, and could not contribute at a level everyone knew he ordinarily would if he were 100%.

While he was working hard at wellness, and rotating between club participation and knee recovery, we continued to encourage and trust that he would overcome the ongoing challenge. He may have already begun to hold doubt, for on Monday, September 30, I wrote Zach to acknowledge receipt of a large envelope from a school in Iowa, and made mention of two phone call messages received from a school director offering to answer any questions Zach might have about the school. I expressed our curiosity about the mail and phone calls, and privately, we wondered if the nagging injury had influenced a next step shift somehow in his master plan of Zach intention. His response was subtle and aloof, asking us to simply set it aside for when he returned. Just shy of 3 months from his flight out to Denmark, his story further unfolds in an email dated Friday, October 25, 2013:

Well, well, well

The last 24 hours have been an emotional roller coaster, for me, for coach, for the team and for the club. The bad news, my knee is not healing and may require surgery. All to be determined upon my return home. I've met with numerous doctors and physical therapists. And they all tell me the same things. I have to give my knee time in order to let it heal and even then, surgery may be necessary. It is just unknown. Meniscus tears, especially small ones like mine aren't a science yet in the medical field.

There are many mixed opinions on whether or not surgery or rehab is the best means of treatment. Thus, the business side of professional basketball trumps the relational aspect and due to the uncertainty of my knee, and the prospect of my future as a basketball player, we have come to the conclusion that I must listen to my body and stop now. So it is with a heavy heart that I'll be returning home. My contract is terminated. The good news, is that I will recover, I will be able to temporarily pursue other venues in my life path outside of basketball and I will now have a true Thanksgiving for the first time in years. I hope this is not too much of a burden for you two and there is much to be discussed and determined, I'm just not in the frame of mind to do so at the moment. Let's still plan on Skyping sometime on Sunday. See you soon!

His scheduled flight home was on October 31, Halloween night. We knew of no trick to this unfortunate storyline. His time back home with us we would consider and receive as a treat, even though there was very little that was sweet about it for him. He continued to present himself as a man of SISU stature, of quest intention and pursuit, and yet greater powers and forces seemed to be at work in this young man's emerging self. The summer quest may have been an awakening to much more than self-actualization. I responded immediately.

Zach love,

I can only imagine the roller coaster of emotions, and we all know that life and its journey is unpredictable. You are our Halloween treat, and <u>*nothing*</u> *about you coming home to us is a burden. We are here for you, and we will be here for you as next steps, next decisions are made. Thank you for such a difficult email, and for your continued efforts to try and make this work, despite the nagging presence of this injury. I think you needed to do this in the manner you have, and I am glad you were in Copenhagen with people you trust versus another country or program with less care and trust.*

Insert 22 • **2013 Copenhagen basketball**

Chapter 13: Bound for a Rebound

Fix You, Coldplay

Rebound, Wayman Tisdale

In classic 'micro manager' fashion, John and I immediately contacted a local team of surgical specialists who had performed various surgeries over the previous fifteen years for both John and Gabby, and now would include Zachary in their patient care. Rebound, as the clinic is known, consists of a prestigious team of surgeons, who among their patient rosters are professional athletes treated for the type of diagnosis Zach would likely be given. We specifically requested a doctor who had successfully operated on John's knee and ankle in the past, and who had a history of working with athletes. Zach had not even landed, and we were already preparing for takeoff. We were confident that he could find out a diagnosis for his knee, schedule necessary treatment, and rebound from this setback. Pun intended. Zach arrived home from overseas a month before Gabby was to arrive home from Spain, finishing her internship and then going on to finish her final five months of college. This window allowed the three of us necessary time to be focused primarily on his immediate care. On November 4, he had an intake evaluation, a physical and an MRI scheduled. Found to be a healthy 25year old with the exception of the presenting tenderness and pain in the right knee, the patient review of systems was negative for symptoms constitutional (weight, fever, fatigue, malaise), ENT (ear, nose and throat), cardiovascular, eyes, respiratory, gastrointestinal, genitourinary, musculoskeletal, skin, endocrine, neurologic, hematologic, pulmonary, and psychiatric disorder, quoted directly from the medical profile record sheet. The MRI findings revealed a right knee lateral meniscus displaced bucket-handle tear, small joint effusion, and pre-patellar fibrosis. On November 14, the surgeon discussed surgery for a right knee arthroscopic lateral meniscectomy, a common surgery for the knee treating a common injury for basketball players. The surgery was approved and successful. At the 10day post op appointment, the exam showed proper healing and response. Zach was eager to get back to training and would begin a physical therapy routine he was extremely dedicated to following for the next 6-8 weeks. It was his hope and plan to secure another overseas team destination and roster spot by February or March. In the meantime, home cooking and holiday meals were on the dining table while post graduate school flyers had his name on the mailing label. Alternative plans were in the makings, but 'Plan A' remained playing basketball. Some observations by John and me at this time of Zach's healing and recovery, included an easily aroused state of agitation previously unseen in Zach's personality, a more withdrawn, contemplative, and anxious mindset and disposition that we thought might just be about the impact and outcome of injury setback, and a feverish desire to lay plans for finding a destination other than our hometown and our living room.

It would be difficult to return as a 25year old to the confines of your parent's home and the hometown parameters that once defined you but no longer were relatable. He had travelled the world through basketball, and he had explored the self at a deeper level, finding meditation, and alternative spiritual views to guide his own personal journey. John and I knew he was frustrated at the physical limitation of his knee, and how it might force a shift from his immediate intentions of playing professionally more quickly to the next steps of a bigger vision he held for his life direction. We again observed some previously noticed physical changes since his last visit home, and these included knee clicking noises that sounded like repetitive knuckle cracking especially when climbing stairs, extreme and persistent lower back pain whether standing or sitting, and a certain subtle malaise or fatigue that lingered. There continued to be an awareness between us of how argumentative he was becoming, how his body seemed to be responding to the years of physical wear at what we thought was too young of an age, and just how something about him simply seemed off balance. His whole body presentation felt ironically in contradiction to the joy and peace he had found and practiced through meditation, yoga, vision quest integration, and through written expression that had previously been vibrantly smart, loving, playful, and hope driven. Depression might be present, we considered, but he was not isolating nor was he without desire for and contribution toward work, personal and public engagement, and laughter play amidst the subtle shifts. We confidently knew him to not be drug affected, as he was not a user beyond the occasion of recreational participation in various social circles, or the social indulgence on occasion with beer, wine or cocktail. Addictive drug use and abuse were in contradiction to his mindful intentions and his personal athletic commitments and priorities. He was never a user of this definition. Increasingly, even his casual social use and participation disappointed his intentions, particularly in the power and pull of excessive alcohol influences within peer circles. He would share this with us and we understood he was attempting to distance himself more from such youthful, unproductive behavior. We accepted all of this to be part of a life stage transition, leaving behind one's wilder, younger days, which might include some relationship separation temporary or longer term. A case could be made that he began to isolate from local friends, but it was named by him as intentional because of personal changes and choices. Again, the shifts felt normal enough to accept without question, not unusual enough for deeper concern.

Zach and I would more frequently encounter conflict through assertive debate and discussion, followed by eventual resolution. This was especially true when exploring and confronting what I would call the mindset move to 'Plan B' from the professional basketball circuit of 'Plan A'. Perhaps because I managed the minutia of the household budget, I was typically the adult who would ask the tough questions regarding personal finances, health insurance, plans for work and earnings, especially if not offered up voluntarily. The conversations seemed parentally responsible to discern and establish mutual expectations between dependence and independence. The primary personal conflict for him in this unexpected setback window of time was that he just wasn't sure about his knee healing. No matter how hard he worked at rehab, the pain and discomfort lingered. His body ached and he could not kick the fatigue. None of us had any idea that a health crisis of huge significance might be hovering, already awakening and soon to be hollering! Rather, the pressure to decide next step choices toward work or schooling was what hovered and all was without clarity. John and I felt no heightened alarm about our son's overall wellbeing at this time, or that he lacked the discipline or drive while in the midst of sorting out his young adult perspective thrust into this unforeseen circumstance. But, we were all confused about how the increasing expression and desire for independence and severance would intersect with the increasing reality of necessary dependence accompanied by some occasional behavioral irreverence! Each of us was still equally vocal and demonstrative in our affection and respect toward each other in these transition months, just as we were to the wearying ever present conflicts of career uncertainty and next step options. In general, it felt like healthy and important dialogue, even if our exchanges sometimes got verbally assertive and voluminously expanded! We each had opinions and we each wanted to be heard. Love was never in question, but loud was sometimes the escalation! The anxiety level and adult exchanges were new territory. But old territory still balanced the heat, for a common expression of love and appreciation that this family had adopted and exercised often was to message on special occasions through thoughtful cards as gifts. Many of these examples are provided within the chapters to offer comparison as written and spoken messages get darker and more disturbing in time, revealing some form of sickness shift.

On my birthday eve of 2013, I received an email directly reflective of Zach's 'Plan B' perspective, after much conversation of departing 'Plan A'. In the grander scheme of personal career development planning, and quite likely the simultaneous subconscious weight of parental pleasing and channeling, Zach delivered me an email gift in the following decree:

> *Before I forget again, what better day to share my future plans than today. This is the program and place where I intend to do my doctorate upon completing my masters at MUM. Specifically, their Ph.D. program in depth psychology with an emphasis in Somatic studies.*
> *LOVE YA*

The mailed packet that had arrived at our doorstep in late September was from Mahareshi University of Management (MUM), and since then, we had received school literature from Naropa University in Boulder, Colorado, and Pacifica Graduate Institute in Carpenteria, California. Zach had been researching schools with programs that honored and aligned with his beliefs, his interests, and his larger vision of purposeful work. He still intended to bring the acquired skill from this higher level of education back to the athlete community that he perceived to be holistically in dire need of healing pathways. When the birthday email arrived, I quickly responded with written encouragement and support, even though, in classic Beth/mom mind, I was simultaneously wondering how he would fund all of this. Did he have a 'Plan C' (cash)? Racing through my mind were thoughts that included, 'his earnings and savings would be eaten quickly by these programs, he would need to explore student loans and grants, we cannot afford to take this on!' Anxiety was a nagging friend of mine. Worry was its finger wagging partner.

But Zach was busy building his own plan. He had sold his big green beast, the Ford Expedition, and this would be a kick start. Getting work and eventually finding an apartment to live off campus at MUM were goals for creating his coveted independence again. He made it quite clear, emphatically stating, that these were HIS plans and that HE would figure out how to make them happen! In other words, back off, Mom. All too often, I would fixate on behalf of both my children about minimizing any debt in the startup of one's adult life and creating strong credit. Zach had no debt thanks to his athletic job at college, and smart self-control around opportunities for credit card use, so why not build up more income rather than take on the debt of schooling, I would reason. And how will you pay for a health issue should you get sick or injured, I wondered. Be sure to afford health care, as you never know when you need it, even if you are a young, vibrant, active athlete in your prime. You never know. But we all would come to know soon enough. Between health insurance worries, financial debt fears, and teachable moments around independent living, I could become a 'negative Nellie', an 'anxious Annie', and a 'controlling Connie'. These were fine examples of transference, not transcendence, as I had begun my own adult life with very little means or guidance, had some occasions of sloppy spending or budget stretching, and often felt the chase of catching up as life offered one expense after the other. Various unexpected surgeries along our family journey caught us off guard and cost us plenty even with quality employer insurance. Coaching my children about adult life transition strategies and future possibilities of choice and outcome that it took me a lifetime to learn and find balance around, seemed responsible and smart. I never thought of it as controlling or manipulative. Even when I pushed about getting work, helping out, being prepared, there were no regrets then and there, nor here and now. Independence carried these responsibilities, so welcome to adulthood! That is, if you are well and able.

Frequently, I would read about their peer generation wallowing in college debt or credit card abuse. I had been intentionally teaching them to establish good credit and to manage credit and monies wisely. A planner to a fault, though, I was all too often thinking and organizing around future events and expectations, trying to be prepared for what is yet to come. Often, I would lose sight of appreciating the here and now of the present! Apparently, it was in the future that I hoped to be more present! I would no doubt benefit steering a bit more to the here, and bowing a bit more to the now. Zach and I had to find balance in these truths we both held. I presented that my fears and worries may not be helpful, but that my planning for the future was. He responded that his own anxiety around past choices may not be helpful, but living for the present moment in time was. Today was all we were guaranteed, he would point out. Tomorrow has to be funded, I would respond. We both held truth and we all persevered. Mutual respect mattered. While Zach would strive to be fully present in his practices, his studies, his adaptations to what life offered, and his forward moving actions on decisions and choices to influence life purpose and direction, it became increasingly obvious to him how hard it would be to practice the 'here and now' mantra while living under the today and tomorrow and beyond principles of our seasoned self-supporting selves. John and I had not evolved enough yet to embrace and value a balance of 'here and now' mindfulness while yet so ensconced in a futuristically driven pace and mindset of bills, work deadlines, home projects, relationship demands, and overall life management. Adulthood, it has its burdens and balances, and we certainly were not meditating nor transcending to relieve and release them! Rather, we were constantly balancing future home and lifestyle upgrades and the budget allowance to pay for them, all the while approaching our retirement years with intentional preparedness and decisions to fund that! This was our reality mantra of our here and now! For Zach's intention of shaping an immediate future, he felt he had to move out of the house to make clear and timely next step choices. He began to explore alternatives, bound elsewhere for sure, but with an unexpected rebound that would shortly follow.

Happy Birthday!

Thanks for putting up with your Butterfly - Monkey son throughout this transformative, volatile and vulnerable time. I'm most grateful for your efforts and desires toward understanding me, because they further us both to a new place of growth. This unexpected block of time "home" will forever be the foundation of our adult relationship. It has been a much needed period for healing and has given me the opportunity to make peace and celebrate the natural severance that is taking place.

Naturally, pain hurt and confusion precede comfort, healing and understanding. I am turning a corner within many relationships of mine; setting boundaries, burning bridges and strengthening others. Ultimately, I know that the next time I leave, I'll be a better man, son, brother, friend, lover and person.

My time here is dying, and is soon to be dead. Vancouver does not offer me much anymore, in the way of my growth. My path and its direction are being dictated by events and opportunities which are manifesting themselves in my mind, body and soul. It's my responsibility now, to forge my own path, outside of your jurisdiction and most likely outside of your understanding. It is my way and I have to go it alone. Our home, our family, friends and community have been a perfect platform, but they are no longer a fitting base camp.

These reflections have reminded me of how much I have to be thankful for. A loving mother and father. A best friend as a sister. Deeply embedded bonds of brotherhood between an ever-shrinking circle of old friends. Closure with coaches and teachers. The closing of not only chapter but of the book of youth and young manhood. Due to the strength of your love and support, I am finally ready to be a man — finally ready to own my plans and create my realities. Trust in your work as my mother and rest assured that you taught me well!

Thank you for the unconditional love of motherhood. Thank you for your humor. Thank you for letting me be an ass. Thank you for letting me call you a bitch. Thank you for the comforts of home and for a childhood unparalleled by my peers. Thank you for accepting that it's time for me to go out into the world on my own. Thank you for my foundation and thank you for my faith!

Embrace this new year and perhaps my enlightened transformation into adulthood will help inspire your own open minded evolution. I look forward to future conversations that may arise from your curiosities, because spirituality, for me, has no one creed and demands no devotion. The subjectivity of spirit is a fascinating enterprise and in my mind, no two souls are ever truly alike. The soul is the fingerprint of God, and is a means of individualized, ethereal identification. May we all continue to imprint our spiritualities upon ourselves and each other, celebrating the universal truths between us, along the way! →

I LOVE YOU VERY MUCH!
                    - ZACH

Insert 23 • 2013 Mother's birthday card message

Chapter 14: MUM'S the Word

The World at Large, Modest Mouse
Soul Meets Body, Death Cab for Cutie

When Zach arrived home in November for his knee surgery, he was eager to speak to us about a desire to visit a school he had been researching for quite some time as a post graduate possibility in the 'Plan B' stage of alternatives to playing basketball. The packet that had arrived to our Vancouver address while he was in Copenhagen, and the phone calls seeking a Mr. Zachary Moritz were from the Maharishi University of Management (MUM) in Fairfield, Iowa. Now, if that is not a school name that has all kinds of stereotyped perception around it, a basketball is not round! John and I even had to get beyond our own personal stereotyped fears and pre conceived notions of bias about the school name itself. Thanks to Zach's resource referrals, as well as the link he sent us to Oprah Winfrey's taped interview with the town mayor about the school premise, we became increasingly more receptive to understanding and acceptance. It was, of course, an entirely different challenge for us to develop the comfortable choice of language and message content spoken by either of us when introducing the school, especially its name, to others less comfortable with different. Locals and family friends would often inquire about the whereabouts of Big Z, and we would not shy away from whatever his truth was, even if we didn't fully understand his choices or how to define or describe them. We were preoccupied with trying to broaden our own consciousness as we learned to embrace our son's pursuits, working to not steep ourselves in judgement as we earlier on found ourselves doing, and often felt others did within our community. The look on people's faces was priceless, especially within the church, but pretty much anywhere when you would tell locals he was visiting a school in Iowa called Mahareshi University of Management to consider for graduate enrollment. It didn't take long for us to not only understand how someone like a Zach needed to leave behind a small town mindset, but also how important it was for us to stand in his corner and help bridge that process. Increasingly, there was a consistency in his interests and a symmetry to the design of something significant in his life. We felt we were witnessing claims within his quest proclamation from August 2013 moving in the direction of actualization. We were amazed and impressed at how he had accepted this knee setback and reassessed his path. Zach introduced us to Transcendental Meditation and a clearer understanding of transcendence, invited us to the closing ceremonies of a rite of passage quest, exposed us to the cleansing ritual of a smudge, and now introduced us to a unique consciousness-based educational community that Oprah featured on her TV show in March of 2012. He was convinced that detail would win me over, avid Oprah fan, I am. Never a dull moment in the life of Big Z.

Our son made a decision to travel out to the school to participate in a visitation weekend, thus scheduling a flight to blustery Iowa in the midst of a brutal winter, February 7-10, 2014. His knee was not feeling well enough to currently pursue 'Plan A', so he decided this was his here and now window to 'Plan B'. The visitors weekend included facility tours, staff introductions, TM talks regarding school philosophy and instructional format, course visitation, and financial aid options. Returning enthusiastically inspired, he shared schematics he had drawn of a business plan concept for his vision of a mind body spirit institute specifically for athletes. He envisioned yoga, breathing techniques, meditation, music, various forms of therapy as tools to enlighten and enrich an athlete's work toward successful personal management of both sport and life demands. He aspired to help athletes strive and thrive, his words. The visit inspired him. Zach was drawn to the Master of Arts in Maharishi Vedic Science program, but he understood he might have to take some prerequisite undergraduate courses. The idea of enrolling as a full time student and not a student athlete, enrolling in a school that required two twenty-minute meditation practices daily by all students, staff and faculty, provided only organic vegetarian meals, required a drug free, alcohol free and tobacco free campus, emphasized the arts and entrepreneurship, and offered a block system of courses where only one course is taken at a time, seemed a slam dunk score for Zach. And yet, former fears and latent labels laced with insecurity haunted him with residual doubt. His K-12 education's negative teacher to student messages, the average to possibly even sub-par academic outcome at university, and the resulting university transcript records he felt should be stronger from someone who had more intelligence than he felt he had applied, all influenced his concerns as to whether he would receive a formal MUM acceptance. Upon reviewing transcripts, would they view him differently from the manner in which he was so wonderfully and respectfully received at visitation, offering them his vision for athletes and sharing his idealized schematic sketch, he worried. He was a changed young man from those youthful days of high school and undergraduate studies, and he truly wanted to apply himself differently in a community that would nurture and value each individual's holistic intelligence. Upon return from this Iowa visit, and immersed in some worrisome self-doubt, Zach momentarily considered moving in with his uncle to a small town east out on the Columbia Gorge where he might focus on healing and find work. He even reconsidered seeking work locally while living at home and training for a hoped fall season return to basketball. But with sudden determination, confidence and clarity, his fire and focus rekindled. He sought out his undergraduate transcripts, contacted MUM and arranged to enroll by the end of the month. We were enthused yet still concerned about his physical health, the increasingly familiar but uncharacteristic exhibition of anxiety that would surface frequently in conversation. and a very vague plan for long term financial management. Something felt increasingly uncertain about Zach's shifting persona, and we could not name it as anything beyond a 25year old seeking a productive path in life. He spent the week before he left eagerly preparing and enjoying the remaining days with us. Mom, Dad, and son attended the recent Lego movie as a sendoff, and the theme song lyrics resonated with our moment in time. It would be awesome for Zach to become part of a new team, a new community, a lived out dream. In just two weeks post visitation, Zach returned to MUM as an enrolled student, eager to once again, find likeminded community and personal relevance to support his intentions. Classes began February 24, and we agreed to his respectful dependence seeking request for some severance from parental support and nurture, lovingly and eagerly provided his entire life.

This young, ambitious adult was trying to teach us to let go and let be, so as to personally grow and soulfully be set free. He pursued his independence through redirected intention, effort and execution, and he encouraged us to reclaim our own lives, shifting our adult launching focus and attention to Gabby, as needed in her final months at university. Zach asked that we refrain from Skyping or calling for four weeks to allow us all transition, and we welcomed the idea, encouraging him with love and prayers as escorts toward his continued journey of self-fulfillment. We felt optimistic, but there was this looming loose ended concern Mom would present first about health insurance. Only three months remained on John's employer insurance coverage for Zach, which meant upcoming insurance severance took precedence over adult independence severance! The two of us exchanged emails within the first week at MUM, and the Affordable Health Care Act became our new best friend. Enrolled in Washington coverage should he return home before June 6, his 26th birthday, and also enrolled in Iowa coverage in the event he would remain in school and find employment there for the summer, he could drop whatever plan was not needed prior to his birth date. Mom would now sleep at night knowing her son had health care coverage beyond the discontinuation of his parental provisional care. How prophetic that priority would prove to be on the not too distant horizon.

Just weeks after Zach's departure, John and I shared a much needed vacation to the Hawaiian island of Kauai with dear friends in late March, celebrating 30 years of our marriage anniversary. Our son's seemingly settled life drama and movement toward desired independence, coinciding with our daughter's upcoming college graduation and intended life launch to follow, lead us to believe we were moving beyond these demanding and consuming parent years. The island respite offered itself as another rest stop interlude in the 'life as a highway' metaphoric road. The intersection of our agreed upon 30day severance from any initial Iowa contact expired on Hawaiian time. We had earned the green light to call! But, he sounded strangely frightened and vulnerable, which left us equally frightened and vulnerable. The light at this intersection now turned yellow. What to do long distance other than to encourage and love? Upon return and following a short mother daughter spring break get away to the San Juan Islands, John, Gabby and I each shared conversation and concern about Zach's wellbeing in Iowa. Each had either spoken to him on the phone or via Skype in late March early April, and we all agreed that he increasingly sounded confused, paranoid, frightened, and vulnerable. He was not adjusting well to the dietary plan, the class he enrolled in he felt ill prepared for, the winter was 7 below zero in Iowa, and yet he insisted to persevere none the less. Worried, but also wanting to honor his intentions, we gave him time to work through the challenges, and ask for help and support from family or staff when he felt incapable. Our shared conversations continued to be quite uncharacteristic, and we were consequently ready at a moment's notice, to cross the line he had drawn regarding our support and involvement. This former king of thrive had fortuitously developed a supportive relationship with the Director of Student Services at the university. Zach informed us that the two were working together through his various transitions of meditation circles, classroom challenges, dormitory mates, meetings, and protocols, as well as arranging for a mattress addition onto the cold dorm room floor because Z could not fit the standard size beds. Zach attempted to manage it all, welcoming the solitude of the single dorm rooms, striving to thrive while transitioning within this new tribe. The placement was a far cry from his freshman year of undergraduate studies in Boise, when he moved about 30 pairs of his athletic shoe collection into the crowded dorm room, burying the sizeable boxes under the bed and wherever else he could house them as near and accessible! Oh, the excess! I witnessed that to be a chaotic, cluttered, pizza box laden dorm room double, shared with a fellow rookie teammate equally as messy and carefree. That university did, however, have extra-long beds for their athletes of supersized length!

To Iowa, he took few belongings, having acquired an awakening of more practical stewardship and a heightened sensitivity to the American lifestyle of excess. He informally adopted a 'less is more' mantra from overseas travel and quest reflection, now more consciously living with a leaner cleaner approach to existence while seeking a more consciousness based format of formal education. Select significant books, music, clothing and room necessities travelled lightly with him in this life season. With no car to transport himself and a wicked winter waging, his Fairfield footprint would be simple and restrained in design, comfort, and impact. We hoped this destination of choice combined with his determination and developing voice would find common fertile ground. Instead, that ground shook uncommonly so by mid-April of 2014. Holy Week, and a mystery series was about to erupt.

Chapter 15: Reawakening in Iowa

My Sweet Lord, George Harrison

Help! The Beatles

Zach's correspondence with us via email from Iowa through most of the month of March had been clear of thought and well written. Contradicting this were the phone call conversations we began to receive in early April, when we began to hear fear, uncertainty, conflict of thought and emotion around his health, strange delusionary and paranoid projections about people within his current environment and from Denmark. These were the first encounters with spoken thought patterns and ideas that made no sense to us. "She's here", he would begin to hauntingly declare. "Who is there, Zach?", we would ask. "My true love is here. I have seen her. She came with her father", he would continue in a dreamlike sequence. Ok, we thought, maybe he thinks someone at MUM is 'the one' for him. It began very innocently and unsuspecting of being unusual. The mention and legitimate acquaintance name held a possibility for truth, but the dreamlike delivery and listless lunacy was so extremely uncharacteristic of the Zach we knew. The behavior did seem odd. Random statements that we had no connection or association to, and logically did not even seem feasible, would be spoken in the middle of coherent conversations. "They are all against me!", Zach would claim, about whom, we did not know. John and I would gently but with persistence, ask questions and try to reason with this now stranger named Zach. We queried possible food challenges, temperature issues in the dorm room, access issues to health care support for the now mentioned fever and swollen glands he had, anything that might be triggers to these new and strange conversation pieces he offered. Did he need more protein, should we send some bars, could he get out on foot in the vicious winter weather and find his way into town to get himself supplements to the vegan only menu in the cafeteria? Was his room warm enough, especially sleeping on the floor with winter temperatures well below freezing; could he access additional blankets?

97

Was there someone who could help him get to the doctor or the medical clinic to check out the fever and glands?

Were we micro managing possible solutions when we did not have a clue what the problem was? For us parents, it was an exercise in balance beam discipline, trying to walk right foot, left foot, down the center of deep listening, right foot honoring our sons request for independence and then left foot holding the thought that he was not well and he might need help. A ten performance would include each of us in agreement that care was needed, and then working together as adults in support of one another. A healthy Zach would have understood this. Unhealthy Zach was seemingly not capable. As the adamantly independence seeking young adult, he was at this point driving the 'I am an adult' vehicle, and we were simply passengers in the back seat. He would hold the foot of his independence over the gas pedal of his intentions and either accelerate or decelerate, not understanding when the vehicle would not successfully move forward. Could he pull the car over, ask for help, get a mechanic, believe that he might benefit from help, and then trust that he could eventually get back on the road again? We were wondering if he might need to give up the wheel temporarily, and move himself over into that passenger seat. It seemed a balanced idea to us. Increasingly, it seemed his engine was breaking down. John and I were with growing concern as to just what was happening out there at this consciousness based, educational, meditational, and now 'frustrational' destination of his choosing. We were worried, and the edge of concern was sharpening. Increasingly, we wondered if we needed to encourage him to park that vehicle, service the engine, and allow us to help steer him home.

On the actual eve of our 30th wedding anniversary, April 14, 2014, my celebration was one of these strange phone conversations with Zach. He spoke to me for three hours on the phone, revealing personal shifts in both physical and mental state. Vacillating from gentle and vulnerable to angry and confrontational, he finally shared that he had not been feeling well. I spoke insistently of sending an airline ticket for him to come home and receive medical support in the comfort and compassion of our care. Zach made it clear he did not want to come home, but he finally agreed he may have to for wellness sake. I heard the pulsating pain of his internal conflict cry, and felt the parenting pull of my anniversary try. His message and argument we had come to understand through his guidance and direction. He was a happy go lucky child growing up in our home and in our community, and he so wanted to become a man of mindful matters, leaving his childhood baggage behind, moving his future image forward. A return to the comforts and familiarity of our home and our town at this formative foothold would lend itself to backward, not forward, he firmly believed. Past, present, future. Leave the past behind. Let the present be the gift, the future should be kind. It was a difficult admission when he finally allowed the truth of his circumstances to be spoken out loud. "Mom, I am really sick", he shared almost in a whisper. He told me he was too weak to walk, he had been experiencing fainting spells and black outs, he had lost more than 30 pounds, he was suffering from extreme fatigue, he had severe stomach cramps and an achiness was felt throughout his body. This engine had broken down. He further shared that he had been to the local hospital for help and was given some antibiotics for swollen glands and possible strep throat.

WTF, I am thinking! I begin to implode around the overwhelming sense that we might be in some type of crisis and yet, we don't really know what that crisis might be! Am I overreacting? How did we not know of such dramatic health changes? When did this all happen? At what point would we be notified? How is it that nothing was found at the hospital with such symptoms presenting? What is going on? What happened to the Zach we have known and loved for 25 years? Where is he? Do I need to step in and write 'the coaches' again? But we weren't driving the car, dammit! Pull over! The Family Educational Rights and Privacy Act of 1974, FERPA, was driving under their influence of withholding information without Zach's consent to share. Apparently, we were not quite on the threshold of an emergency where there might be some purpose in reaching out to the family. The medical insurance paperwork from the hospital visit we would have seen eventually, for he was still on our health care plan, but it had not yet arrived prior to this phone call. Our loved one was very sick, far away, and we must rally immediately. Health and healthcare remain the central tenets to a quality of life, and a youthfully naïve lesson in this truth was confronting each of us. Furthermore, any young man or woman's knowledge of access to and skill for navigating through a health care concern and a health care medical system, is typically at a freshman level especially in their teens and twenties. We elder men and women, considered mentors and family, need to faithfully guide them along to a more senior level of responsible knowledge, hopefully graduating them eventually toward a reasonable degree of independent ability for self-care and success. But then, really, when any one of us are sick, young or old, are we fully able to independently manage our care? If we are seldom sick or in the practice of even using a medical care system, what do we even know about how and when? Our young Zach was in need of these lessons, these truths, and a time for action was approaching. He believed he could care for his own health alone and independently in Copenhagen. He feared he could not in Iowa. Health care independence may be the ultimate fallacy. Stop the car and pull over. Get help. Trust in someone. Can we trust in the system?

During this April 2014, Holy Week calendar of time, nothing felt as holy as the health rescue of our son. All of the emerging adulthood, spiritual awakening, transcendence, and consciousness based everything else that Zach had introduced and shared with us took a momentary flush down the other john by this Beth and John. Fear was our #1 and anxiety was our #2, and both needed flushing. We had to clear our heads and hearts of both, and then create a focused plan of action. It was hard not to wonder if all of his searching and seeking had led to this unusual outcome. Maybe too much meditation, too much alternative spiritual thinking, too much visionary work was all to blame. Maybe even too much foot on the gas pedal, while rushing to an intriguing independent destination. Was there even something specific for us to blame? We had no idea. Please put on the brakes, Zach. And he did. In this anniversary moment of time, our son was frighteningly ill, alone, and in a place very foreign to us. He reluctantly asked for help, something against his ideals and hoped for intentions. When I emphatically told him I was coming to Iowa to safely bring him home, I experienced an immediate release of tension and despair shared by both of us. We wed our intentions. He responded to me, again in a fragile, almost wounded childlike manner, but without any hesitation. "When can you get here, Mom?" As soon as possible, son. Know that I am coming. It was Monday night late when we signed off of our distress signal phone call. I immediately communicated what had happened and what my plan was to John and Gabby and my sister Joanne. My sister had increasingly been connected to my concerns about her nephew and provided comforting support and care to all of us. My next necessary communication was with my counseling interns, each of whom I was scheduled to supervise that week. Shifting work around, and researching reasonable and doable airfare and flight schedules, booking rental car and hotel accommodations, the action plan John and I spoke of and coordinated around was both deliberate and expedient. I was to arrive safely to MUM, observe, manage, and resolve this mystery of a situation, and then do everything I could to get him on the plane and return home safely. We would together create a next set of steps once we got him home and under our umbrella of shelter and care. There were unknowns and uncertainties in the solution equation, but the known was that he needed and wanted help and we would be there for him. Of course.

In the fury of emails and communication that night and on into the next day around scheduling this rescue mission, our tender hearted and increasingly intuitive daughter had sent me an anniversary link of love medicine that touched my soul and quieted my angst momentarily in the mystery unraveling before us. I opened the link at 4 in the morning, and a lasting gift it was. She paid happy forward. My daughter sent me the link to Pharrell William's interview with Oprah about the phenomenal response to the release of the video for his wildly successful single 'Happy' from the Despicable Me 2 soundtrack. Watching the interview, hearing the song, seeing the worldwide reaction to the video, and witnessing Pharrell's reaction was so centering for me in the moment of readying myself for this trip and quieting my growing angst. Our own personal reactions and responses to the Happy song were among the multitudes of worldwide, joy filled, dance crazed reactions. It was infectious! To observe this video clip in the shadow of our momentary darkness, my wee hour of sleeplessness, my hoped for light and love and happiness - this was healing and inspiring to watch. I found it irresistible to not find oneself singing along, no matter the wee hour, no matter the fear power. What moved me most in the interview clip was the tender, vulnerably honest, real time reaction of Pharrell in expressing how overwhelmed he had been by this success, acknowledging that so many had believed in him for so long. This captured scene emphasized to the viewer the spontaneous interplay of his exact appreciative and humble words spoken, with the simultaneously unspoken but visibly very evident reaction and impact emotionally, perhaps even spiritually, to him as a result of the song and video's worldwide embrace. The momentary absence of words by Pharrell in the very vulnerable and personal scene stirred a deeply rooted emotion from within him, and likely from within any viewer, including my emotionally vulnerable self, right then, right there. The mere infectious nature of happy, the mere relationship to happy, the very possibility of happy, we all want it, seek it, celebrate it. Happy go lucky Zach, I am thinking. In that beautifully spontaneous, sacred moment within the interview, Oprah's gentle wisdom intervenes and she expresses so clearly and resoundingly a proclamation of what they had just shared in that moment. She, in a calm and confident steadiness, in a nurturing and quite omniscient manner of readiness and resolve, responds to Pharrell, and equally to all of her viewers, and likely even affirming the moment to herself. *"I know, I know, - it is used for something greater than yourself. I know."* Thank you, Pharrell. Thank you, Oprah. And thank you, Gabrielle, for sharing a timeless uplift and reminder. There is an unknown, uncertain, but yet to unfold mystique in what lay ahead of us, but possibly our embrace with some grace would reveal something greater than ourselves and we would find happy. This was how I received the happy link uplift gift in my waning wee hour of wonder. The gesture and the link content encouraged me to carry on and keep faith.

Within two days of my departing flight to rescue some happiness and return with hopefulness, our daughter travelled down from Seattle to come home that final 3day weekend of her college career, eager to greet her brother and mother upon airport return and perhaps add some version of family happy to our truth trial of an unconventional Easter Sunday. Dad and daughter would keep themselves busy together and comfort one another through the duration of that wait and wonder. It had been difficult for her especially, to focus on the demands of her final weeks of college while learning of her brave brother's mysterious health disruption. The family of four would have a brief but meaningful reunion at the Portland airport, intending to reunite again soon after in celebration of her college graduation arriving in two months. The plan was for all of us to attend, with his health setback well on the way to full mend. Best laid plans. The anniversary eve phone conversation between Zach and I had at least generated a university contact name of staff working to assist Zach's situation, the Director of Student Services. I asked Zach to please let the director know I would be calling him. In my preparations to leave for Iowa, and with Zach's consent provided, I reached out to the school and we exchanged call backs until a connection was made. A very kind, caring, and concerned soul was met in the school director, a doctoral of psychology staff member, who, after repeating a few times how glad he was that I would be coming, then proceeded to heighten my concerns and fears as he spoke further. I learned that this man had taken Zach to the Fairfield emergency room on March 31. Zach had been complaining of extreme fatigue, swollen glands, achy joints and body pain. A full laboratory and diagnostic evaluation had been done with no revealing indication of reason for his ailments. Recently, the director continued to share, Zach had been isolating more, not eating, experiencing severe migraines, vertigo and nausea. He recommended we get him home and pursue neurological and psychological evaluation. Excuse me, I am thinking to myself, while I recover from the weight of those two extreme suggestions; what did you just say? What has triggered these symptoms for him in less than two months' time at this school? I am in somewhat of a state of shock, especially when this administrator suggests that Zach could possibly have a brain tumor and that an MRI should be performed to rule it out. OK. I get a grip and refocus again around our first important step, which remained getting our son home safely. He then suggested Zach would likely need a wheelchair to assist transport to and from the plane, as it was uncertain if he would be able to find the strength to walk without incurring a blackout. At this point, I was not singing 'Happy' and there seemed to be something very despicable happening. Something was stirring in Zach, and it didn't seem to be spiritual in nature nor receptive to much nurture. Yet, it was our nature to nurture, and as parents, we were quite spiritually synched and most readily receptive to rescue and recovery. Mom was well on her way, loaded with love and care to share, and a still deeply devoted heart of prayer. Holy Week. Please be holy.

Chapter 16: Rescue Mission, Iowa

The Sounds of Silence, Simon and Garfunkel

Darkness, Darkness, Robert Plant

Spiritually speaking, for many weeks, John and I had been seeking prayer and emotional support from a church committee team we were in active ministry with, and from a vast array of friends and family. The afternoon before I flew out to Des Moines, Iowa, I wrote a massive plea to this faith based village for prayers and love while explaining what we thought we were stepping into. I was specific around details of what we were experiencing, what Zach was experiencing, our prayer needs for safe travel and sound medical care. This plea included an expressed desire to defer any questions for which we likely wouldn't be able to answer for some time. I couldn't fathom carrying that responsibility amidst the work ahead. We needed to receive internally on the deep inhale without the giving externally on our necessary exhale. It may be more blessed to give than to receive, but sometimes we may find ourselves needing to accept receipt of what others more ably can give. This perspective would be as foreign to us as the town and school in Iowa would prove to be. We mastered the art of giving. At this crossroad of our life, however, the giving was going to be channeled into Zach and our immediate family. From within our various communities of connection to social, family, sport, church, and volunteer circles, this servant mindset equation had never been so tipped toward our need to receive. We were a family accustomed to giving of ourselves, and as a result, we had a wide and diverse network of care to draw from in return. It was now time to call in the dividends, while still protecting the personal investments, so to speak. I completed that written confession and absolution to my village with a closing reference to the fact that I was travelling the mission in the midst of Holy Week. I flew out on Ash Wednesday and returned on Easter Sunday, holding this rhetoric more as metaphoric, and hardly euphoric.

In that naked and honest, soul baring reveal of a time, I continued to hold a deep and personal belief in God's plan and promise. I held as symbolic, this overlapped occurrence of the season of rebirth and resurrection, its thematic application to our circumstance and its timing, regardless of Mahareshi vs. Martin Luther. I believed that this strange and uncertain retrieval, this dark and mysterious upheaval, would come to reveal all and we would rise up from it and begin anew. We would approach this with a relentless commitment, not even knowing what we were yet up against. I leaned in to my God and my Savior, prayers and prayer requests, friendships and family whom I trusted for support, and at the time, I held an indomitable personal spirit and active faith. We held hope, wrapped up in love, and we were confident that it would sustain us all for whatever lay ahead. Zach was returning from what was to be another mountain top type experience, and together, we were now headed toward some deep and dark valleys that lay well beyond Japan, Zamora, Copenhagen, Big Pine, and even Iowa. But first, the flat cornfields and soaring hawks of Iowa beckoned. While on my outbound flight to the great Midwest, I distracted myself with a newly published book a health conscious family friend of mine had recommended called *Grain Brain*. She knew our son, and she knew the pieces of our story. This may help him, she encouraged, and in its eventual adoption and application, the message of this book would serve each of our family members toward improved health. The author, Dr. David Perlmutter, a renowned neurologist, promotes the concept that carbs can destroy your brain, and provides sufficient research and professional experience to prove his boldly stated claim. Dementia, ADHD, epilepsy, anxiety, chronic headaches, depression, decreased libido, and many more afflictions could be dramatically reduced from the practice of changing your diet, especially eliminating gluten and sugars. This book felt serendipitous in its timing, for I would decide immediately to promote the idea of this dietary path to Zach and adopt its recommended practices for the benefit of us all. Perhaps this would help us address these sudden health symptoms he had been experiencing. I felt encouraged to at least share with him one worthy idea of healing practice to benefit him and the family.

On my drive from Des Moines to the town of Fairfield, I wondered how my son would greet me. Would he be in a wheelchair? What does 6'10" look like at 205 pounds? I wanted to race up to him, physically pick him up and emotionally carry him all the way home to safety. I wished the rescue and recovery could be as simple to carry out as the thought and desire was that rose up within me. He was an adult at 25 years of age, and I would instead work together with him toward coordinating a respectful, yet non-negotiable from our perspective, return to our home for care and repair. He was not my little boy to carry home and tend anymore, but rather, what I now referred to as my man child, whom I would forever offer care and support should he need it. I fully understood that he was not mine in this existence on earth in the first place. A first home for him within my womb, a vehicle for his birth and entry point into life, and one of many earthly guides leading him on toward his own path, I understood separation would come. An independent pathway would be necessary and normal. It had been a great joy to witness the choices and decisions he was making toward his own path to something meaningful, a path to something greater than himself. We would all be so happy, should this play out. But for now, he needed me, and I arrived. I pulled into the county seat of Jefferson County, Iowa, the city of Fairfield; its fields were fair and the town center had a simple Midwestern flair. Following the map toward the university and to Zach's dorm, I was struck by the campus simplicity. The looming Tower and the Golden Domes were the extreme exceptions, both symbolic landmarks of the town but even more so to the school, Mahareshi School of Management, commonly referred to as MUM. Circling the campus twice while I yet had daylight, and then finally parking the rental in the dorm parking lot, I phoned Zach. In that surreal moment, I wondered how the rental reality would suffice with regard to Zach's body pain discomfort and physical size fold up when we would drive the 2 hour plus trip back to the airport in it together on Sunday morning. It would have to do. We would have to do it. As I stood outside the drab dormitory building, he slowly ambled out to greet me, accompanied by his well-travelled, Chrome Industry cargo backpack filled with a few necessities and his infamous aluminum water bottle in tow. Both were Zach props that had traversed the globe more than I, in their short lifetime of usage by that traveling man. He was also accompanied by an immediate desire to get to the hotel king bed and rest more comfortably on a supersized mattress with a bed frame up off the floor. A continuation of controlled quiet and restricted light was equally desirable. Overcome with relief and instinctive motherly love, I melted into a fragile hug from my towering, kind hearted, slow moving, oh so vulnerable son. He walked to me, no wheelchair! Hallelujah! Risen indeed! Such sacrilege, the metaphor held on this Ash Wednesday eve, ashes to ashes, dust to dust. As I stood in the shadow of the Mahareshi

Golden Domes of Pure Knowledge and in the foreground of the Mahareshi Tower of Invincibility, I am without knowledge and I do not feel invincible. But it all feels holy and full of possibility.

I do still hold onto faith. I can only hope that a universal knowledge of inner happiness, outer success, and world peace will guide us to an invincible strength for overcoming what lies ahead of the Moritz family. Again, metaphorically speaking, in light of the immediate surroundings and the icons of symbolism just steps beyond us, may we each find what we came here looking for, I thought. In that vulnerable moment of time, he and I were crossing a religious bridge and a philosophical stairwell between our personal sets of spiritual beliefs and values, and our individual definitions of healing and wellness need. Compromises were made in the name of love, in the emotions of hope, in the forces of fearless faith, and in the crisis of care. We would compromise conversation immediately for the severe migraines were the first symptom to greet me following the hug. Throbbing head pain resumed. A king bed beckoned. We found our Best Western hotel option once again, although a different couple, mother and son, in a Midwestern Iowa town of approximately 10,000 residents versus a Southeastern California town of approximately 4,000. Travel points for a reduced rate, a room with a king and a sleeper sofa, a hot tub and pool for pain relief, and reasonable access to the campus all played in to this chosen entry point of recovery and return. We were booked for 4 nights, and I had to work diligently and decisively to ready him for the flight home. Our room and the atmosphere within became a darkened tomb quickly, as he lay in bed nonstop the first 24 hours, curtains permanently closed, no TV or music, lights at a minimum and silence requested. It was an immediate introduction to the strange and unfamiliar Zach persona we had never encountered prior and a reality check to the seriousness we were facing. How was I going to get this behemoth of an unwell yet independent adult to his medical care? He had to cooperate. His initial pattern of quiet isolation and very flat affectation interfered with the necessary doctor visit and pharmacy prescription fill we needed to complete together by the very next day. To succeed in that law abiding accomplishment, since I had no legal authority to act on his behalf, I had to engage him, motivate him, transport him, and trust in him. And he had to trust in me. From the moment of hotel and room check in, I finally exhaled a long and slow sigh of relief. Once he was in bed and resting, I noted that at least on the outward appearance, he looked better than I imagined.

SONFLOWER

He was a handsome man, with dark thick eyebrows that appeared as if they were painted so perfectly on his face, penetratingly alluring blue green eyes, and a jawline and hairline not unlike the silhouette of some striking fashion model.

This maturing physical appearance as he aged tended to call attention in his adult life, not unlike his forever height feature, yet I believed him to remain humble and not egotistical by this truth and its potential power. Although he looked reasonably stable to me lying peacefully in that hotel bed, I knew with no uncertainty that he was not. I just couldn't name why. I just couldn't name what. While we were in the car driving to the hotel, I noted from him a flat affectation, a lethargy, and a disconnect to any enthusiasm or clarity of thought beyond the very present quiet of now. That very present now for him was one that included severe migraine, light and sound sensitivity, tingling sensations, ringing in the ears, tremors, pain throughout his back and joints, stomach pains, and delusional thought process around a woman and her father, whoever they were! Once in the hotel room, if I had to turn lights on to see, or use the bathroom, or read a book, or use my computer, he became very agitated by the light and the sound. This was my introduction to a series of reactive responses that our family would proceed to adopt in the months ahead. On this trip, my personal adaptations included tiptoeing, slowing down and minimizing all movement of body motions and volume of sounds, which would include attention to door handles, utensils, papers, pages, and keyboards. The goal was to silence or minimize any possible added noise that would aggravate the steady pain. A soft tone of voice, a gentle delivery, and a limitation to aggravating topics, learned as we encountered them, were unconditionally embraced. These circumstances were unlike any I had ever incurred in the 25 years of raising and caring for my son, or my daughter, for that matter. As my oldest child, I entered each new stage of child/young adult development first with him. I didn't understand this emerging stage, this foreign encounter, this sudden shift. And I could not enforce action, which was conflicting all the more.

That first night, I went down to the lobby to call home, check in about my arrival details, our arrival details, and to share what I encountered. It was comforting to hear John's voice and to receive encouragement around the initial steps toward fulfillment of this mission's intention. He was so relieved that our efforts were underway. It was difficult for him to not be present with us, to focus on his work and accept that his provision of care allowed such a limited physical touch, but such a critical financial and emotional touch. John needed and wanted that hug, that touch from his beloved son, that opportunity to assure Zach of his fatherly commitment to his care. My devoted husband had to rely on me to relay these messages to a rested and receptive Zach, to wait for his opportunity to secure their reconnection, and to trust that I could get our son home safely and in the arms of our mutual care. John and I were a balanced team in this mysterious journey of support and assistance for our son, but both of us suffered and managed our own personal impact to the heartache and despair that for each other neither could repair. Since arrival, I hadn't realized just how much turbulence I had been holding inside until I instinctively, and then intuitively, realized I needed to find a private space for an emotional release beyond the public space of a grand central hotel lobby. I had begun to get emotional during this particular phone call, as did he, and the secured seal of restraint had been peeled partially open ready to pour out. Where could I go to let restrained and reserved sound out, to express my fears and emotions, to speak to my God whom I felt had not yet forsaken me? I discovered what would become my own personal temporary tomb, accessible and private, waiting for me every time the need arose and became unconquerable. The rental car became my safe haven over those four days, and all that occurred behind those car door protective walls was between me and the dashboard. Climbing in, parked intentionally from that point on in a private space on the side of the hotel building, I would shut the door, slink down, lay the seat back, and privately sob hysterically until the need would pass; until fear would flush its way out of those tear ducts, and hope would have a space awaiting its return. I wept, I prayed, I begged, I howled. I so worried that something was happening that was bigger than us all. Bigger than this small window of time. And yet, maybe not; I would hold out for hope to medicate me, to then make me well. I had to be well; I had to be the well. For Zach, for John, for Gabby, I had to be a source of resilience. These tears would fill up that well, as they cleansed me of pain and sorrow. Eventually, after an inexplicable window of rental car care and my well replenishing flare, I would regroup, refresh, and return to our mother son tomb of darkness. By the light of a cell phone screen, I would begin to lay strategy for the next day. Morning of day one brought soft spoken conversation around a few priorities, following some breakfast food delivered to the room. My urgent need and desire was to meet and check in with the medical team he had worked with in Fairfield, to pick up medical records that would return home with us, and to get a sense about what this medical team felt was happening to Zach.

The first morning upon arrival, I began my first negotiations with him and with medical scheduling personnel, who rightfully demanded his verbal authorization first and foremost to any of my involvement. This woman on her mission deemed our pursuit as health care urgent and critically necessary, while the woman seeking his permission deemed it as health care private and legally necessary. Zach held all the power for any action. He was, however, listless, apathetic and quite carefree about any significance to my action plan's ticking clock, as well as the hospital's appointment scheduling indifference, both holding influence as potential mission trip road blocks. The work was an exercise of patience, persistence, and logical presentation which we all managed to work out and get done together. This was my first direct encounter with the combined challenges of helping him in the medical care navigation amidst these new presenting symptoms, amidst his age of legal independence and amidst his ever prevailing illness indifference. Additional goals of this rescue mission were to help clean out his dorm room and pack up his belongings, speak to him of Grain Brain and secure proper foods for rebuilding strength and stamina, check in with the Director of Student Services and clear up any outstanding health or enrollment concerns, all the while building an emotional bridge of acceptance and assistance for a successful airplane ride home scheduled Easter Sunday. My greatest edge around day one, a Thursday, was the ever ticking clock for securing an immediate appointment at the medical center for that very same day. I was told the doctors and the pharmacy would not be available Good Friday through Easter. And due to privacy laws, of course, my calls to the office were not getting returned. Finally, when a human was reached and not a machine, the medical team were only willing to schedule if their adult patient Zach would speak to them. We secured our appointment, motivated action, located the center, reviewed the records with the physician, and received a migraine medication to be taken at night, along with a suggestion to reduce any meditation frequency and intensity. The doctor felt that the meditation could be causal to his collection of symptoms, a professional advisement that seemed a casual and aloof response to my heightened and expressed concerns, matched by Zach's dazed despondence and placated participation. All the lab records in review revealed nothing, thus she pointed to a possible something. Perhaps, she suggested, Zach might also be battling some depression adjusting to the campus routines and his recent personal setbacks. She prescribed what she called a 'happy' pill, an SSRI, and attempted to downplay the rash of symptoms presented. Zach did not want this prescription; he was not clapping along. She went on to suggest that the majority of his symptoms, including depression, could be a result of the migraines, and that the migraines might even be a result of the excessive meditation. Wow. Really? Seems contradictory. It happens, she said. I remain mum about MUM. I meditate about the meditation.

When John, Zach and I later research migraines, we did find a mention of excessive meditation as a possible cause to some of these symptoms. But he had no history of migraines prior to this outbreak, having meditated consistently for two years now. I had no idea prior to this experience of how painful and debilitating migraines are, never having experienced one or having been in the immediate presence of someone who was having one. It seemed feasible that these symptoms would be healable and treatable given rest, time, and treatment. Maybe this was all in fact a response to this strangely new environment, I couldn't help but wonder. I tried to trust this medical team, they trusted their diagnostic tools and professional knowledge, and Zach trusted none of it. But he had no strength or stamina to resist or persist. I could literally feel the conflict of his personal principles to reject the idea of these prescriptive drugs as not curative, but only sedative. Nevertheless, he complied within this medical care corner, round one. I so wanted to trust in getting him home and getting him well. I, too, complied. As we left to fill the prescriptions and find some acceptable food, this was all he could give of himself for day one, and it was exactly what I needed him to give. Back to the dark tomb we returned, and while he slept, I escaped to find some trails to hike and some peace of mind to strike. Reliably and religiously, while in the car ride to and from my outing escapes, praying out loud incessantly, I would weep those April showers in hopes of bringing us May flowers. May, please be. Just maybe.

The next phone call series was to the student director and the school nurse. As was typical with Zach throughout his emerging adult evolution and his varied communities, they spoke of his welcomed presence, embracing and adoring his charisma, his humor, his intellect, and his engagement when healthy. The staff shared how they had held great hopes for his success and happiness at MUM, encouraging his return when well and able. This was always heartwarming as a parent to hear messages of welcome and appreciation

111

for your loved one. There was, however, accompaniment of increasing concerns expressed by the school team about his overall holistic wellbeing. The two felt there were increasing indicators of something gone wrong, despite medical examination giving no red flags. I was aware and appreciative that thoughtful, respectful language use in message delivery was exercised by both staff members. There was consideration and courtesy given to not judge or label his circumstances or behaviors, but to message sincere care and genuine concern. While new student Zach had displayed strange and unaccounted for behavior, with no drug use or external stimuli of any altering influence as possible or obvious explanation or truth, there was no shaming, no assuming, no character assassination in their response. I found this exchange to be comforting, honest, and validating. They honored his dignity and character as relevant and to be respected, actions I will never forget. But still, no one knew what was causative. The school director volunteered his opinions of how brilliant he felt Zach's ideas and long term plans were, and that Zach's potential to accomplish these things was perceived as strong and significant. His words were affirming, and offered a momentary respite from the heightened immediacy of the health mystery unfolding. These shared conversations reminded me that Zach had traveled here accompanied by a healthy intention to accomplish something mindful and meaningful. This community could have been a safe and thriving next destination if health breakdown hadn't interfered. The sudden and swift shift in Zach seemed to genuinely baffle the MUM staff as to what was actually happening. We all voiced hope that he might return when he was well, possibly in late summer or fall. He had completed the FAFSA paperwork application and explored various campus jobs in anticipation of continuing on in Fairfield through the summer. Maybe in the fall, we agreed. The simple but necessary steps to clean out, lock up, and close down his enrollment and housing status for now were then reviewed. My pledge to them was to have the work done by the next day. Micro manager Beth could then check them off her rescue mission's mobilizing mandates. Now on to the food nutrition and its healing intuition.

Unlike Zach, and the MUM community, I was not vegan, nor organic, nor holistic, nor puritan in my food shopping, cooking, or consumption. I was a practical shopper of meats, fruits and vegetables, grains and dairy, but my mantra was price versus pure, and the organics of my budget were typically about financial sustainability! My consumer habits were often thoughtlessly tied to familiar loyalties of brands, tastes, and recipes acquired while growing up rather than those more consciously chosen with healthier intention and assessment. So, to acquire food supplies round one, I drove to that nearby WalMart superstore I had passed on the way into town. I proceeded to shop for our 'Grain Brain' recommended food selections, pick up a pair of sunglasses to shield his light sensitivity, and purchase some purified water in bulk. Returning with what I perceived as practical, affordable choices, I was greeted by Zach's immediate questioning as to whether the food was organic. My eye rolling response was one of irritation reasoning at this point, for I had begun to feel lost appreciation for all of the extra efforts involved in this ongoing mission. Of course, the truth was, he was vulnerably not himself, desperate for physical relief, and determined to hold on to his developing personal principles if possible. How could I expect thoughtful logic and reason to accompany the unfamiliar patterns of illness presentation? Would they be reasonable expectations? No. He wasn't well. I was to be the well! Still, it seemed reasonable to want appreciation and to be valued for your efforts even if we had no idea what wellness we were actually seeking. Organic? Organic appreciation, that would be swell. This entire trip was not an inexpensive rescue mission, at least by our standard of living and means. So to judge the food rather than be grateful for the provision …I mean, child to adult severance was sounding quite healthy of a separation in that innocently delivered yet irritatingly received response! This here and now was not his self-focused severance mission, but rather our health focused rescue mission. I would locate and acquire food that met his needs, enrolling with google as a student of 'Organic University', studying healthier food origination, selection, and preparation. My first textbook was Grain Brain. My first classroom was Everybody's Whole Foods in Fairfield, Iowa. I OW A lot to this personal awakening. Dr. David Perlmutter, our new dietary guru, would have sided with Zach, encouraging one's food choices to be organic or wild whenever possible. I needed to personally grow in this nutritional arena of health care, and if I was going to get on board the Grain Brain train, I was going to have to learn to shop organic, learning the new and very different to me language usage for proper selection and understanding the differentials in quality food sources and selections. I would then practice the new habits that grain free and sugar free endorses.

Googling the local area natural grocer, I headed over to the nearby location, and bravely stepped out and into the doorway of one more foreign country to me. Campus field trip, it was. I hadn't learned the language, understood the culture, nor practiced the adaptations prior to this classroom expedition. Insecure and intimidated, I was. Somebody smudge me! Someone sage me, please! I ventured forth into the aisles of health conscious education, self-conscious of my ignoramus toward the unfamiliar products, labels and brands of supplies on the shelves. My overall lack of knowledge and integration of the Ayurvedically advanced, organically organized nutritional course of study prior to this was inexcusably indifferent. I was now drawn in. Everyone I walked past seemed to either smell so deliciously clean, or body odor raw. More often, an earthy, sensual incense type smell would emanate from shoppers as they confidently perused shelves, casually selected grocery and personal care products, and then cavalierly moseyed on into their seemingly conscious lives of peaceful transcendence, meditation, and universality. This out of town novice just wanted to walk along behind the calming smells, and the confident strides, pretending that I knew what I was doing and exactly what I was looking for. I became sarcastic with myself, feeling insecure, uncertain, uncomfortable, and right back on that balance beam exercise, balancing a different yet similar wave of energy. Right foot, Zach's lifestyle choices, left foot, Beth's lifestyle familiarity. The burgeoning balance of embracing and integrating organic foods and natural grocers we would lifetime embrace blissfully over months to come. But for now, in this Fairfield mission field, Zach would need to return with me. Help me, son, to get over myself, and get on with yourself. Out I went, empty handed and heavy hearted. The loyal rental car knew my recovery routine.

Zach and I managed to get through the second evening together with an attempted use of the hotel pool and hot tub. Short lived it was, but to try was at least a step out into some effort and exposure. We were able to share some engaging and logical conversation during that effort, laughing lightly, loving gently, and listening carefully. This gave me great hope. The morning of day three we agreed to take a leisurely drive around the area, something Zach had not done in either of his trips here, given that he visited and then enrolled deep in the throes of winter without any transportation either. Spring was now in bloom, and the fresh air was medicinal to both of us. He was too weak yet to hike, but with sunglasses offering shade to the sunlight, and dietary shifts offering quiet to his stomach plight, we at least ventured together out beyond the hotel haven. Seizing the fact that his energy and attitude were currently stable and stronger, we also chose to clean out the dorm room. The room was small in size, hosting a simple sink below a single wall cabinet that held a few cans of tuna, a can opener, a personal hygiene bag, and some bottles of Ayurvedic oils. I later learned that these oils are used with the intention to cure about 30 systemic health issues. I had never seen or heard of these oils. Add them to the growing list of my inclination to ignoramus. Two mattresses were laid on the floor in a manner that provided length for his body, with bedding bunched up as if someone was going to get back under the covers. The room, his clothing, the closet, the desk, his notebooks….it was all so 'less is more', which I observed as simple and refreshing in comparison to his undergraduate rookie year of dormitory life I had witnessed 8 years prior! It would not take long to complete this task together. Glancing at the bedding on the floor and visualizing him in that barren space, it saddened me to imagine him isolated in this small corner of the first floor struggling to overcome while experiencing blackouts. His inability to listen to his treasured music or to peacefully meditate due to body and brain pain, his inability to digest meals because of stomach pains, and then the avoidance of calling home because of growing pains; I was in pain. Copenhagen seemed so far away, and yet it was a mere six months ago. Where would we follow you next, my son. How will we help you launch again, healed of whatever ails you, proceeding on the quest, and succeeding by your own measure? We cleaned what little needed cleaning, turned in the linens, loaded the car with his belongings, and returned the room key with checklist completed. How about optimizing an organically designated homework drop in, suggests the freshman student Elizabeth to the associate professor Zachary of 'Organic University' imagination as we drive away from the campus! We stop at the natural grocer for a teachable moment or two, he finds a few things as I shadow and take note, but shortly into the assignment, the principled professor voiced his exhaustion exodus. We both leave our respective campuses and return to another early eve of collapse and confoundedness. Reading silently under the tent like covers, holding my cellphone flashlight, I prayed we could successfully complete one more day until heading home. Zach was so strangely not himself.

Saturday was a long, slow day of waiting and passing time, but I managed to escape the doldrums with a drive out to the Jefferson County Trail system. I listened to music on the radio for the first time since arrival, singing along in glory rather than sobbing the song of my story. I walked the trails for a long stretch, lost in thought about what life might have been for Zachary here. What would it have looked like if he were healthy here, I wondered. Would he return in the summer or in the fall? Zach's symptoms had improved somewhat during the three days of quiet rest in our hotel hideaway, reading quietly when his brain would allow, and soothing his digestive pains by shifting to a meat based, vegetable balanced, gluten free, sugar free diet. But I was no doctor, no neuroscientist, no nutritionist, no psychologist, and I still had no idea about what was going on inside him. We would explore that further from the comforts and operating base of our home, accelerated around the remaining 6 weeks of his insurance coverage on our family health care plan. We would cancel that Iowa State healthcare plan after all, and activate the Washington State plan. Had I somehow willed this circumstance into being as a result of my conversations the last few years with Zach about eventually turning 26 years of age and needing stable work with employer based healthcare or at the very least, the financial means to purchase your own care? Self-fulfilling prophecy, it seemed. Hush now, ego. Stay focused on the present here and now, Beth, for the past is just that, and the future is yet to unfold. Within 24 hours, the MUM chapter will be part of the past, and soon enough, something else will present. We finished loading the car that Sunday morning, checked out, and began our return drive to Des Moines airport. I had been coached by the medical doctor to make sure he took a 'happy pill' before the flight, ensuring cooperation and an agreeable mindset for the flight home. He took it very begrudgingly. Escorted by wheelchair up to the gate at the airport, we then boarded, flew home, and soon landed in Portland, Oregon, our home airport. Mission accomplished. He rallied in exiting the plane, willing himself to walk slowly from arrival gate to baggage claim, only to plop down on the floor exhausted, next to his stalwart of a sister who looked on at him in wonderment and warmth. Much like old times, the four of us found food and headed home together happy in the now. Happy Easter eve it was, with no filled baskets, no church worship, no holiday ham or hard boiled eggs, just safe travel, safe arrival, safe son. Safe. Another SISU moment of survival in the face of adversity. Sometimes, there's just no place like home.

Insert 24 •   2014 Easter Sunday PDX return

Chapter 17: Home Front Hellth

I Am Here, Pink

I Won't Back Down, Tom Petty

As early as the very next morning, during living room conversation about the selection of caregivers and the scheduling of appointments, Zach made it known that he did not want to be in this home or in this hometown. His deliberate attempts to create independence over the past three years in Fairfield, Copenhagen, and Zamora, solidified his desire to resist family dynamics in the face of his adult emergence, especially while trying to discern this mysterious health situation. Until he was well, however, our home was his option. Fortunately, the physical structure was such that he had a private daylight basement bedroom, a bathroom with a 7' shower, and access to a large living space downstairs. This would grant a unique degree of separation and space initially thought to be quite accommodating. A hoped intention was for the space to also soothe the onslaught of light and sound sensitivity that everyday living and conversation in the world which now seemed to tease and taunt traumatizing response. John and I did not hold his insistence to privacy and separation as an act of rejection but rather as a necessary healing space required to recover, refuel and ready oneself to launch again. We understood that. And yet, our lives also had routines and rhythms within the home, and each would require adjustments to these unique living circumstances and personal health presentations. Within the first two weeks, Zach opted to communicate by email, because the living room conversational check ins stirred aggravation and suspicion. If we were too loud or excitable, it was experienced as painful physically; if we were too soft or simple, it was perceived as condescending and strategically manipulating. He would zigzag emotionally between tender and grateful expressions, then angry and judgmental proclamations. Paranoia manifested and it was increasingly indicative of brain illness not brazen independence. Zach was convinced that on John and Beth sanity walks, as we called them, the two of us were meeting imagined persons and strategizing with them about his developing delusional thought. We agreed to accommodate his written communication request, but what if we hadn't? Was a battle worth it? Would it be the actual battle or just the battleground? While this choice initially seemed a workable solution, it became a burgeoning problem of increased isolation, proliferated paranoia, and exaggerated interpretation. We were challenged continuously in our efforts to engage this man child in pursuing proper care.

As Zach's chauffeur to the appointments we did get scheduled, I was at least privy to some civilized, face to face conversation between us. In the initial three weeks of his Iowa return, before extreme isolation set in, he would agree to assist me with the grocery store shopping, only to ask for the car keys shortly after our entrance into these noisy, populated spaces. Quietly and patiently, he would sit and wait in the car, eyes closed, with meditative pose. The lights, the noise, the public glare and stare of physical size combined with an inability to banter with strangers, he managed the surging anxiety that accompanied the relentless physical pain. I recall feeling deeply saddened and continuously confused about my son's experience. The confusion was baffling because externally, other than the listlessness and flat affect noticeable to his parents but not to those who did not know him, he presented and appeared quite normal. Internally, he was a wreck. Who knew what was truly going on in his brain, his body, his spiritual soul. We didn't. Nor did he. Help was hard to find. Our agreed upon action plan for immediate health care attention was to schedule an MRI to rule out brain lesions or growths, select an acupuncturist (his choice) to physically address his multiple symptoms, revisit the surgery clinic and surgeon for a knee checkup, and explore what a psychological evaluation would offer in hopes of addressing his odd expressions of thought, his odd displays of behavior.

Zach selected medical professionals within our insurance plan and across the river in Portland, choosing professionals whom he believed would best align with his personal philosophies. Unfortunately, he no longer had an established history with a local general practitioner who personally knew and understood him nor held a meaningful caregiving relationship. We had outgrown our routine pediatric caregiving practice by the end of middle school days, utilized a small family practice for colds, flus, and referral needs, and essentially adopted sports medicine caregivers as our primary care to the many miscellaneous sports related injuries. Because we were a family without major health management needs thus far in life, we seldom accessed medical care. The negative of this positive is that we therefore were not savvy. We were not familiar enough with nor had we established proper teams for more efficient access to the medical pathways, prescriptions and protocols of our modern day health care system. Unfortunately, this can lend itself to not even knowing what it is that you don't know. The power plays and profit driven practices often improperly present when in the hands of an ill-informed physician, an unfamiliar relationship, or an ill-informed, unfamiliar illness diagnostic. You might not know any different on the front side of intake. You might be run around in circles, unwell, unsure, and unsuspecting. John and I did not speak the health care system language fluently nor did we have the navigation experience to best interpret information. Despite disconnect to the practice of health care protocols, we were always quite capable of learning and we would persistently exercise research and readiness.

Fortunate as it was to be such a physically healthy family, we now needed to quickly and responsibly establish new healthcare relationships with and beside our son. He was already well into an illness that held us clueless around cause, diagnosis, and necessary treatment. What we did know, is that we would do all that we possibly could to work with him, not for him, as he made very clear, while beside him, not in control of him, as it might sometimes appear. What a dance in this interlude! Regardless of any childhood severance, adulthood proclamation, or independence celebration, this rapidly revealing reality we faced would necessitate steady unconditional love and care regardless of hurts, happenings, and hardship. Love expression from our son became a blur in the mirage of his wellness condition and strange superstitions. His behaviors, responses, and messages were misleading. Zach selected a holistic acupuncturist in the Pearl district, and a therapist/career specialist in the Multnomah Village area. We contacted my local family practitioner to get a physical checkup, tell our story, and hopefully warrant a needed referral for the MRI, since an established local physician relationship was not currently in his wellness wheelhouse.

Securing the MRI referral meant subjecting our son to my physician and her surprising projections onto his story and circumstances. A series of rapid fire questions and facial formations delivered a bedside manner of doubt, bias, and challenge. The strange school named Mahareshi with its questionable religious affiliation, the inquiries about meditation and the implication spoken of cult like concern, she was not building trust with this patient nor his parent as to obtaining unbiased intake and evaluation. It was evident that this doctor did not comprehend nor indicate wellness value to any of Zach's personal life choices nor their significance to him emotionally, spiritually, and physically. A patient knows when they feel unheard, judged, and invalidated. Zach would later remind me why he preferred to avoid Western philosophy medicine. Medical ethics, as to the dignity and value of a patient, does it include how one's illness message is received and mirrored back from a physician, unfiltered from their personal bias? Personally, this doctor had been a fairly solid physician for me, but revealed herself differently in her discomfort and detachment to my son and his story. Whatever she personally felt, however, she was still professionally able to focus around the immediate health concerns presenting, and the vital intention of our visit. She validated our purpose in the appointment by authorizing the prized possession of an MRI referral after observing and assessing the multitude of symptoms and unusual circumstances of such dramatic shift to this former professional athlete's health and wellbeing. We were grateful for the referral, but wounded by the encounter.

This particular doctor visit, and many that followed in the months to come were not without a patient and caregiver encounter that reflected judgement, bias, and stereotype. Credibility to any possible illness other than mental health, suspicion of previous drug use as a likely ongoing abuse, and even resistance and ignorance to a more holistic evaluation of a very real and present culprit residing in his broken down body were battles we faced regularly in our constant pursuit of medical diagnosis and treatment for comprehensive care. I began to understand why he did not want to be working with Western medicine that seemed to be consistently failing him. Zach's former fitness was failing, and his meditative mindset was bailing as we kept asking questions on our purpose driven home town quest. We could use a mind, body, spirit institute about now; so we crossed the river in search of answers. The acupuncturist was helpful as our son found some level of relief from the use of Chinese medicine practices. As part of the proposed care routine, medicinal teas and cupping therapy were employed. I did not ask too many questions, nor did I judge the again unfamiliar health care choice Zach insisted on utilizing. Driving home after an early May treatment session, he revealed a circular mark under his left arm. I assumed it was a cupping mark. This was the first time I saw a circular mark he spoke of time and time again from this point forward whenever he entered hospital and medical care. It was visible, circular, and noted in records as either a rash or a lesion. We came to this knowledge in the future from medical records as well as from future conversations held with Zach. While noted on record often, the rash and its circular nature never held an association to something more significant throughout 2014. We didn't know, but we would eventually learn to know better.

The therapist/career counselor chosen seemed a bit old school for Zach, guiding the 25year old through career cluster worksheets that I recalled utilizing with middle school students while employed as a school counselor just a year prior. He requested Zach read 'What Color is Your Parachute?', a book I had read in 1980 while preparing to interview out of college. The thought occurred to me, will we be needing a parachute? After all, we were still on an incomplete rescue mission. What would we need to escape from, or leap toward? Probably, and sadly, it was likely this chosen 'therapy' we needed to escape from, with a leap toward more specific psychotherapy warranted, but who among the uneducated knew? We sure didn't. We needed guidance badly. The short time together for Zach and this therapist gravitated toward career counseling and less toward emotional therapeutic care. The two of them discerned that Zach was at a crossroads of career, work, and direction, so they focused on career work over therapy. It was logical from a therapist standpoint, for Zach had just experienced a career setback that might prove to be permanent. And Plan B had just erupted in Fairfield. Career counseling was the wrong choice at the wrong time for the wrong curative focus. Those sessions never got beyond three appointments. It likely would have been quite challenging for this particular mental health professional to address adequately the strange series of mental health symptoms that accelerated rapidly just days from Zach's last appointment cancellation. This had not been the psych evaluation care treatment suggested by the Iowa staff. We were further behind and not catching up.

Primarily because our family did not know what it meant to get a 'psych eval', nor did we yet adopt any idea that he might be psychiatrically ill, we did not fully understand why or how to follow up with that suggestion. Did it just mean evaluate and care for your mental health through talk therapy? What did it mean to be psychiatrically ill, anyway? Furthermore, Zach did not welcome any idea of a therapist or mental health practitioner at that time. How were we to convince him otherwise? What were we to evaluate? Depression? Anxiety? It was a baffling consideration as to why and how, let alone what, where and when. We were unfamiliar with any mental health concern beyond the two aforementioned common encounters for many. As a school counselor, I knew our school psychologist to do evaluations on students, but typically this would occur after a series of presenting problems and symptoms to reason the necessity of the evaluation over time. This suggestion/idea we were presented with was sudden, abrupt, and presenting from an unprecedented health shift for Zach. We simply didn't understand, and no one suggested or explained the possibility of a mental health diagnostic sudden onset, or that a psychologist should run Zach through a lengthy evaluation process to discern a diagnostic disorder. As parents, we were not aware of any history to draw from other than normalized depressive occasions in Zach's life that did not appear to us to be out of the ordinary, or of any crisis proportion. The anxiety that he had spoken of, he had shared repeatedly that he was finding healing and satisfaction from TM. Maybe a sudden personal history was awakening and forming at the age of 25? Would mental illness be the cause then to his multiple physical ailments, we could not help but question? He had increasingly not been himself over the last six months, but he was so in the midst of personal transformation, that the recent oddities felt explainable, almost understandable. A full and deeper understanding of the mental health world was yet quite foreign to us other than some basic generalities. A licensed school counselor knows more about building school schedules and teaching bullying curriculum than she/he knows about mental health diagnosis, unless previously a social worker or one who walks within a life of mental illness. School psychologists are hired to be experts in this knowledge, so I personally did not have a depth of knowledge to draw from. What was now so different for our son in this adult emergent season of deep reflection, healthy living, and holistic vision? There was a certain something interfering, something festering, something stirring. Zach checked out of the counselor/therapy commitment by mid-May, and the acupuncturist shortly thereafter. Neither of them would have been ready to face what was to come.

With no medical support team in place, or advocacy group to guide us, we were increasingly at a loss as to what was wrong with Zach's health. His collection of symptoms and behaviors were not caused by a brain tumor, for the MRI results were returned via a simple mailed sheet of paper indicating 'normal'. No phone call, no discussion, no physician follow-up, no interpretive review. Who would we turn to with this giant of an adult escalating in strange behaviors, physical symptoms not diagnosed by labs or by clinicians to reveal treatable illness? Ourselves if no one else. Team Moritz continued to rally along independently with best friend Google, while the two distinctly different parties to the process, Zach and his parents, would continue to try and synch ongoing efforts and reasoning for health care diagnosis and treatment. In this ongoing pursuit of healing, both in the home and in the community, it became evident that there were elements of residential environmental distress for Zach other than simply residing in a place he did not want to be. Our home and neighborhood had been besieged with daily construction noise and vibration for the past eight years during his absence. Former acreage lots nearby including our own back field had been short platted, additional roadways had been developed closer to the property line, and the steady sound of hammers, nail guns, noisy delivery trucks, and music blasting contractors had displaced the pheasant calls, coyote howls, and owl screeches of his childhood memory. For a physically healthy, nature loving soul, this would be disheartening and disturbing. For a severe migraine sufferer with light and sound sensitivity, this was hell on earth. Large evergreen trees were being cleared and hauled, chain sawed and chipped, while houses and the peering eyes of their windows were rising up into the shadows of the fence line west of his bedroom window view. Privacy was rapidly diminishing while noise was rigorously replenishing. The basement was not the refuge we all thought it would be. He sought relief through the use of sound barrier headphones and earplugs, and yet, the construction vibrations could not be deterred. These additional disturbances also contributed to stirring the agitated state he had already been predisposed to from his collection of ailments. What would be the perfect refuge? While Zach's disposition was influenced negatively on a daily basis from the outdoor environment, it was in equal balance to what was occurring within the indoor environment of his noisy mind. The confluence of these environmental disturbances almost seemed prophetic. They were simultaneously, literally and figuratively, comparable to his own physical discomforts, his own internal eruption and erosion of mental torment. Destruction, construction, displacement, replacement – I can recall sensing this symbiotic connection to both worlds; his personal state of mind and his surroundings in like kind. Neither would offer enlightenment or encouragement regarding outcome.

Our cozy comfortable haven of a home, which we thought would be an oasis for Zach, proved otherwise. Built in the 1970's, it offered creaky floors, noisy plumbing, and thin sound barriers between the active kitchen upstairs and the common area of entertainment space downstairs. His ailments suffered, particularly with a bedroom space below his parents' bedroom, whereby the sounds of closing closet doors and frequent footsteps to and from their bathroom above became daily disturbances. The space for yoga, computer work, and occasional attempts at video game, mind numbing enjoyment were subject to family foot traffic and the typical pots and pans noise of the upstairs kitchen space. These features were seldom an issue over the years, but in this deteriorating state of mind and body, all was heightened and made issue. Zach tried to adapt with regular use of earplugs and an altered time of day rhythm for home and space utilization. Basically, he avoided more, isolated more, and expressed anger more. We tiptoed, we opened and we closed anything that had a noise to it with more careful intention. We flushed and used sinks and disposals less often, and we tried to repair the floor squeaks, even stepping softly and selectively around them. I had practiced a version of these adaptations in Iowa. Eventually, the noises, our behaviors, his reactions, seemingly anything would fuel a rage built up and expressed from some vulnerable vitriolic source of disturbance. Each morning, and sometimes early afternoon, depending on his battle with fatigue or insomnia, Zach would climb the stairway to our kitchen, his knees cracking loud at an even steady pace. He would chop vegetables, mix them to cook with eggs and meat, or combine yogurt with fruit, consuming the healthy meal methodically, quietly, almost robotically. Always careful and thoughtful about cleaning up his mess, putting dishes and equipment away, he then would disappear into the downstairs abyss, communicating primarily through emails, taking frequent and long showers to calm anxiety, and soothe the skin sensations that aggravated him. In my worry window of his long showers taken, I would enter his room to do a safety check or a snoop loop, to find yoga mat, books of Greek mythology, science fiction, philosophy and mysticism, poetry, all among journals of drawings, notes and personal poetry strewn across his bed or in piles on the bedside floor. His room and belongings were often scented by the remains of an incense stick burnt in its ceramic iguana shaped holder I had gifted him years ago. When I entered the room, his personal space felt sacred, almost holy, a cool comfort in the sanctity. When I exited the room, my personal space felt unstable, imbalanced, a caustic discomfort from security. I was afraid for my son. Little did I know how afraid he was for himself.

When Zach wrote us an email early on in May, he expressed his desire to heal and evolve within a different community other than the sheltered experience of his hometown and childhood home.

My interest in Fairfield is as much motivated by the meditation and philosophy as it is by the networking world at large. There is so much inspiration, intelligence and innovation within the forward thinkers who meditate. It is a creative curious community that has been calling to me for a very long time. There is unparalleled potential for continued understanding and application of self-knowledge, within and around those who practice TM. Yes, this is the last place on earth I want to be after accepting the truths about myself and my time here.... Vancouver, on a broader scale, as much as the paralyzing prison cell that the here of my room has felt like lately. Right now, my intention is to heal so that I can continue to help myself.

Zach would write these messages with such clarity and honest expression, and then within the same written message or immediately following it, he could swing to a message of anger, agitation, and random verbal attack. Sometimes, he would react out loud to the simple daily life sounds and noises of an active home, experiencing them as hugely disturbing and painful sounds, screaming out profanity and unleashing what appeared to be uncontrollable overreactions. Who was this person? Did his college days incur that much duress and stored aggression, we wondered? Had we not been the parents we thought we were, and had we somehow induced this pent up angst from what we perceived to be normal parent child development in the upbringing of this child, this young man? What we were now experiencing made you question everything, because answers were so hard to find. It led you to question yourself.

Mother's Day weekend 2014, I travelled north to Seattle to spend Friday and Saturday evening with Gabrielle, escape the imprisoned fortress of our home, check in on her health and wellbeing, and enjoy the gifts of a Mother's Day brunch and flowers. It was heart medicine, and I badly needed it. I like to think she needed it as well. Her life was a month shy of college graduation, and she was doing her best to manage her own fear and confusion regarding Zach's circumstances. Her knowledge of and respectful care for her brother's expanse of thoughts and feelings prior to this strange development, now more often expressively cycling with unforeseen rage, sidled up to her parent's previous postures and now growing fears and uncertainties; it made for a challenging family member perspective. She was physically outside of it all, but emotionally well within the

126

walls. This was a complex placement for his sister, straddling both positions within the family, respectful daughter and trusted sibling. Emergence surrounded us, for she, too, was in a season of transition. As the next and last emerging adult child in the family, who would she become and how would she express herself, seeking personal independence and self-discovery? Gabrielle would circumstantially be subject to a personal postponement of sorts, while the family meandered through this mystery walk. She would loyally and lovingly stand beside us all in the sudden uncertain realities of our pathway projection, until an obvious seasonal shift of her own pace and her own space would need to quicken and widen, pained and hardened by life's unforeseen offerings. Our Seattle time together and our opportunity to visit alone renewed me, and yet, it also fueled further concern about her distance from the home front hell(th) happenings and behaviors increasingly stirring in Zach. I would withhold some, but not. I would divulge some, but not. How do you protect her heart and soul, but respect her relationship and desire to fully know what is happening and to possibly participate in the care? Hell, we still had no idea what we were dealing with. We couldn't even name it, to accurately share it. Whatever the hellth it would be named, whatever the hellth we could blame, none of it would change the fact that she would soon complete her own successful 4year mission of college degree in hand. Our daughter would graduate in June, finish her Seattle apartment lease through August while seeking further employment in design, and then ideally launch her own young adult life beyond the conforming collegiate years and these presenting family smears. She was readying to soar while he was readying to roar.

Meanwhile, John was in Atlanta for a 2week training in his new work assignment, travelling with continued regularity and demand, while trying to contain his own emotions and fears around this mystery unravelling before us. The four of us felt it was a doable trip for me to leave Zach alone that Mother's Day weekend, especially since he would have immense quantity of comforting quiet other than the uncontrollable outdoor developments nearby that possibly would occur. I was uncertain if he would acknowledge me in any way this Hallmark holiday for moms, as he had begun to aggressively measure and criticize my manner of response to his more recent behaviors, escalating our shared conflicts to heightened new levels beyond my comprehension of how I ever thought either of us previously held. Thankfully, I had plenty of loving, playful, and creatively expressive Mother's Day messages to draw from in my collection of memories and cards over the years. To my surprise, he sent me a thoughtful, lengthy email, and I was touched by its sincerity, the outreach intention, and the simple subject title.

Thank you.

Considering the intensified reflection of not only the last three months, but 25 years of mother/son energy, I wasn't certain that words would be able to come in time for a card. I am grateful that they are coming now, and will celebrate them for whatever they are. They are not without equal parts healing and heartbreak. Warmth and frost. Love and loss. Learning and growth. Understanding and forgiveness...After a long, cold winter between us, many things have been melt this spring. And likewise, I am confident that the cycle will bring with it a beautiful bloom, full of life, and with the promise of a summer of love. My hope, is that many things have been better put into perspective, that many things have been purged, and that the many reopened scabs will only heal over that much stronger.

Certainly, many judgements have been made, some warranted, some not. I hope amidst my mood swinging, that you can accept this wholehearted thank you. It is in admiration for your courage and strength, while weathering this storm with me. I know it has not been a place of comfort for you, so I thank you for being brave enough to partake in one of many adventures, and on as many of my terms as possible. I thank you for opening yourself to new information and for embracing the wisdom of the world. That being the world at large, but also the individual worlds of our own subjectivity, and the objective world we share as mother and son.

More than anything, I thank you for being the best mother that you could be. Your heart has always been in the right place, and the impurities that you project, have been more often than not, not your own creations. I thank you for forever nurturing my feminine side, while simultaneously embracing your masculine side. As terrifying as it may be at times, I thank god for your masculinity, because more often than not, it was the most consistent male role model in my life.

Moving forward, I will have faith that understanding and acceptance can be the foundation for our fresh start. As mother and son, as well as a functional family unit. My hope, is that through your now enlightened empowering of me into my adulthood, you'll in turn be better equipped to empower yourself.

In matters of love, and because of our bond, I can say with confidence that I am not and have never been a male chauvinist or aimless objectifier. And, that my womanizing has always come from a place of identifying, respecting, and understanding a woman's needs as much as my own. My evolution as a spiritual being, and as a man, would be nonexistent without you and the other strong women who've surrounded me thus far. It's given me the foresight to seek out a partner who possesses similar strengths, and to know, that behind every strong man, is a woman who has had to be considerably stronger.

My prayer, is that the animosities and anger that I do harbor don't continue to inflict feelings of inadequacy upon your motherly nature. You are a great mother, and always have been. You will forever have my confidence and support, as both my mother, friend, and as the spiritual healer that you are evolving into. I look forward to the true healing that space and time will give us. Empowering us all to become closer as we naturally drift farther apart. I will always love and respect you, yet I will never understand you. I hope you can mirror the same my way. Happy Mother's Day! Zach

This beautiful, well written email was sent at 1:36 pm that day. Rage was at rest. But when I returned home, walked in the doorway around 8pm that same evening, eager to thank him, I was greeted by his empty stare from the dinner table, eating dinner directly across from the front entryway. The email love was currently lost in translation. Rage would awaken.

Zach cleared his dishes, walked away assertively, noisy knees clicking and stomp stepping his way down the stairway. I anxiously began to clean counters, put away my belongings, and ponder the contrast of the day, of these past weeks, of this man's life! Within moments of this strange transition back into the home, Zach screamed up the stairs, 'fucking stop all the noise!' He ranted about noise and intention and scheming and how the whole neighborhood had been against him all weekend. This was a bizarre outburst, as was pretty much the entire remainder of May. Mayday, Mayday, we're going down. Mission? Rescue. What color is your parachute? A crisis was building well beyond what we thought we had in front of us. John was travelling nonstop in his new management position learning the job on the run, resolving problems left behind by previous managers, and adapting in the shadow of sudden management changes at the company. I was finishing a university job assignment and readying to apply for a recently opened leadership position within its guidance and counseling program for the following calendar year. Our daughter was alone in Seattle, attempting to authentically participate in end of senior year events and obligations at school, while holding the dramatic and uncertain truth that her brother, her best friend, was in crisis at home, far from her access and support. By now, she was utilizing professional therapeutic care in Seattle with a therapist that wasn't really serving the full scope of her immediate needs, but generally provided a safe and accessible outlet, a drop point for the emotional overload.

Our social life had been on sabbatical by choice since we brought Zach home from Iowa. The only shared outlet as a couple had been the frequent walks we would escape to for conversation about all of our work and home stressors. We were starved for the physical exercise and for the exercise of certain freedoms and truths that had been quarantined. Outdoors, we exercised the freedom of speech and noise out from under the imprisonment of the silent library of a home, desperately holding on to each other's hand, knowing that the direction we thought we were headed toward, the one after the 'empty nest parent rest' exit ramp had taken a sharp turn to an unknown and possibly dangerous destination. In the mere three weeks' time since we brought Zach home for healing, his wounds seemed to multiply and deepen, becoming a contagious infection of family destruction, waging an unwanted war between wellness and wildness. All four of us were in this ever elusive battle defending his health, protecting our love's wealth, defending and protecting the health and wealth each our own. Following Mother's Day, Zach began to increasingly empty his room of belongings. Early on this appeared to be an intentional message of 'minimizing excess', disposing or recycling stacks of papers, folders, books, clothing, shoes, furnishings, and childhood memorabilia. Further on he would irrationally message acts of silent rejection by removing his previously most meaningful and useful remaining possessions such as his cell phone, his computer, his backpack, even his treasured books and journals. At first, we reasoned with ourselves upon early morning wake up and front hallway encounter of stacked items by the entryway. He is simplifying through stewardship, he is preparing to travel light in this modern world of extreme excess, we told ourselves. Our rationale seemed reasonable to the philosophies and values he had been shifting toward prior to illness. We would discreetly relocate select items to the garage, decisions made from within our clear minds but also from confused valuation perspectives. We would allow for his future discernment when in a right mind. One early foggy morning, upon returning from a volunteer role at a high school breakfast in our church basement, I found Zach hauling all of his college recruitment correspondence, basketball literature, personal written notes from recruiters and even notes from his college coach to the recycling bin which had already been placed roadside for pickup. Once I realized what he was doing, I asked him to please reconsider. He raged at me about their insignificance, their falsehood, their imprisonment, their role in holding him back. He believed he could not move forward if he held on to all of this baggage, most of which I had saved on his behalf. Some of what he spoke made logical sense, and some seemed an illogical penance. Truth and delusion were courting, while riddance became sporting.

The duality of his messaging push and pull and even his emotional swings would become standards for Zach's behavior expression, both written and oral, for a very long time beyond the month of May. He was logical and rationally feasible yet simultaneously irrational, delusional, and disturbing, becoming increasingly more difficult to sort reality. Between the purging of belongings, his sobbing and pounding on the walls in the shower at night, his increasing isolation, and the ongoing pain and suffering of physical symptoms with no relief, I had begun to fear he might choose to make an attempt on his life. He refused to go out of the house, and I wasn't sure how to get help. I damn sure was going to do all that I could to keep him from harming himself. I would not allow even the thought of this to slip by me as possibility without taking precaution, finding help, standing guard. There were collectively too many recent signs to not be ignored, including my own internal intuition. In my career as a school counselor, I had training in suicide ideation, prevention and education. I had comforted school communities in the aftermath of suicide, I had presented prevention materials to middle school students, their families, our school staff, and even my own counseling peers. This could not be training I would then need for my own son, I recall thinking! Too many threatening signs were present. I phoned John long distance for emotional support and then spoke to Zach's sister. I asked that she let us know if there were any strange indications or possible threat of self-harm in his communication with her. We were deep into a different level of crisis now. In vigil, I sat all night by Zach's door listening for sound, movement, indication of life. I had spoken to the crisis line, but I had no evidence of suicidal intention spoken by Zach or any written proof. I just had perceived indicators and personal intuition which wasn't enough for outreach response. I was on watch. Every so often, during silent spells, I would peek into the room and he would bark, "Get the fuck out!" Music to my ears, exhale release to my inhale hold, for my son was alive. Gripped in gut wrenching fear that night, I prayed in desperation, still trusting in my faith, while wondering how we ever got to this place in our lives. As the evening quieted, I drifted to sleep, awakening very early that next morning, and finding a strange email in my inbox from Zach. He shared that he had plans to travel to Fairfield ASAP, that he had laid out his camping gear on the floor of his room, and that he had no desire for our travel assistance. Living here was killing his soul, he said. He had to be with her, he continued, further sharing that he would prepare to leave on Memorial Day weekend. He advised that he would reach out to his sister to let her know he would not make her graduation after all. The email vacillated between logical clarity and angered resentment. It was a different kind of balance exercise than the beam. It was a truth balance scale, much like a Libra scale, and this Gemini Zach would express both retainers on the scale, well and unwell. The scale weight leaned unwell.

In response, John and I participated in an immediate series of email exchanges with Zach, that we believed offered feasible consideration. Ultimately the content proved to be more mind altered ideas from him, and more wishful wellness wants from us. We chose to consider that the woman he would refer to as his true love, that he said he saw in Fairfield, that he imagined he saw in our home, that he said he met in Copenhagen, might be real and possibly a genuine part of this urgent desire to return to Fairfield. Ok, love can get ahold of us strangely sometimes. Love can drive us a bit crazy, we convinced ourselves! Our written exchanges that night of May 21, 2014, included the following segments of a grasping attempt to believe and hope that Zach leaving the home, meeting a potential true love, and returning to a community that embraced him might actually assist him toward necessary healing. Desperate hopes they were by all.

Zach email to Mom at 4:56 pm: *Airfare not my route. Taking a backpack yes, a cooler yes, other camping necessities, please. I need to go ASAP, like I've stated. Flights are irrelevant. And the new moon will be seen upon our Fairfield arrival. Thank you for Dad's note, I'll respond to it shortly.*

Mom's email to Zach at 6:20pm: *May I ask who you are travelling with? Remember this is the most active camping weekend without any reservations - just sayin…Could you at least not leave til you hug your father? He returns tomorrow eve.*

Zach's email to Mom at 9:30pm: *You know good and well who…..*

Mom's final email in the series at 8:32 am the next morning: *If you are referring to me knowing that the two of you (female fixation) are travelling together, then duhh!!! I meant from here to Fairfield…are you going it alone? Is she coming here and travelling with you? I am confused as to how you are travelling….. maybe I don't get to know. Dad shared his note from you and I am so grateful for that* *message of connection. He was so broken by all of this, he was like a child in my arms the night before leaving for Denver. I could not sleep and so when I attempted to get up he pulled me back and begged me to stay. He was terrified of losing you physically, as was I. Oh so fragile we are, at the mercy of your swings, your fire, your rage. I hope you never have that experience with your own child. The pain, fear, anger unbearable. What is bearable is the ever fleeting hope that we grasp onto when we see it, when we don't, that you will rise again like the phoenix and begin with the grace, love, and power we once witnessed in you. Hope is what we hold onto and love drives it. If it has been your true love at the baseline of all this turmoil, illness, and deep inner work, then it must be a crazy powerful force that I hope can find balance in each other to bring forth the greater love into this world and from each of you outwardly to the greater good. This is, after all, what I have wanted for you, Zach, in all my urgings for you to go and do. No shame, no big worldly expectations, no superstar illusions, just finding oneself, one's loves and passions, and sharing it in the world. Perhaps by the end of July, the quest that was begun last summer will have come full circle in this initial cycle. Blessings assured. Mom*

In response to his father's letter to him, Zach went out and set up the tent. The tent was left set up most of the summer, a symbol of their many trips together, a symbol of hoped for future trips together, and simply a reminder of May's madness. John writes to Zach before heading to the airport for his next flight:

My Son;

Today I leave home in tears more scared than I have ever been. I am not allowed to speak to you and if I were I know not what to say. Please be smart. You have so much to offer this crazy fucked up world. The world needs men like you. I need you in my world. Your mother and I want nothing more than for you to free yourself from the past to move to a place where you can exist in your own right. We do not know what it looks like. I have tried to talk to you but apparently I am a hollow core to you at the moment. I am sorry I have failed you in this way.

What I can do is offer to get you out of here. Your mother and I are well aware you need to shed this skin you are trapped in. The best we understand is that you are desirous to return to Fairfield. We all then need to make that our focus. I understand you are ready to go now. So I ask you to focus on your needs and tolerate our space until we can get you back to Iowa. You for most things have been more than gracious and have shown much gratitude.

If I may offer one last piece of fatherly advice – if you are taking a tent – please take the time to set it up to be sure all the parts are there. Please be safe and try to understand we are in this with you as long as you want us to be. Can we grasp where you are – no we can't even imagine. And that is the scary part to

us. And you should know we actually look forward to coming to Iowa to see you. I think there is
something great brewing in you.

With love, concern, and respect, Dad

One more critical email that month sealed the fear deal, crushed the Fairfield trip, and catapulted us into the cellphone couch of an Employee Assistance Program with another desperate attempt to get Zach into crisis counseling immediately. Our daughter frighteningly forwarded a Zach email sent to her that implied self-harm, implied death, implied farewell. We were all traumatized at a despairingly new level. John and I offered one of us to go up immediately to Seattle and bring her home for the upcoming long weekend. She had a longed for and well deserved art department trip to LA scheduled to depart that weekend, which would now remain tentative while we sorted out the urgency of the situation. We contacted the crisis line and continued to build our case for emergency care. We contacted employee assistance again and received more counsel and advice. How do you tell the vastness of this story over the telephone? How do you capture the seeking truth of this man and his found collection of downfalls and health eruption? Do the experts even care about any of that when assessing an immediate risk situation that is truly a power of now assessment? The gift is in the present, right? These professionals are trained to assess the presenting risk, offer resources, and work with whatever current knowledge they can reasonably attain. Direction is then drawn from this intake while their previous training and experience helps them further explain. What to do, what to do, our minds raced with uncertainty. Keep the vigil, keep the watch. Work a little harder, work another way. This now was bigger than a migraine, the joint pain, a collection of symptoms, an adult life transition or some spiritual emergence. Zach's email to his sister woke us from our Fairfield haze, accelerating us into an even more aggressive pursuit of crisis care.

Clarity is something I have in abundance these days, despite all the bullshit that is scarring my senses
in its stench. Among such insights is the notion that it's best I do not attend your graduation, and that I
let it be a rite of passage for you and your parents, as much as a severance between our sibling energy.
You'll always be in my thoughts, and a pillar for my power, within this strange, shrinking world. Yet time
and space are needed between us, as much if not more, than they are within other extinction oriented
relationships of our shared past. I will die and be reborn, first like the Eagle, and then forever cyclically
like the Phoenix. For my lover has a power that is unparalleled, but before that death and new life can

occur, my dying wish as your big brother, Zach, is that your partner can one day empower you to the extent to which mine is empowering me.

In closing, I want it known that I didn't cut myself <u>tonight</u>, but god knows I wanted to. I wanted to feel cold steel and warm blood commingle. I wanted to hear the heaviness of each thick droplet hit the floor. I wanted to taste the bitter sweetness of myself. More than anything, I wanted to release the pain of everyone else. I thought and think of draining all the bad blood that courses through my veins so that all those thirsty bloodsuckers can starve. I will leave them to their own ego deaths, from here on out. It's been a month for me, imprisoned within the walls of my blood. If anything, it's shown me I need to be bled to death, never to return, and never to look back. I look forward to whoever we are in the next life within this cycle and I'll see you when I see you, knowing you will embrace my alter-ego upon its looming unraveling. Until then, love always.

Holding all of our accumulated fear, past, present, and anticipated future, and then being told we had no actionable or justifiable legal means at this time (has he physically harmed himself or someone else?) to secure for our son active help or treatment without his compliance, we were advised to remain vigilant, and call 911 if emergency actually presented. Our emergent Zach was presenting as emergenZ. We had to up our game in notifying the various villages of support. John communicated to his work that we were in need of him staying home this next week as we discerned our next steps to advanced care and how to actively enact them. I withdrew my application for the university job, and with our blessing, and her own personal discernment that it might be good to get away and be distracted, Gabby went to LA. She would be surrounded by a team of professors and art students who knew her and cared about her, holding sacred whatever she might have been willing to share with them about her family crisis. The three of us agreed she would come home for his birthday, the following weekend, a weekend before her graduation, and she could reconnect in the home with her brother in person. For now, John and I would stand guard, keep him safe, and continue to google the hell out of our computers to figure out assessment and action.

It was at this point that we also called our siblings, who already knew we were having health challenges with Zach, but now would be asked for prayers specific to life versus death, specific to timely assistance from our community healthcare system, and specific to support and sustenance for John, Gabby and me. We called the quest leaders, for they were a recent community of love and support for Zach, who would embrace and respect his personal philosophies and shifting life priorities amidst this health mystery unfolding. They all attempted to reach out to Zach, but to no avail given that he had shut down every vehicle of his to communication. His computer and phone once again found their way in the middle of the night onto the rejection counter of the kitchen. Of course, we welcomed prayers from our family, church and friends, but the truth was, we had no specific sense of the what and why to offer them. The broad blessing of prayerful love and support for each of us was without question necessary, despite our specific request for Zach prayers. At any manic moment in this journey, one of the three of us could have had a physical or mental breakdown ourselves. I had never known stress and fear at the heightened levels this imploding crisis delivered. A lingering taste of metal in my mouth had to be a body chemistry shift, I reasoned; the taste and metabolism of fear. The hard to swallow knot that would sit at the base of my throat, would rise and fall as the measure of safety and risk vacillated. It was all very suffocating. We had wondered for some time if Zach was having a mental breakdown, perhaps a onetime event triggered by a huge measure of loss and identity, maybe even a desperately broken heart. We had no family history, no previous medical occurrence or even any acquired knowledge as to mental illness cause and effect, but we increasingly felt we may need to accept this as possibility, explore this as probability. Medical experts would soon advise us to accept this as probability without any accurate exploration of possibility.

Zach, meanwhile, was quiet again in his isolated and aggravated state. Our clues to his existence were measured by shower noise, house squeaks and creaks from his footsteps, and the crackling knees accompanied by neck cracks as he would, from the dungeon of his space that the basement shelter had become, venture up the stairway to seek food and sustenance. The smell of incense burning was the smell of life. John and I continued to write him, trying to enter into his physical and mental space safely and respectfully, encouraging him to allow professional help. We would help him help himself, our message would invite. The intentional privacy violations would then escalate the excessive and unusual use of 'fuck you' and 'get the fuck out' type responses, so we carefully tapered and tempered our push. No need to waken the rage or risk setting the stage. Until knives came into the picture, and not to chop vegetables. Following a day full of noisy tree work and repetitive construction noise outside his bedroom window, and an early evening rant about how we were all creating these disruptions intentionally, he flippantly flipped chairs, posing like the Incredible Hulk with a raging intensity of delusional delivery, and then collapsing onto the basement floor, curled up like a fetus, crying childlike for help and for whereabouts of a female avatar imagined. We compassionately yet frighteningly tried to calm our loved one, immediately aware that we would contact the crisis line again, working to build a legitimate enough case to warrant professional help. Zach retreated to his room and shortly thereafter we heard him shower, sobbing while trying to soothe his suffering. The parental pain penetrated. The protective vein perpetuated. The opportunity when he showered to enter his room without invoking rage or an awareness of our presence was thus perpetrated. We found two camping knives stabbed into his plastic trash can, which we removed and hid. Filled with intensified fear for his safety, we called and made our report. We did not yet fear for our own safety, as we had never known our son to be violent. But this illness was violent. We pledged to keep him safe from himself and from whatever demons and evil nemesis he was battling. That next morning, we found Zach's computer and a third knife, one he had been gifted with at high school graduation by an outdoor ministry hiking leader, displayed on the kitchen counter. We were relieved to see the knife volunteered for riddance, but the computer meant we could no longer write him. This was a disposal tactic now familiar to us, as he would use it when he would rid himself of various belongings as in the aforementioned 'minimizing excess' and 'rejecting value' actions. Left out for eventual retrieval, he would in time retrieve the isolation friend and foe. Zach would cycle between his like and dislike of the computer, social media, and the search engine madness of trying to understand what was happening to him. John and I certainly had our own version of that madness.

But thank God for search engines! John and I were so alone and unguided without them. Our computers became our mistress/lover substitutes as they accompanied us to bed each night, snuggled close, fingered and manipulated to give us an occasional orgasmic release when we found anything that might guide us or steer us through this mess. Intimacy between us as a couple was so heightened, yet it was so not organic sexy time. Rather, it was organic sanity prime. We were inseparable in those night hours, curled up into each other spoon like, as if we were newlyweds in bliss. But our honeymoon was over; we were searching our mistress for whatever was amiss. Sleep was rough on this road, for turning back was a mission impossible. We would map our way forward into the dark night, until morning's sunrise promise of a new direction that might shed some light. Then with creaks in the floor, shadows at the door, and mysteries on the counter even more, the energy of our passionate interlude would fade, for a mistress never really resolves the problem. How would this night time love affair confront this now daily display of family dysfunction? The fact that Zach left the knife on the counter for us to secure was perceived as his attempt to communicate that he did not want to harm himself. It was a silent gesture that begged us to appease, at least we believed. Then it became a screaming gesture to help him, please! On the eve of Friday, May 30, I found Zach lying on the kitchen floor, crying out for help. I shouted for John's attention, while tearfully begging Zach to calm down, assuring him I would help him control this impulse. He was so frighteningly vulnerable, this near seven-foot sweet child of mine. We were all so fucking vulnerable! He had taken the kitchen knife he regularly used to prepare his breakfast, and stabbed it into the tissue box from the counter, fighting some uncontrollable urge to harm himself with it. Whatever this monster was within him, he was struggling to resist its power and grip on the unrelenting symptoms of physical pain and uncontrollable anguish. Zach lay curled up, all 6'10" of him, sobbing and trembling, pleading and questioning. "I cannot control it, why can't I control it?", Zach whimpered. "It'll be ok, Zach. It'll be ok." I am stroking his shoulders, gently touching him to allow the hoped for magical healing of touch I had so often wanted to deliver. And yet, touch was not comforting, sound was not comforting, life was not comforting. Could any of us actually make it ok? Would it be ok?

John gently coaxed his fragile son out to the front porch, while I called 911. I was frantic, near hysteria, describing the threatening moment, while the calm, reasonable voice on the other end of the call had to assess if immediate danger was at hand. 'Is anyone bleeding, where is the knife, what is he doing now?' kinds of questions were delivered in her steady and direct response. I just wanted someone to help us, to help him, right here and right NOW! After setting aside the knife and tissue box for safety and for evidence of the severity of our situation, and accepting the fact that this operator was not sending anyone just yet, I located John and Zach on the front porch to ascertain the situation. They had engaged in some calming conversation, away from any obvious threat, and it was determined by crisis standards that we were all currently 'safe, and unharmed'. This experience was a heightened depiction of insanity. I could not believe that these

138

events needed to be worse in measure for help to arrive! Realistically, I knew those words 'safe and unharmed' to be false, misleading, and painfully uncertain. At what point in time would it be justified to receive help? I was coached to call back if he escalated. I joined the two men on the porch, and witnessed Zach speaking all kinds of nonsense about this imagined true love, her father who was in conspiracy against the two of them, and the belief that his own parents shared knowledge of her whereabouts in conspiracy with this future father in law. He paused amidst the madness meandering and suddenly rants on about how we and all the neighborhood had been torturing him continuously with excessive noise, screaming out, 'Great job, great job!' to the darkened empty space of the front yard field. John was exceptional at listening and gently reasoning with him, allowing Zach to settle down and return from this delusional outburst. Zach responded well to John's care, calm, and fatherly love. His father would later share that he could always see flickers of our Zach from within this mysterious persona for there would be a certain look, gesture, phrase, or thread familiar. We still held so much hope. Having spent day after day, night after night on the home front, witnessing, fearing, and holding all of this recurring madness up close in real time, I opted to exit this secured scene, collapse into our bedroom space and weep like Multnomah Falls. John assured me all was stable for now and that Zach was eating quietly. Mom passed out into a long overdue, melatonin induced deep sleep, emotionally and physically depleted from days and nights of this torment, but keenly aware that I had John in the home and by my side to help. Not unlike our parenting work over the years, John and I would balance each other in the work and the care. The next morning was quiet. Afternoon and evening ironically offered reasonable conversations with our troubled son, who was still deeply committed to the idea that this woman's avatar was in the house. He had seen her, and was convinced we were continuing to withhold information. Zach had an eerie calm about him the day after that knife on the kitchen floor collapse. He vacuumed and cleaned his room and the downstairs, he did some laundry, behaving as if we were expecting company. It dawned on me that he likely believed she was arriving, whomever she was.

A strange premonition in the early evening of that cleaning frenzy day, was the experience of the family cat racing up the stairs, tail fully fluffed out and eyes bugged like he had seen the devil. If I had a tail like that, it would have fluffed out weeks ago. I understood the cat. The cat would begin to avoid our son, cognizant of a stranger danger.

139

Zach had become the stranger, and his behavior the danger. Or maybe the cat saw her, just sayin'. Crazy. June 1st was a Sunday, and Zach carried forward the calm of the previous day. He even joined us for dinner. Often he would choose to eat without us, but on occasion we would catch him in an agreeable state, and encourage the shared time. I missed him so. We missed him so. Who was this strange and unwanted guest residing within the soul of our Zach? Not the guest he felt sure we were accomplice to hiding. We dined and cleaned up together, with no sign of his avatar friend. As the evening progressed, there seemed to be a growing uneasiness in Zach, for we would hear him pace up and down the stairway. John checked on him in the kitchen, and then Zach followed his father to our bedroom door, demanding to hear from us just what his love's father had directed us to do. "What did he say?", Zach insisted, hovering in the doorframe, leaning forward with a blank stare. He was intimidating. John again gently escorted him to the living room, and managed to keep Zach calm, as he spoke to his confused son in a respectful and attentive manner.

John allowed Zach's delusions to be spoken, and did not challenge them. I followed my treasured men to listen and observe, phone in hand to dial those three numbers at a moments' notice. I overheard Zach say to John that suicide would be a dignified end for both he and his woman, for they would be together and no longer under the power of this man, her father. Zach wondered out loud just how powerful this imagined man was, and whether he (Zach) would need to go after him, take him down. In that revealing moment of madness, with words spoken so uncharacteristic of our Zach, John stayed and reasoned with his son, and his son sat talking calmly but with such commitment, as if these ideas held legitimate truth and reason. I nodded to John that I was going to call 911. Begging for help, I explained as best I could to the operator how we were increasingly fearful he would do something uncharacteristic of him in this sickened state. He was speaking the words suicide. What if? For the first time throughout all of the fear filled moments, I actually wondered if Zach, in a broken mind, could or would act out from these delusions. John and I were in agreement, and so was the responder, who by now, had a series of desperate phone calls on record from our household and enough situational tracking to warrant concern of Zach's harm to self or others. We had to keep lovable sane Zach, who we would see and hear deep within this shell of a being, safe from frighteningly insane Zach, who was getting sicker in ways that we could not help him on

140

our own. Finally, we believed we could solve this baffling mystery with the help of experts who could safely lure Zach out of the home, into the hands of capable health care, and on to a healing pathway. Help us, please!

Our good fortune at the end of this exhaustive chapter, was that this 911 operator was wise enough to send to our home 3 officers, one of whom was crisis trained and exceptional in the practice of these skills. After all, Zach's size and strength were intimidating, something in his well mind he would have worked hard at presenting as less so. Add the maddened state of unpredictable thought and possible matching behavior, these officers were coming prepared to assist but also protect one another. It was a terrifying thought to have officers come to your home prepared to draw a gun in defense of a perceived angry giant. It happens. In the early hours of Monday, June 2, 2014, an EMT transport came to the house, and Zach was finally convinced by a respectful and responsible officer to go to the hospital and get evaluated for his mental and physical condition. Six weeks after we left Fairfield, Iowa, we were hospital bound again, hoping to finally get a full understanding of what ails Zach and how to find wellness. We were exhausted.

Chapter 18: Bi-Polar Blip

Float On, Modest Mouse
Wake Up, Arcade Fire

Relinquishing our perceived control was necessary to getting help. This was true as much for Zach as it was for John and me. Control was not something any of us felt we had much of, but that which we did have, we could now choose to surrender. Our parenting role shifted in that living room moment from active care giving, safety providing participants to active resource using, safety pursuing advocates. Our 25year old son, Zachary Charles Moritz, was calmly and willingly escorted out of the house by the two emergency medical technicians and three police officers. It had been just a year since he was eagerly preparing to escort himself up to the Inyo Mountains. This living room encounter was not at all the vision any of us imagined occurring after that sacred journey toward personal transformation. Both departures were quests in search of healing and direction, one by choice, the other by circumstance. Looking tenderly into each other's tear filled eyes upon closing that front door, John and I collapsed into the sturdy pillars of strength we had attempted to be for him, now for one another. We were alone in our home without our patient, nearly depleted of patience. There was little concern in that empty house moment as to the placement of our footstep to avoid a noisy, creaky floor, the placement of our word choice to avoid conflict or quiet a voice's volume, or even the placement of our emotions from the madness and mystery within this midnight hour. Our guard let down in the absence of his hauntingly strange presence, the erratic shadow of his precious but now precocious soul. There was grave concern yet in the still unknown mystery of our son's body and mind breakdown, and in the uncertainty of any next step our shared predicament would suggest. Standing in the entryway moment, we could now dare to exhale a sigh of relief, we could now wonder out loud the why of disbelief, and above all, we could now physically release the ever so lonely cry of accumulated grief. We did.

Safety from harm and direction for healing; only the confidence in these intentions would allow us to quietly stand by and watch our son driven off by uniformed, armed, authority figures, whom we trusted to be more familiar than ourselves in situations such as we found ourselves. What was to be next beyond activating 911 support, and enabling the hospital transport, we were not at all clear. There were some next step possibilities we had been researching as the necessity to exert action was becoming more obvious, more critical in nature, each passing day of the Mayday mayhem. We were blindly seeking direction, primarily trying to discern the what and when and how of getting our sick son to help. In the hour of accumulated desperate need, the who arrived at our doorstep, calmly coaching Zach to consider and then act on leaving the house for help. The where to the care was merely a 15minute drive from our home, and we would head out shortly. We needed this assistance to determine direction and a persistence to initiate supportive action. He had isolated himself in the home since cancelling care appointments mid-May, unwilling to leave the home, and what we came to eventually understand, was that he was unable to leave the home. The grip of his illness twisted his desire and his fire, his ability and his clarity, into a tangled brain foggy mess. He was fearful to leave for many reasons, some of which we believe he could not even understand. Sometimes, I heard the fear in his written or spoken message. Sometimes I heard the defiance. I understood both as truths. He had nowhere else to go. We had nowhere else to go. We now had a place to go.

John and I changed out of our bed clothes, gathered up our hope and a prayer, and continued to follow the ever evolving footprint of Zach's quest for a fulfilling life. Hospital bound we now were. The emergency room and the crisis call center became our gateways to finding help, given that Zach still had no primary care physician established, a mystery illness upon him, and an unfamiliar knowledge of any other method or resource with which to seek assistance. John and I, as primary providers and caretakers for Zach, continued to cheerlead ourselves with messages of encouragement about how we were bright and capable adults, that we could figure this out together, the care pathway, the health diagnosis, and ultimately, treatment care. We were doing the best we could with the resources and knowledge we had. It was and is far too easy to focus on what you have not yet done or what you are not yet doing, when the solution pathway seems to evade you and the problem itself begins to expand. This was our truth. SUDDENLY, YOU REALIZE YOU DON'T EVEN KNOW WHAT IT IS THAT YOU DON'T KNOW! And that, is a sickening feeling that can paralyze your present. You feel the clock ticking in the measure of lost time; you hope to survive the calendar of ongoing turned pages, the life of distinctively lost stages. Between that time past and the future page yet unturned, the present must be endured. Often, the work was all about endurance, for while hope hovered, despair loomed. Faith was without question, daily on trial. You be the judge. We would find her soon enough. For now, we would go to find him.

Zach was resting in a room referred for mental health observation. In the wee hour arrival to the hospital, we would be greeted by a social worker who would listen to our story, attempt to piece key links together, and then further sort out relevance to the vast array of information detail provided. Of course, everything about him felt deeply relevant to us, his parents. This man was a mountain on the landscape of our lives. But of late, he was more like Mt. St. Zachary, erupting with lava, clouding his own vision, and altering our own visual viewpoint. We rambled on to the health practitioner about his explosion of physical health issues, the mental health delusions, the anger and accusations toward us and yet, simultaneously, the sane and loving behaviors that coexisted under the roof of our home, inside the dome of his mind. His health crisis in Fairfield was shared, our attempts to find help, the approaching parental concern of 5 days remaining on our employer health care plan, Zach's strongly independent mindset and his eventual rejection of help, his obsession with a woman and her father in Copenhagen, and our consuming fear for his own personal safety. It was a fevered sales pitch intended to achieve endorsement as to the severity of his need for care, thus our own need for care. John and I had become quick studies to learning next step options. The medical team would collaboratively assess through intake, examination, and observation whether Zach was physically or mentally ill, gravely disabled, and whether we, as his parents, were credible sources in our intention and our messaging regarding our son's health. This last assessment seemed to always be in question, and the implication felt insulting and demeaning. Before any decisions would be made, the hospital lab examinations would be completed, an evaluation of their results considered, and a further consultation necessitated. If there was no illness detected other than mental, the next step of care would be involuntary hospitalization, should Zach be determined incompetent to discern and provide for his own care needs. Dependence, not independence, would become his new truth. We felt conflicted on his behalf, and yet relieved to have assistance options on our own behalf. Fortunately, we would learn, this local community had two evaluation and treatment centers, and a bed would need to be available at one of them for his placement. We were encouraged to go home, get some rest, and return around 6:30 or 7am to engage further in this decision. It was now 3:30am and home was just a mere 15 minutes away. Home; it would allow us a brief respite, and a short window to research further all the new and unfamiliar names and labels, decisions and responsibilities such as psychosis, designated mental health professional (DMHP), gravely disabled, 72 hour hold, involuntary hospitalization, least restrictive alternative, evaluation and treatment center (E&T). We were entering the mental health care system at its most intense entry point, psychosis, and we sure could use a mentor or an advocate other than each other. Search engine to the rescue. Finding a path to care continued to be our own assigned homework.

We returned early to meet the DMHP and engage in the evaluation of whether Zach was gravely disabled at this time. A determination would warrant a 72 hour hold as legal and necessary, until a court proceeding could further determine if a longer stay at an E&T hospital was necessary. In Washington state, definition of gravely disabled (WPI 360.12) qualifies as *'a condition in which a person, as a result of a mental disorder, 1) is in danger of serious physical harm resulting from a failure to provide for his or her essential human needs of health or safety, or 2) manifests severe deterioration in routine functioning evidenced by repeated and escalating loss of cognitive or volitional control over his or her actions and is not receiving or would not receive, if released, such care as is essential for his or her health and safety'.* Zach was approved for the 72hour hold based upon our testimony, the assessment of the DMHP, and the behaviors and actions witnessed in observation and examination. The care team would seek a bed at one of two local E&T centers, and a court hearing would follow for longer care assessment. Exhale. The mental health care system had not been what Zach had been seeking, but it apparently was what found him. We were looking for mercy, and we now were at their mercy. Would there be mercy? Things were no longer as they used to be, and blue skies had disappeared. I missed the Gaye music of our lives.

The hospital had run its standard intake documentation, and upon much later review of these records, we noted that Zach had either told staff he had an ADHD diagnosis, or the diagnosis already existed on the medical records software. This was a diagnosis John and I were still skeptical of as diagnostic disorder for Zach, but Zach must have believed and shared that the ADD diagnosis (no hyperactivity) was a truth for him since his summer of 2011 doctor visit. So be it. Whatever he shared was printed on record as truth. We wondered how these records would responsibly reflect upon intake whether his delusional mind was trustworthy and reliable of complete accuracy versus exaggerated or confused thought. How would the information be used for or against him, whether true or false, accurate or exaggerated? Among many questions asked at each intake procedure, he was asked about drug use. He had, in his lifetime, used marijuana, cocaine, and hallucinogens, and he offered the honest admission of such. This admission, without accuracy as to frequency or occasion of use, would then become fodder for diagnostic bias, implied repeatedly to be a causative disorder contributing to his illness. So be it? Not so. During future caregiving time of more stable health for Zach, we learned through clear headed and pure hearted confession, the extent of this admission. He had used drugs recreationally in his lifetime, this we knew to some extent, introduced to alcohol, marijuana and some cocaine in high school, exposed and indulged on further occasion in college and overseas. There had been plenty of occasions for recreational indulgence in the past ten years, but excessive use and abuse was not his truth or reality. At this stage of his life, Zach was not proud of these admissions, nor was he ashamed. We knew that his use and experimentation was not at all uncommon in adolescent and young adult years, approve of it or not. He would make no excuse for his choices and experimentation. Nor would we. He knew the risks and he argued that he understood and drew boundaries around use versus abuse. He owned his choices, and he had in the last year come to an awakening around how these choices of his past were not moving him forward in his present. Zach did not have a substance abuse disorder, and to this day, on behalf of his character and reputation, we would challenge any suggestion or implication otherwise. In the path of the medical intake system for an adult child aged 25, our word held no weight. The medical records were not provided to us, nor were they requested by us to note this pattern on record until well after the consuming and preoccupying pursuit of his care and treatment for wellness recovery.

Unfortunately, Zach's unfiltered and unleashed mind dump upon each hospital admission would travel forward on record, describing him as a substance abuser with substance disorder. Drug abuse became a misleading accompanying descriptor of his ongoing treatment needs. Where was the validating evidence beyond his admitted use not any ongoing abuse over the course of his last ten years to then justify an extrapolation into a diagnostic disorder and an assumed causation of this sudden onset of mental illness presentation? The lab tests repeatedly showed zero indication of drug use. Could all medical teams read Chapter 2-16 prior to assessing this individual with such offensive assumption and ignorance? If only. It is true, the heavy use and abuse of a variety of drugs is known to create devastating havoc and disruption in the lives of individuals, their loved ones, and their communities. An increasingly devastating truth in our society is that severe and consequential abuse and overuse of drugs impacts socioeconomic status and mind/body presentations, destroying many an individual, family and community, thereby presenting commonly and frequently in the revolving doors of hospital emergency rooms. Assumptions and stereotypes are likely to occur when a mentally unstable young man enters emergency care and shares that he has used drugs, consumed alcohol, indulged in tobacco use during his youthful and young adult years. Substance abuse and mental health often hold hands. But what else holds hands with mental illness presentation? Plenty! Is anyone even clinically evaluating this question? Zach's circumstance of honest admission to drug usage now intersecting with this health implosion, it was just too convenient for an immediate association by the medical establishment. Substance abuse and severe misuse were never part of any life experience we ever had with our son. Our parental word, however, was perceived as naïve. His now recorded drug use history and the medical community interpretation of its relevance, repeatedly became the reasoned information in his travelling medical history that drew focus and assumed purpose at almost every single future entry point of care. The negative drug screens and repeated lab results from each hospitalization carried just what kind of value to redirecting this stereotype and judgement, we wondered. What about the consistently negative blood lab work ups? Were they reliable? John and I believe, as actively engaged and informed adults in the scope of our sons amazing young life, that there was misplaced bias and assumption around drug and alcohol use as causative influence to our son's mysterious medical disruption. The multiple signs and symptoms of physical health deterioration he presented with at every entry point did not appear to be given the same measure of merit for evaluation of cause, nor did the spoken parent history provided about Zach's character and lifestyle prior to the mysterious awakening of this illness receive any credence.

147

Credibility to diagnostic alternatives proved hard to come by when psychotic presentation was front and center. What would a documented circular skin rash indicate anyway?

Strange and unusual stories ventured out of Zach's mind in the madness, and he could sometimes express himself and present himself in a manner that was quite believable and well. This was not unlike how his once exceptional writing skills shifted toward bizarre as illness progressed. His dual messaging would offer loving and clear thought or idea, and then raging and illogical thought would weave into the thread of those messages, spoken or written. Commonly, it was difficult to sort legitimate truth from legitimate mind fuck, and this was first evidenced in the midst of the Fairfield health implosion. Even Zach was tortured by the truth of this occurrence, crying out at random occasion about the unknown something that held control over him. Strange shit would just come out of the brain, facts and truths mixed with fiction and ideas and imagination and exaggeration, and he could not control its impulse or its fire. Malfunction it was! It was as if an alien lived inside his brain and altered all thought and behavior. The physical examination records of that first emergency evening checked off no neck or back pain, which we knew to be ongoing complaints of daily agitation for Zach. Fatigue, weakness, headaches, and skin rash were checked negative in the review of his body systems, which we also knew to be inaccurate, having listened to him for 6 weeks speak nonstop of these ailments and challenges. In this and every single lab workup, his urinary drug screen was immaculately clean. Neglectful intake, it later seemed. No bacteria or virus was found in whatever workups were done, but then, what was being evaluated to accurately trace that possibility anyhow? Blood and urine? Outdated and ill performing diagnostics, perhaps? No one ever spoke of the possibility of a bacteria or a virus as a potential culprit. All of the physical symptoms which we shared with the intake team, were apparently to be interpreted as mental health disorder or substance abuse symptoms. For the past six weeks, his ailing symptoms in addition to this steady onset of rage, agitation, delusion, paranoia, and confused thought included migraines, light and sound sensitivity, tinnitus, back and neck pain, fatigue, tingling and crawling skin sensation, cracking knee and neck sounds, a circular rash, tremors, digestive pain, flat affect. John and I would repeat this very relevant information time and again, and we were clear minded, direct witnesses to all. Did anyone see these additional multiple symptoms as relevant, possible clues to something more comprehensive than psychosis? We were at the mercy of Western medicine practice, and we had no reason to not trust in the care we so badly needed. We certainly had no ideas nor had we found any Google suggested possibilities.

Leaving the hospital by late morning that Monday, we decided to push ourselves beyond an extremely fatigued and run down state to attend a previously arranged noon therapy appointment in Portland, scheduled through John's Employee Assistance Program. It was an appointment originally intended and hoped for Zach, but now claimed as necessary and timely for the two of us. The therapeutic exercise was one of being listened to, but not one of shedding any enlightened possibility for us or for him. We returned home exhausted but rallied to complete two necessary priorities yet in the dusk of the day. We needed to contact our daughter and John's employer, in that order. Our proposed original plan with Gabby was to celebrate Zach's birthday in some fashion together at home this coming week but those plans did not include an involuntary hospitalization for Zach. His birthday, we knew, would be oddly different this year, but we would all four be together under the same roof, or so we believed, and she was eager to have direct contact. John and I had conceived an adjusted new plan to propose to her once we shared about our past 24hour development, and it would still involve her coming home. If she wanted company immediately, if she wanted to come home immediately, we would make it happen. Otherwise, we would travel north to retrieve her following the court hearing scheduled for Thursday morning, the day before his 26th birthday. Their aunt, my sister, would also be in town for a nursing conference, so there would be additional family care and support. It would be painful to tell our daughter of her brother's story, our story, and to tell it long distance over the phone. It would be equally painful to imagine her alone in her apartment, pushing herself to carry on with deadlines, details, and then the onslaught of such disturbing news from home. I cannot fairly speak of how it must have been experienced for her to receive this call, to listen and to feel the lonely ache and sorrow. I can only imagine the helplessness, the sibling loyalty and love, the staggering weight of the fear. I desperately wanted to hold her close, to make everything all right. John would reach out to his manager, hoping to rely on and trust in his understanding toward this unexpected family crisis. He counted on his management's leadership support to filter out customer deadlines, service needs, and project follow up. John was the kind of employee who had a long trail of corporate dedication and loyalty, working ridiculous hours, travelling extensively on an almost weekly basis, and willingly, practically to a fault, availing himself to help any and all, both coworkers and customers, as a collaborative teammate and company member. Surely, in this time of crisis, he would be respected as the hardworking, loyal, and dedicated employee he had a history of proving himself to be; surely he would not have this unpredictable, unexplainable circumstance held against him in the self-management of his personal and professional life balance and demand. Not unlike our trust in the medical system, we faithfully trusted the employer support system, even though no mention was ever made of Family Medical Leave Act (FMLA), something we later learned should have been mentioned by management. Our character, our honesty, our perseverance would matter; we believed that would make a difference as to how we were treated, how we were supported, how we were respected. And we hoped the same for Zach.

It had been quite a testament of resilience and perseverance as to how John, Gabby and I withstood the fear and uncertainty of Zach's health while navigating our own life balance and personal health. John managed to bear the demands of a significant and demanding job transition as well as the tremendous weight of financial support for the entire family. Gabby reflected great will and determination as she managed to uphold and even complete her schooling, accomplishing academic and artistic accolades while crisis was erupting at home. I had miraculously withstood the unpredictable days and nights of cycling insanity, alone and constantly in pleading prayer and vigil. All three of us remained loyal to our dedicated roles in walking by Zach's side, by each other's side. And yet we were afraid and uncertain. Coworkers, friends and family knew little as to the depth of devastation that was happening to our once healthy family core. It all escalated so quickly, so mysteriously, we could barely hold our heads above water to dare shout out for help, to even understand what help we needed. Well intended nonstop questions from family and friends were increasingly harder to answer, while unwarranted and usually unintended judgements were painful to hear. All too often unsolicited advice was confusing and extremely presumptive. Managing outside input became exhausting, sorting out the ideas, suggestions, comparisons, when the speed and intensity of the situation was accelerating. We could choose to spend time tending and responding to the curious and suggestive community, or we could spend time responding to our crumbling and overwhelmed immediate family needs. Our energy and lack of knowledge could not support both. Increasingly, it was lonely and heartbreaking to not have a broader lean in community or knowledgeable advocacy that felt safe, comforting, and helpful. John and I at least had each other. We worried for our daughter, so alone. She chose our Thursday afternoon pick up arrangement, granting herself the needed time to wrap up course demands and work deadlines, then allowing herself three days off at home. Next on the family notification schedule would be my sister and brother, who would get an up close and on time dose of our current state of Zach affairs. Our extended long distance family, which basically by definition, included all of our living family with the exception of my brother and sister in law living an hour away, knew we were in crisis at home with Zach, but none knew we had just hospitalized Zach involuntarily. Joanne, a woman of deep empathic care, an aunt of creative individual flair, and a medical professional mental illness informed and aware, was travelling to town the very next day. We would telephone and update the other long distance family chain of support. I had previously arranged to take both my brother and sister to lunch for their respective birthdays on that day, Gemini pairing that they were. Often, the third Gemini in the family clan, Zachary, would benefit from birthday celebration inclusion with my siblings. My sister was flying in to attend a nursing conference in Portland, and chose to also spend a few days with us, hoping she could connect face to face with her loved nephew Zach, whom she knew was in deep despair.

My sister Joanne had become my compass rose of directional guidance, for she understood mental illness and she knew how to fully listen and hold sensitive, supportive conversation. Perhaps the most meaningful skill she soothed my soul with was her innate ability to know when and how I needed to be told what a great job I was doing. The first time I heard her tell me this, tell John and me this as a team, I emotionally broke my personal thunderous tsunami wave of cresting self-criticism and self judgement. Over the course of our sudden onset storm system, when John and I were striving to navigate a stable and clear direction, she helped me throw overboard the self-imposed measures of unmet expectation and inability to effectively solve Zach's presenting problem, to answer accurately and knowledgably to medical people and others who inquired, and therefore to obtain the necessary life jacket or life preserver for my son. She would orient me like a compass at sea, steering me with words, resources, well timed silences, and validations to calm the stirring seas within and steady the daily tides surrounding and seemingly swallowing us up. Her messaging emails, her tending, her deep listening and even her available responses to my nighttime messaged cries of fear and despair, were all soothing sustenance amidst washed out beaches and redefined shorelines left behind following each recurring storm we weathered. For her timely love and care, I remain grateful. It had been a rare occurrence in this baffling mysterious health crisis journey, that someone would simply listen lovingly and respond by acknowledging effort, commitment, and strength in the caregiving and advocacy for your loved one. Early on in Zach's mind body breakdown, when I would share our confusion with family and friends as to the contradictions of his behavior, I inadvertently found that I opened myself up to more vulnerability and distraction. The inappropriate questions, the judgements within questions, the assumptive inquiries, and the comparative stories of negative outcome shared from other's mental illness lives and encounters were not helpful in measure of support. Often, they drove more fear not hope. Suggestions as solutions when the problem had not been clearly identified were unwelcome expressions of perceived care and concern.

It was especially difficult to hear criticism and judgement of Zach, when you understood him to not be himself, to not be well. Loved ones would perceive themselves as protecting you while in criticism of him. Pain would multiply; the pain on behalf of your own suffering and struggle, and the pain on behalf of your loved one's suffering and struggle. Both matter. Zach's pain and suffering needed the same careful filter from judgement by us, regardless of his strange behaviors and messages. As personal as his verbal insults or other's suggestive messages might be experienced, we had to develop skills to not hold or own them as personally intended wounds. There were lessons in this for all of us. Joanne had the professional skill and the Auntie heart to understand illness, its role in his behaviors, and thus weave her understanding into compassionate care for her nephew. She had the ability to not judge or critique Zach for something he was in struggle with to overcome, maintaining the knowledge and belief of who her nephew still was in the midst of his chaotic confusion. If she did have doubts or fears, she withheld or filtered them from us, not burdening us but choosing to lift us up and strengthen instead. *'You are doing amazing work, Beth. You and John are working so hard, caring so deeply for Zach. You are both finding healthy pathways for him, while still taking care of yourselves and Gabby in such loving ways'.* Acknowledgement of our parental care and dedication renewed us, fueled us, validated us. Affirming value is a strength bearing gift to offer someone in crisis. We lose sight of our value when success feels unattainable, when our efforts appear to not make a difference, when our loved one is so sick that sometimes, they may even reject our necessary care. Affirm us with love. Listen without judgement. Weather a storm together. Gift your care unconditionally.

On June 3, I picked my sister up at the Portland airport, updated her that Zach was on a 72 hour hold at an evaluation and treatment center, and confided that we would participate in a mental health court hearing on Thursday to determine a diagnosis and treatment plan for mental illness. She received it with sadness, hope, and love. We met our brother for a birthday lunch overlooking the Columbia River, and I then brought him up to date about his nephew Zach's status and our family status. Having the available expertise of my sister to respond to the questions and explanations I was still ill equipped to provide was helpful. Getting comfortable stating my honest, hard to accept response to most questions anymore became increasingly important, and I could practice in this safe family moment. "I just don't know." There it was. Spoken out loud. My answer and my truth, dammit! My brother loved his nephew, and held a budding adult relationship with him. In the last few years, they developed a special bond in the shared mutual respect of nature and mother earth, of spiritual perspective and practices beyond the scope of Christianity, and inclusive of alternative pathways to meaningful life choices. Rob Roy expressed a genuine sorrow for all of us in the known and unknown of these dark and difficult days, and I welcomed his additional comfort. The tone of the lunch occasion was certainly altered despite its original celebration intention, but we made the best of the circumstances, checking in further with each other's lives and life stories. Happy Birthday, I would remind them, as we wrapped up the gift of our time together and placed a Moritz bow on the bill. We would find ourselves increasingly in contact, as our family saga took center stage, and our blood family would lovingly try to stand alongside us in the lonely, unfamiliar, uncertain hours, days, and weeks ahead.

Within just 72 hours, Zach would turn 26years of age. The day before his birthday, he would sit in a mental health court, judged gravely disabled, placed in lockdown care, and subjected the next day, on his actual birthday, to medication against his will. There would be no cake, no candles, no happy in this ceremonial song. Have you ever just greeted someone on their birthday and simply said, 'Birthday.', as your greeting? This would be the first time in 26 years of his life that we would not celebrate and we could not bring ourselves to acknowledge any happy. The hospitalization, the forced medication, the mean and hurtful statements so uncharacteristic of our Zach, the surreal nature of our lives in this here and now, it was just so hard to fathom. We were affirming our love in these agreed upon actions of protection, and he was not experiencing any of it as such. Not here in lockdown, not now in madness. We had to keep reminding ourselves he was not himself, he was very sick, and thus we must be resilient. His own resilience in enduring such struggle for weeks now, was warrior like, not unlike the mythic heroes he so loved to read and muse about. Joanne, John and I tried to visit Zach the night of her arrival, his second night in lockdown. We found him curled up on the floor of his stark room, not fitting the bed, mattress on the floor, in great pain, lights out and earplugs in to minimize light and sound sensitivity. Understandably, he was angry. He told John we had a funny way of showing our love, and asked us to leave. There likely was an accompanying 'fuck', as it had become his favorite adjective, adverb, noun, and verb of choice in the colorful array of vocabulary he utilized in madness. In fact, John recalled a slow yet deliberate message from our son when we attempted to visit him early on.

"Get......the......fuck......out!" This became his madness mantra when he really wanted to be heard, when he really wanted out of his head.

The physical exam upon entry to E&T was just the day after the physical exam performed upon entry at the hospital emergency room. On these records, migraines are noted, and a skin lesion is also noted on his medial left upper arm. A pinkish, round, 3 cm. lesion is the written description, and further into the report, the nurse practitioner writes that it is probably a linear lesion on that upper arm. This would imply that the mark was a scratch or that it was generated externally. Zach tells them the rash has been present almost a month, and this is recorded in the notes. It is a confusing discovery to once again find that just the day before, the hospital medical notes specified no rash or lesion. Furthermore, a linear lesion is not round, so even within these E&T exam notes, there appears to be contradiction. His mark on the arm was round, pink, and visible, according to the E&T notes, not linear in description. Records also revealed a prescription written for a Clotrimazole cream to treat the observed lesion/rash. The observation of this lesion/rash was the first of many more recorded on Zach's medical journey, with no relevance given to any significance. The rash appeared after acupuncture treatment, Zach and I later recollected. An even later recollection by Zach, was his discovery of it months earlier. And that psych evaluation suggestion we had been encouraged to explore when leaving Fairfield in April? We learned that Zach was evaluated by the E&T team of medical professionals, and psychiatric evaluation diagnosis had been determined; Bi Polar Affective Disorder I with psychotic features. This was not the evaluation procedure initially advised by the MUM school director, but it was an evaluation process necessitated and secured while in this psychotic state, while in this treatment center. The critically necessary diagnosis in E&T would determine medication strategy, payment coding for services rendered, and outpatient planning. Diagnosis would drive the path to patient wellness and recovery, we all now believed and trusted. The prescriber notes from the day after his arrival, would remind us of how Zach's mind was clear enough in the delivery of some statements, yet deluded in others. He was quoted as saying that the feeling of no control was new and frightened him, and that he regretted scaring his parents, likely two truths. But then within those same progress notes, he was asked about family history of mental illness such as bipolar, and he was quoted as saying, "Fuck yeah, there is bipolar all through my family!" News to us, son! Nothing substantiated those statements yet they were received and recorded as truth! Untruth. Without implying shame or negative stigma to anyone with mental health diagnosis, this statement for us was delusional, exaggerated, and untrue. A different example of truth logic came in the form of a worksheet he completed upon hospitalization entry to identify goals while in treatment. He humbly wrote, *"To heal as a person, both on and off the court. Ultimately, to achieve my ambitious plans ASAP, while living a balanced, mindful, and respectful life."* I would bet that few other goal sheets at that evaluation and treatment center reflected that kind of clarity, honesty, and intention from an inpatient goal sheet, especially from a perceived to be drug using, substance abusing young erratic adult actively in psychosis! Fuck yeah! Get the fuck out of here.

Obviously, the challenge in accurately assessing credibility of patient intake information was complicated for any medical team assessing psychotic illness. He could be convincing, and certainly our parental word and input was not deemed relevant on record. The discernment challenge of believability was the same kind of assessment duality John and I as medical caregiving laypersons faced daily with him in our home. Zach worked hard to deliver logical thought and action, but mind fuck interference was not uncommon. Verbal aggression, exaggerated thoughts, mixed with delusion and hallucination would sabotage the holistic intention and actions he had previously been working so hard to develop. He somewhat mystified the staff at the facility, for he was an anomaly of sorts to the norm of patient enrolled. These days, he mystified all of us. But he was there to be evaluated and treated, and there was no question something about him wasn't well. Among many ironies in the treatment plan path, was Zach's resistance to the facility's administration of drugs prescribed for treatment, considering the stereotyped interpretation of drug use disorder previously placed on record. His desire to lead a life choosing alternative methods to healing other than drug treatment would not be within his control while hospitalized. He would have to relinquish that control. In the emergency room care of June 2, his records note he had been given Tylenol for the body aches, Ativan for the anxiety and insomnia, Maalox for the stomach pain, and Haldol and Cogentin for the psychosis. Of course, this is also where he was on record for having no pain at intake documented. And yet, the Tylenol and Maalox administered speaks to some kind of physical discomfort he must have presented with even though those very pains and symptoms were not recorded. Confusing accuracy, or lack thereof. Upon arrival at E&T, he adamantly declined any Depakote or Olanzapine prescribed for mood and psychosis, and that freedom of choice would soon not be an option once found gravely disabled and approved for mandated treatment. We are so very sorry, Zach, and yet we are not. We compromised your hard fought values to keep you safe. We hospitalized you to keep you safe. Safety meant medication. Moral values versus medical values. Libra scale. Balance beam.

The court hearing was Thursday morning in the center conference room. We sat in circle with lawyers, a judge, the medical team, and a recorder, while Zach entered the room with what looked like security personnel. My God, we had thus far survived raising up a young man who managed to divert trouble on a significant scale, lead a fabulously active and healthy upbringing, and discover a satisfying sense of self that would bloom into a future we so looked forward to witnessing. Here we now sat in a mental health courtroom to decide if this same young man would be qualified to be held against his will, medicated to resolve this episode, and then released to pick up all the pieces and somehow move on with a renewed vision. Here and now, Beth, here and now. In the courtroom, I was an emotional wreck, blubbering when spoken to, quivering, trembling, and frightened from the foreboding circumstances we faced. If he was not approved for some kind of care, then what, we wondered? Personal safety fears for our big man Z hovered like a storm shadow darkening our heavy hearts. We shared information, the team shared information, the lawyers represented him, and the judge ultimately appeared disappointed with the inability of Zach to match behavior and choices with his pulled together physical appearance. While attempting to defend himself, his projection of arrogance combined with his continued strange mix of speech and ideas contradicting logic and clarity with delusion and confusion actually demonstrated the instability, just as we had experienced at home. I looked around the room, wanting to make individual contact with each person present. My imploring eyes searched each set of exploring eyes, hoping to tap into any empathic energy around the table, advising each of them that this is not our son, this is not Zachary Moritz. Allow me to introduce my son, his beauty, his humor, his care for others, his loving family, his adoration of sister, his devotion to teammates, his 'happy go lucky' demeanor. Here and now, Beth, here and now. That man was missing in action.

The evidence presented that morning was enough to approve treatment for up to the maximum 14 days, with two particular provisions from the family helping seal the deal. Unfortunately, these created open wound around family trust for Zach. We had all compromised ourselves, each with a different definition of saving a life. He was battling desperately to save his definition of an intentional life, one whereby we were considered allies. Now, we were perceived as enemies in a different definition of a battle to save his life! Damned if we do, damned if we don't. One damning piece of evidence was a cell phone recording of a sickened Zach which we made on an evening of outburst, capturing his madness, rage, delusion, and childlike plea for help. He responded in the courtroom with justification and blame for his recorded behavior and message as a reaction toward enemies that included his colluding parents who collectively provoked his outrage. The defense was illogical to listening ears, revealing truth about his ill mind affectation. He didn't make sense. Hidden behind the striking physical presence and the skilled verbal attempts to present intelligently while seated around that table of judgement, were the invisible to the observing eye inner functions and dysfunctions of that infected mind. He could be eloquent, for sure, and he had physical features that were visually appealing in presentation when they were not focused at you in a gripping glare or a listless stare. Looking at him, he was normal and in control. Listening proved otherwise. The request to read out loud the other family provided piece of evidence came as somewhat of a surprise. We had given a copy of the frightening email sent to his sister in May that alluded to potential self-harm, possible death. Everyone present could have chosen to read it silently without revealing to Zach its utilization in this moment, but likely the judge or medical team or legal team wanted to witness Zach's response. John and I worried that Zach might feel betrayed by his sister, that she might feel betrayed by us in the use of this shared evidence that further proved safety risk. We all might claim betrayal in this read out loud choice without a voice position of compromise. But court was adjourned and Zach was hospitalized. Upon departure, John and I thanked the lead nurse practitioner for guiding us through. She coached us on expectations and evidence, having recognized early on that Zach was in dire need of treatment care. John and I were in unfamiliar territory, but we were fully invested in securing support for his care, and this professional recognized our urgency and our trustworthy parental dedication. Brooks became our angel answer to prayer in this mess of a situation. She worked to develop a trusting relationship with Zach, treating him with respect around his personal spiritual beliefs, his multiple discomforts, and his family significance. She was equally respectful and collaborative with us. We would finally locate an advocate we could team with, learning from each other in this most unusual case presented. She did, however, work for corporate, not us. There were boundaries, legalities, and procedures she had to follow. We would learn much from her. She would learn as much from us.

Our drive to Seattle following the court hearing was quiet and contemplative, until the news flash of an on campus shooting around 3:30pm at Seattle Pacific University. The campus was on the other side of the city from Seattle University's address in Capital Hill, but both were private school systems of local collegiate village for students, staff, and community. We had friends with children in attendance, and our concern was immediate. Traumatized by our own recent fears and experiences of unexplained aggressive outbursts influenced by our son's sudden health implosion, we held an awakened and deeply sensitized empathy and compassion amidst unexplained tragedy. We cared about victims and victim families, but also perpetrators and perpetrator families. Could it be, we feared, that an uncontrolled madness of mind could instigate these actions so violent? The tendency would be to believe someone would have control of their mind and actions. This incident in Seattle was not unlike a news story read a week or two prior out of Santa Barbara, California, when the news reported a mentally ill young man opened gun fire at UC Santa Barbara. The community had organized around the wounded and traumatized victims and their loved ones, but also around the family of the mentally ill perpetrator, who were equally devastated. The perpetrator family spoke of how their son was never this kind of person but that he had become sick and obsessed, out of character. They had been seeking help but were not able to get effective help for their son. What happened to their loving son? How could the family or our society help prevent such atrocities? We read about the Santa Barbara case and wondered, even feared, for our own son. Could he act out such horror in an unstable and confused state, despite his nonviolent nature? We were ever so grateful Zach was getting help, even if involuntarily, as we listened to this immediate Seattle tragedy and respectfully reflected on all perspectives of family impact measure. By phone, we checked in with our SPU parent friends to ascertain safety for their children, and express care, concern, and a transportation home offer. Care and safety had already been secured and gratitude for the offer expressed. Just another fragile encounter of health, safety and violence intersection that happened to occur in the emotionally vulnerable window of our Seattle Gab arrival and our Vancouver Zachary departure.

Our daughter was swept up into our gripping and lingering embrace once we arrived to her apartment. The day's events reminded us of such fragile life and death encounters, seemingly more heightened and feasible to threats within our own lives of late. We dined home-style at a classic Seattle trendy spot named Skillet, and resumed our I-5 southbound travel home. The car ride captivity allowed us the opportunity to review the court hearing procedure, and to share the choices we made to save our son from the stranger in his head. To hear about it secondhand is to not fully understand or comprehend, but she carefully listened. John and I hoped this family would not return from this sickly season as lost and misunderstood strangers to one another. We would come through this, wouldn't we? Would the family bond we had dedicated our lives to building as solid now begin to crumble? How would this illness wound each of us, wound the family? Could faith, hope and love yet prevail? The three of us made it home exhausted on so many levels, and yet, we were without worry of safety securement upon arrival to the house, now empty of our momentary madman of mystery. Deep sadness prevailed in the literal and figurative emptiness of our hearts and home, but his physical safety had at least been secured for now. Pink Martini seemed so long ago. We woke the next day on June 6, 2014, Zach's birthday, not happy. He turned 26, he was in a lockdown mental health treatment facility, and upon discharge, he was unemployed without health insurance and unable to resume the employment he had previously been engaged and thriving in. Life had flipped him on his backside, and no matter his intention, he could not work a little harder, work another way. The date and possibility of him being uninsured I had dreaded well before this mystery illness, and now the actual fulfillment of this fear arrived. I had not imagined, ever, this particular health care crisis and the resulting devastation of his own personal mind body spirit vision and practice. Had I somehow willed this to happen through my parental anxieties and personal drive to be prepared for tomorrow, to emphasize the kids to be prepared for the immediate future, I absurdly wondered? Could I be to blame for this monstrosity before us, I considered again? Such an egotistically ridiculous mother's thought, to guilt herself, to carry an unnecessary blame, to take on the burden of the backlash. But I was so willing, if it meant freedom from sickness and healthful opportunity for my child.

At least Zach's health insurance enrollment had been initiated while in Fairfield. Thankfully, the Affordable Healthcare Act was enacted and available as a tool of support, I reasoned. He agreed with me that the enrollment get done, and he participated in the process this past spring. What we found, however, with the help of the E&T staff, was that we had not fully completed the sign up process for Washington state. Suddenly, we were catapulted into crisis not only ill prepared but underinsured! Fortunately, staff helped complete Zach's enrollment, and our employer insurance plan coverage completed the pre-existing hospitalization and care while our patient was yet 25 years of age and on his parent's plan. Financial considerations always held a past, present and future, despite the here and now of payment preparation. This I would preach to my son, and certainly we were living it. In the near future, we would wonder if these medical expenses and the frightening crisis of our son were held against us by John's employer. Illegal, yes, but feasibly discreet and possible. That paranoid thought would have to be set aside and taken in stride, for it was not productive, nor legal, by employer human resource and health care law standards. Families had unexpected health crises. This was what insurance payroll deductions, human resource management guidance, and employee benefits were believed to support and assist. Quit the worry and assumptions, Beth. Be thankful for coverage and care, but maybe it would be wise to remain aware. We had reason to feel insecure. Paranoia had become familiar in this household!

Gabrielle was eager with anticipation to see her brother the first time since his fragile Easter return from MUM. Because he had not welcomed his parent's attempts to visit, we hoped her reception to be different. She knew his favorite local foods, and planned a special birthday visit bearing gifts from not far. Local Burgerville blessings! Unbeknownst to her, the birthday gift he had already received this day was unwanted but mandated. Medication. Olanzapine, Depakene (or Benadryl if refused), Ativan, and Zyprexa were one hell of a birthday guest list. When his sister entered his room at the center, he did not receive her as hoped. He told her he had not trusted any of us since Fairfield and he yelled at his sister asking her to leave. Unfortunately, she too got an immediate up close dose of the rejection curse which we had shared about with her by phone. That response reminded us that his behavior was not simply a parental push away, an independence day fireworks display, or a parent and grown son exaggerated interplay. He was sick. Her food gift was rebuffed, and her gesture of love quickly rebuked and handcuffed. Birthday. The evening remained fragile for the three of us at home that Friday night, seeking some adult beverage abuses while nursing shared battleground bruises. We would self-prescribe wine for the wounds, and home isolation adding some tunes. Together, we distanced the attempts to visit in hopes that Zach might focus further on diagnostic treatment, healing his way back to some form of whatever a new normal might look like. My sister Joanne returned to the nest of our home after her nursing conference, and the four of us strived further that evening to create laughter and enjoy music, both loud and pleasing. Laughter and music had become woefully absent for months in our soundproofed home, robbing us of their therapeutic healing qualities and our previously unifying shared experience between offspring and parents. We leaned gently into family, craving the additional company of the charismatic and engaging nephew, brother, son, our healthy Zach. By Monday morning, Joanne returned to Boston, and Gabby accompanied her father travelling north to the Emerald City, resuming his work and travel while she went on to complete her senior year of college. I reached out to my sister in law, welcoming an invitation for overnight getaway and additional support from accessible family. An initial observation upon my exhale to the heightened stress of recent events, and the respective return to our life routines, was just how surreal it felt that the world surrounding us did not stop and wait with or for you while in the darkened depth of crisis. There is no pause button, mute button, or rewind button for the work, bills, chores, and daily upkeep to life.

SONFLOWER

All responsibilities and obligations resume, while one has no idea of your eventual outcome and necessary adaptations. This is a universal truth for any one of us, whether in crisis or not. Darkness can block our path to enlightenment if we allow. We must transcend.

Treasuring the opportunity to leave the hauntings of our home in this short lived freedom spell, I drove eastbound along the Columbia River Gorge to visit my generous and concerned sister in law at her oasis of a nestled in cabin along the White Salmon River. The drive along state route 14 in early June was spectacular, full of evergreen silhouette, winding narrow roads that seem to have no end, and monoliths of volcanic rock formation with spectacular waterfalls that define the river canyon edges. All framed in blue sky backdrop and juxtaposed by the bleached white snow blankets of Mt. Hood and Mt. Adams in the distance. For me, the drive itself cleansed my soiled soul with a *'Calgon, take me away'* commercial enticement of ease, escape, and expanse. So in need of a deep soul cleansing was I. A long slow soak, rinse, and renewal, followed by a sip, a stroll, and a sizeable sigh would be my high. Frequently, Marta had offered me to come and seize the respite from our heightened stress, and finally I could accept. White Salmon was a beautifully scenic destination. Her intention was to help, and to show and share her love for our family, her family. While her gestures of hospitality were comforting and generous, her words and messaging about her nephew and our situation were sometimes discomforting and teased mischievous. People were presumptuous, we found; even friends and family. A mental health diagnosis will earn you that! Not unlike many who loved us and felt worry for us, she, too, wanted to protect us, wanted to help us solve the presenting problems we faced. But the projections onto suggestions and questions, both uninvited and ill informed, about forcing accountability onto Zach and drawing grown adult boundaries for his behaviors and actions, were both hurtful and harmful. The implication was that Zach had control over his situation, and that we should also take control over our own situation, when in fact what we had witnessed and lived appeared less about our control necessity and more about his illness struggle. To be comforted and cared for so thoughtfully, but yet simultaneously confronted and challenged as to whether we as parents were enabling, or whether this child was taking advantage, or whether our son had ever held a 'real' job, or whether we as parents had established healthy enough boundaries, I could feel the trend of her own assumptive transference transcending!

162

Advice was being given without full intake and understanding of circumstance. I knew my son, I knew our parenting, I knew his work ethic, and I knew these implications helped in no way to discern his sudden and bizarre illness nor drive toward his ever elusive wellness. Marta was known to be direct and forthright, perhaps the seasoned trait of a Brit, the trusting honesty of a sister in law, or the undisciplined ignorance of assumptive impulse. She was speaking out loud what I would continue to sense or hear spoken from so many adults along this baffling journey. In response, I would learn how to speak up, to educate, to defend, and eventually advocate. Or sometimes, I would isolate to protect myself and my loved ones. Other people's life experiences and acquired wisdom can on occasion be helpful and enlightening when the fit into the presenting puzzle is not forced, when all the edges and color markers of the pieces legitimately match up. The full picture on the puzzle box cover is most helpful.

Strolling together arm in arm along the river's edge, our body chemistry nurture did not match our thought processing nature. Conversation was not all comfort and caring, and some of it was quite judgmental and rudely daring. But she also extended a gracious offer that forgave all aforementioned transgressions, and reminded me, that regardless of hurtful implication and perception, this family member was vested in Zach's healing reception. She and my brother Rob Roy decided Zach was welcome to come and live with them upon discharge, under agreed upon guidelines, and with Zach's acceptance of their offer and expectations. If home was so difficult, perhaps the beauty of the gorge, its surrounding quiet, and the safety of extended family would allow Zach a more effective place to recover. Perhaps even her conversation had to push some edges to best assess their own personal safety measure in extending this offer. I wept with gratitude from the gift of outreach, the gesture of love and support, the gamut of possibility. Thank you, Marta and Rob. I inhaled the oxygen of renewed hope for healing change, and exhaled any angst of uncertainty around upcoming discharge. We could begin again. John and I had evaluated over and over again, where we might have sent our son to heal while he was sick at home demanding to heal elsewhere. At the time, we could not act or even ask, because we did not know what his health needs were, we had no professional support, and his symptoms of illness would accompany him wherever he would head. We became very clear around these truths in May when we believed he might return to Fairfield and meet up with the supposed true love he had been talking nonsensically about. To live with relatives, he would need a supervised, provisional set up, we discerned quickly. As parents, we were naïvely gullible a mere 3 weeks ago. Now that he had a diagnosis and was in treatment, this generous offer was a viable outreach alternative to returning home. For now, we would wait to learn of Zach's response to treatment, one day at a time. This was a mantra I would be motivated to work harder at embracing, after years of anticipating, organizing, and activating future preparation and readiness for any and all household and family demands, obligations, and responsibilities. I could change. I wanted change. I would change. We all would be changed.

Zach changed. He called me Tuesday and again on Wednesday, and I heard a tone and a tenderness I used to know. Within the conversation, however, there was also continued misconception. He did not remember making phone calls to me nor the content of our conversations held just a day after making them. We continued to have faith in the return of a conciliatory Zach, but we would wonder and even worry about possible recurrence of a contradictory Zach. What would continue to transpire for him within this final week in treatment prior to discharge? What was reasonable to expect? In the here and now of our temporary and short lived caregiving freedom, John and I sought release from our tremendous amount of tension and built up anxiety through an isolation float tank. The night before graduation weekend, we would finally use the gift Zach had given us at Christmas 2013. Sure seemed ironic that the one who gave us the gift certificate of floatation therapy, to benefit our stress filled lives prior to all of this health crisis, would, in fact, be the stressor influence in the timing utilization of the gift's stress reducing promise! Too much symbolism, mysticism, and altruism in the wonder and magic of a float. The float would come to represent a recent memory of the generous and thoughtful young man we had known Zach to be prior to this personal upheaval we had grown to resent. He had been a student of alternative healing therapies, and a disciple among friends and family for sharing his experiences of finding enjoyable and effective therapeutic tools. We gave thanks that evening, for a gift from healthy Zach, so reminiscent of good times past. Despite the current circumstances of our lives, the floats were glorious, and over time, we would continue to find healing energy from them, passing the gift concept forward to others, just as Zach had done for us. To gift a float was an exercise in paying Zach forward.

On Friday the 13th, John's favorite calendar date and favorite number, we travelled north again to Seattle. The weekend intention was to lift up our daughter's collegiate accomplishments and successes, and participate in her graduation ceremonies. For days prior to this hospitalization, we had worried how the two of us would attend, given that we increasingly could not leave Zach alone in the house. We had been strategizing how one parent would travel up and back for Friday thru Saturday graduation events, and then the other parent would travel up and back Saturday night through Sunday culmination. The safe and secure placement for Zach at E&T allowed us the unexpected ability to attend her graduation together. Zach phoned us during our drive up the interstate, begging to come home, speaking lovingly, and having no recollection of his sister's graduation. The mandated medications were doing their work with regard to reducing agitation, but were they numbing and dumbing him as well? When we researched the prescriptions, we read about short term and long term side effects, and we were privately concerned beyond the here and now quieting of psychosis. Those pharma TV commercials are reality speak. Were we making right decisions by him, by us? Would this treatment strip him of his creative fire, his drive and adventure, his future fitness and stamina? To tame the presenting demons and dragons, was this price tag too high? We *always* came back to measures of safety, his first, ours second. Damn it. How could you not look into the future when you are evaluating these here and now decisions. Compromise and risk. Weigh the options. After hearing from Zach, we called and spoke to the medical team asking if we could meet next Monday to discuss Zach's improvement and discharge status. Marta and Rob had decided the best accommodations for Zach would be their alternative home space in Stevenson, as it was closer to us, had a designated room and a more accommodating layout than the cabin. My brother had prepared a space for him, and they had together drawn up rules to abide by, should they feel they might need to remind or rescind. Obtaining permission for them to join us at the E&T meeting Monday afternoon, we would present this idea to Zach and make decisions. This was our anticipated plan, now allowing the celebration weekend to focus attentions toward Gabby, her beauty and wonderment, her bloom so ready to burst forth yet so impacted by our sudden freeze, our slow thaw, and our early summer squall. On Sunday eve, while the three of us descended from the ceremonious peak of the weekend, we returned to the hotel pondering the possible discharge outcome of the following day. How would our family frame the impending future focus? Gabby would remain in Seattle seeking work and finishing her lease through August, and we would resume responsibilities, John with work, Beth with caregiving, both with Zach's healing in mind and her wellness in kind. Our moods shifted from solemn to somber as we curled up together post-graduation on that luxurious hotel king bedding without our king size Z. We ached in his absence and pined for his presence. Southbound we would be in the morning, but directional clarity for our lives still held uncertainty with regard to Zach. Many more a compass rose would be necessary to journey us all safely home.

While the winds whipped and the rain fell torrential, John and I entered the parking lot of the Vancouver community health complex the next afternoon. Searching for my brother's van, we hoped the weather would not cause delay, for a wicked windstorm weather pattern all along the stormy gorge escorted my siblings in route to the rescue. Would this be indicative of what lay ahead, I would wonder? Anymore, everything appeared symbolic or metaphoric, as we had just seen and heard the earth shake, rattle and roll recently right through the soul of our son. I really wanted to behold and believe in a rainbow promise. A woman of such unbreakable faith for so long, my spirit waxed and waned in these desperate days. Marta and Rob arrived on time, and the four of us ventured in as the storm's rainbow promise pot of gold. Zach greeted each of us tenderly and lovingly as we gathered once again in the confines of the conference room. The offer from his aunt and uncle received an emotional warm embrace. Their guidelines were simple in form, necessary in content, and specific to concerns driven by their knowledge of our own personal concerns from at home encounters prior to hospitalization. John and I agreed to supply his dietary needs, transporting food to and from weekly, also commuting him to and from his outpatient appointments in Vancouver for therapy and medication management. An intake appointment was scheduled locally for the next morning to initiate outpatient care, so Zach agreed to stay at our home until Thursday, the original expected timeframe of anticipated discharge and arrival to Stevenson. The five of us discharged to our Vancouver home address, a mere ten days after his 26th birthday, resuming this medicated beginning in treatment care, and the mitigated continuation of family care. We ordered and picked up our favored Thai food, gathered in gratitude and grace, and faithfully leaned into our family and future.

This entire breakdown incident may have been a one-time bipolar blip or even a schizoaffective dip. We didn't yet know for sure, but it had been quite the traumatic trip. Whatever this was, we were all trusting the turmoil to taper down, clear up, and get under control. Zach wanted to figure out how to reclaim his life, get on with living, and so did we. The first task at home, and in preparation for Zach to be independent at my brother's home, was to organize his medication schedule. What to take when, and how much of what were the primary treatment tracks to trace. Olanzapine, Remeron, and Cogentin were the treason to Zach's trust, while wellness response remained the troubling reason to medicate we must. Micro manager mom went right to work, readying food and food transport, with coolers and mini fridge in tow. Ever so grateful, I did not want to disturb my brother's spatial footprint in his home, nor the ever conscious cheapest of budgets imprint he always owned. An Aerobed mattress with bedding would serve as Zach's king, for the couch and chair in the comfortable space allotted could not accommodate sleep. Ever mindful of the back pains, size restraints, and consciousness mindset, we all collaborated to create a safe and sufficient private healing space. My brother soon experienced his nephew as a quiet, respectful steward of his home. Zach had become accustomed to minimalizing and simplifying, aligning well within my brother's lifestyle. A meds tracking sheet was created and medications were carefully monitored to minimize confusion and maximize organization. Zach was still quite dazed by the drugs and their dosage. Sleeping at least 12 hours a day, he was frequently hungry, tired, gentle and yet still very odd.

The first outpatient intake appointment, which I was permitted to attend, revealed to me that he continued to have strange revelations from dreams and about random topics, yet he presented himself as together and quite self-assured. He spoke intelligently with sophisticated grammar and word choice, yet his content remained questionable. I wasn't sure if this was illness still manifesting, or drug affectation. At this point, I wasn't even sure *what* I was sure of anymore! By the evening of the day after our son arrived home, this exceptionally written, yet strangely timed email arrived in each of our mailboxes.... mine, John's, and Gabby's. We were asked to keep the shared declaration of his future name change to ourselves until it became legal. Zach's email address from this point forward in his life would utilize his new chosen name.

SONFLOWER

Hello family

Two things, among a million other things. First, the obvious. This is my new email-gmail account. You can reach me here during the coming future instances where I'll be phoneless.

Second, the subtle. The name, Ajax. I will be legally changing my name from Zachary Charles Moritz, to Ajax Zachary Moritz. The reasons for this are many and I am not apt at thoroughly explaining my reasons for such, without some effort on your parts. I can give you superficial reasons, but for more depth of understanding such said efforts would include reading Sophocles tragedy titled, Ajax (a light read), Homer's work (not a light read), The Iliad (book four) and The Odyssey.

The gist of my decision is that in antiquity there have been two famed individuals who shared the name, Ajax the Lesser, and Ajax the Greater. I see myself in each of them, and especially so in the metaphors of their deaths. Likewise having two stories to draw from aligns with my being, as a person of extreme polarities, paradoxes and dualities.

Ultimately, my complexities seek satisfaction among the stories of the two and I have been drawn to the name time and time again over the last five years. Starting first with the film adaptation of Troy and secondly upon further research into the epic of their life stories.

Please keep this decision amongst yourselves until I have legally changed my name. Feel free to call me Zach or Zachary in the meantime, as I will let you know when my transformation feels complete and my new name can settle in.

Thank you and I love you!

Somehow, I could not help but wonder about the Greek mythology books I had seen on his bed in the midst of mad cycles. And yet, I also held the thought that his choice made sense and felt not at all that unusual. My brother had changed his name in his young adult years, musicians change their names, athletes change their names. The request did not seem that strange, if you could remove it from the context of what we had been dealing with for weeks. He, too, had been subject to dealing with all of the mysterious personal disruption, and sudden onset of interruption while in the midst of life transformative changes activated while in a previously curious but clear mind. I would respond to him in good faith, with a formal, guarded tone, but also with respect and validation to such sincere outreach and explanation.

Son, Thank you for sharing this very personal piece of your ongoing transformation. I trust that you will guide us as to when you would like us to refer to you as Ajax. I hope we can continue to have open dialogue so as to develop increased understanding in relationship today and beyond.

I am not as well read as the rest of you, so I will indulge in some referred reading in hopes that I have greater perspective on your vision and self-perception. My greatest personal hope for your future lies not in the metaphors of death, but in the reality and beauty of living, but then, I am making it about my need and my interpretation not yours. And, I am likely misinterpreting what you are sharing, so pardon my simplicity and ignorance. I embrace and welcome more conversation if allowed.

I will work hard at understanding what you share and embracing your needs and desires as the life you choose to lead and define. As family, I hold onto the hope and desire that we can remain in each other's lives, despite our divergent paths and perspectives. Our love will not falter.

Thank you. I love you all so very much and I am grateful for conversation and sharing. Mom

We were trying to adopt an attitude of gratitude these days, for we were a far cry from where we had been. I drove Zach to my brother's home Thursday, delivering all of his gear and supplies, prepping his room, setting up his medication directions for both of them to manage, establishing his food zone, and then departing for home. I was prayerful, hopeful, and trusted in the day by day arrangement of it all. John and I again updated the quest leaders, who had leaned in with us in the dark days, and welcomed continued connection. Elatedly, the team shared with us that they had just come down from the mountain, holding Zach up in prayer the entire time. So meaningful, this message was. They were truly a loving community of support and understanding who could hold the scope and depth to Zach's intersection of earlier driven intention and now destined intervention. Other than my sister, and of course, his own sister, this group was who we safely allowed fully into the belly of the madness monster, trusting they would still hold up Zach with a pure heart amidst the darkness and delusions. His former teammates were overseas and clueless as to what happened, his local friends of earlier years were distanced and unaware following Fairfield, and local family were now extending a willing but wary helping hand. He had become an island to all, by choice and by circumstance. Zach focused on rebuilding, and in no time, he negotiated with his prescriber to wean off the medications. He was adamantly not interested in long term drugs and their lingering side effects.

Zach and I would commute each week for appointments, food replenishment, and an occasional overnight in which he would join us for dinner followed by ping pong with his father when his mental focus and physical strength returned. The report from Stevenson was that he isolated and slept a lot, there was little conversation, and he presented without agitation but also without enthusiasm of any kind. The drugs had to have some effect on this. We planned a family gathering in Stevenson over the Fourth of July holiday with his sister joining us, and John and I seizing the opportunity to escape as a couple to nearby Skamania Lodge. My brother was travelling, and sister in law Marta would join us for a shared window of family time. It had been two weeks since Zach arrived to his new home base in Stevenson. Following his therapy session in Vancouver prior to the Fourth weekend, the four Moritzs would return together to my brother's home for a holiday happening. Along the gorge-ous drive, midway in route, we stopped at Beacon Rock, a favored hiking destination over the years for father and children, commonly chosen as a Father's Day outing. The former collegiate and semi-professional athlete, now a recovering tower of tremble and trepidation, actually engaged with us in the slow, monotonous climb up the steep, methodical ascent of this historic site. We were elated to witness his herculean effort and successful climb. Silently, the truth of his physical vulnerability in less than a year's decline was startling. Our son was both humble and fragile that late summer day, but innocently willing for the first time in weeks to attempt something so physical. Just a year earlier, he had been in optimal physical condition to return to professional basketball in Copenhagen. Today, we were praising him for accomplishing a reasonable hike at a doable pace. He was oblivious to the height stares once so prevalent in his days of self-consciousness, more fully focused and conscious of the day hike's formidable height in stairs. Our weekend included board games, and laughter unlike we had shared together since Christmas 2013. His range of health symptoms so present previous to this hospitalization seemed either less intense or more silenced by medication. Our hope was once again fueled by this trip's outcome, and Zach chose to return with us to our Vancouver home on Sunday, July 6th. We had decided in advance of this special weekend trip to surprise him with a belated birthday massage at Bonneville Hot Springs. A month off by calendar, the birthday gift seemed symbolic as right on time. Happy Birthday, son! Zach asked us if he could stay the full week with us, beyond his beginning of the week appointments, and we agreed. During that Sunday night drive home to Vancouver, he held very lucid conversations with us about wanting to move on with his life and we all felt encouraged and inspired. Just a few nights later, lucidity flirted with lunacy.

Tuesday nights had long been my 'mermaid' night of deep water exercise and often a dinner out afterward with girlfriends. This then became a night out for father and son on the occasion John was not travelling and Zach was staying with us post hospitalization. The two went out for dinner and a movie that Tuesday evening following the family weekend together, and all seemed well, in fact quite normal. However, as was common in our movie outings, movie titles, and movie topic relevance during Zach crisis and recovery days, the movie choice title could have been a premonition. The *"Edge of Tomorrow"* found its edge in tomorrow. The very next day, a father and son vibe at lunch time in a kitchen moment of unanticipated reactivity, shifted abruptly from movie companions to antagonistic adversaries. Uncertain to us the specific provocation, Zach got up from the lunch, threw the entire contents of his pill containers down the disposal, and argued that all had been the same shit around here, directing angst toward his father, and pounding his fist into the pillar wall of the kitchen entry. Traumatized by progressive behavior patterns from those weeks prior to the recent hospitalization, I intervened immediately, assertively, yet still fearfully, insisting he return to the hospital with me to allow professionals to assess this outburst. We feared he was reducing medications too quickly, that he might regress and isolate again, and that we would all fall back into a repeated dilemma. What just happened? Zach amazingly agreed to go with me, argued that Dad should stay away, and continued to rant like an angry adolescent while in the car. It was bizarre. He had settled down, but I convinced him that we should still go ahead in to discuss this sudden outburst of behavior and receive evaluation from professionals. The two hour wait for care seemed to work in his favor, for he resumed a calm and organized presentation of himself while his name was eventually called for evaluation, diagnosis, and treatment plan. I was left to wait until the social worker reappeared and discussed with me their observation and examination results. The drug screen is negative, of course, and the advice for him, for us, is to review anxiety tips, and discuss medications with his prescriber. It was an anxiety attack, they named it, and it appeared we now had all under control. Zach shared with the medical staff once in that calm and reflective window of evaluation that he understood he needed to get these outbursts under control. If only it was that simple, to understand it, to anticipate it, and to stop it. We left and returned home from our 4hour adventure. The ride home was quiet until Zach opened up to share that his spirit held no sense of hope, no noticeable changes, just nothing. He complained the outpatient therapist working with him was young, naïve, and unaware, so he confessed to going through the motions. His prescriber was reluctantly working with him to reduce meds so that Zach might feel less drowsy, lethargic, detached, and empty, but then, we both wondered together, would rage filled outburst be the outcome of that reduction? Or would these rages be a result of feeling trapped, directionless, and a shrinking shadow of his former self? Was this rage moment a reaction to the bleak life lingering right in front of him? Likely, the rage served all of the above.

Our first bump in the outpatient path had been experienced, and we wondered if the bipolar blip was just to be the tip. Or, would it at all be possible, he was simply feeling defeated, needing a change of atmosphere other than the bedroom of my brother's home, or the routine confines of our home with the daily reminders of a life just passing by. I wrote my brother and sister in law, thanked them for their care, updated them on Zach's disinterest in returning, and signed off. Defeated, I then wrote my sister, knowing I would receive a tender boost needed, while keeping her in the long distance loop to her nephew's status. John and I wondered about everything. Mental illness, spiritual emergence, drug and bipolar disorders, Kundalini awakenings, drugs to medicate, alternative treatments to drugs, faith influence, power of prayer, random life disruption, health care solutions; we still suspected something was definitely eluding us among all these considerations. We made a decision, however, that it might be wise to become students of mental illness in the event Zach's health eruption is more than just a bipolar blip. Motivated by a friend's advice and suggestion, we signed up for a 10 week, Family to Family-NAMI (National Alliance for Mental Illness) course in late August, the next available local program offering. What else should we do, we would endlessly wonder?

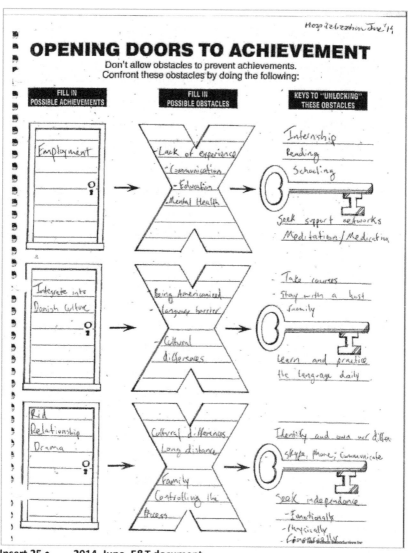

OPENING DOORS TO ACHIEVEMENT

Don't allow obstacles to prevent achievements.
Confront these obstacles by doing the following:

Hospitalization June '14

FILL IN POSSIBLE ACHIEVEMENTS

FILL IN POSSIBLE OBSTACLES

KEYS TO "UNLOCKING" THESE OBSTACLES

Employment

- Lack of experience
- Communication
- Education
- Mental Health

Internship
Reading
Schooling

Seek support networks
Meditation / Medication

Integrate into Danish Culture

Being Americanized
- Language barrier

- Cultural differences

- Take courses
- Stay with a host family

Learn and practice the language daily

Rid Relationship Drama

Cultural differences
Long distance

Family controlling the process

Identify and own our differences
skype, phone; communicate

Seek independence
- Emotionally
- Physically
- Consciously

Insert 25 •   2014, June, E&T document

173

Chapter 19: Kundalini or Spiritual Emergency?

Unwell, Matchbox 20

Losing My Religion, R.E.M.

A day after the unexpected hospital visit in early July, John traveled for work, Zach isolated other than for meals, and I stewed over possible tools, resources, and options to help Zach move forward from this paralyzing circumstance. He wrote us an email that spoke of resentment about what is 'being done to him', and how badly he would like to be somewhere else to allow continued healing to happen. Feeling void of physical, emotional, spiritual, even sexual energy and mere existence, he wrote, he was an empty shell of his former self, and increasingly he felt he could not find his way out of the pull down under. He pleaded for understanding and expressed deep and heartbreaking hopelessness. I tried to swallow that old familiar lump that would sit at the top of my throat when the fear from within the depth of my own soul would rise up and hover, nauseated by the possibility of death from despair. At what point does a person's state of hopelessness move toward action choices, and what would those choices consist of, I constantly worried. If only my actions could make the difference, shift the direction of thought, change the circumstance, point us in the right direction, I always prayed. Guide me, Father. Show me, spirits. Protect us, ancestors. Someone help.

Sometimes, answers would arrive as guidance, and the divine thoughts would in fact intervene with those death thoughts, my worrying wonders from deep within. An idea stirred in the fertile soil of my maternal heart, generating warmth and new hope, pointing me in a direction of possibility for my vulnerable, pleading son. I eagerly shared the seed of thought with John before presenting its germinating possibility with Zach. We both agreed the idea might actually set this young man's weary soul free, to connect again with people who are safe, loving and understanding of him in the present life transitional stage, easing a reentry to nature and spirit in hopes of refueling the empty well from which he was drawing. I prepped the soil for thought in anticipation of tilling the seed for action.

Zach, what if you were to work the land at Three Creeks and stay for whatever time the community would grant you to heal and redirect yourself while earning your stay through stewardship of the land, I intended to ask him. Perhaps this could be made possible, I imagined. Would this be something you would wish to do, Zach, that you might feel drawn to doing, I considered probing further. These new crops of thought and idea would need clearance and legitimacy before being fertilized and cultivated, spoken and arranged. John and I commit to exploring further the feasibility and receptivity of this blooming idea as well as the necessary safety and logistic considerations. Could he physically, would he emotionally, should he mentally? There were concerns, and we would never want to compromise truth or trust with this valued community. We did not yet know what he was confronting, and his eruption had been within the first year following his quest. Had a sprouting seed been planted or propagated then fertilized beyond from that garden session?

Gathering the courage, the clarity, and the compassion, I spoke of these thoughts and ideas to Zach on Saturday morning, July 12, 2014, and he responded with an enthusiastic glance, a sparkle in his eye not seen in quite some time. Spontaneously, we wept in response, releasing the pent up sorrow from so much sudden and mysterious personal pain and upheaval. In that tender, vulnerable moment, our tears reflected a cleansing readiness for community cultivation, a bouquet of belonging. The moment felt laden with love luster, as grace and mercy waved hello, acknowledging themselves as partners in play. It was assumptive, however, to seed this with our son prior to affirming possibility and feasibility with the caring but calendar committed quest leadership team. John and I had reached out to the Big Pine community and Zach's quest guides a few times in the recent months of shaken behavioral shifts and stirred awakenings. While in the epic elation of this epiphany's euphoria, we would do so again, leading with hope not fear. Acknowledging our continued gratitude while seeking further support, we inquired about this proposed possibility with Gigi. All concurred that Zach should return at this juncture, almost a year since his quest passage of the previous summer. He appeared capable and stable enough, as well as quite motivated to go; it seemed the right time, the right choice, and the right mind. I wrote dear Gigi.

As we await the Moon of Rebirth to reveal itself to us here in Vancouver, Washington, we are reflecting on gratitude and grace. The Moritzs have been working through difficult times, and yet, the serendipity of so many people, moments, events, prayers, and timing has been nothing shy of God's grace and love.

You have been a power force, and those who have prayed with you, among you…. we have felt this love and witnessed its healing. Gratitude in abundance. I cannot find the words to express the love I feel for you and your work, and how the truth and unconditional nature remains embedded in my son's soul, and in my own. There has been brokenness, deep vulnerability, rage that has worked its way up and out, exhausting Zach, exhausting us, but on the other side of it has been possibility and discovery. He is ready to leave and move on, out, beyond.

It is our hope that he can begin with a time at Three Creeks, to serve the grounds, continue to rest and heal and discover, and be surrounded by people who matter deeply to him, to us, to each other.

Gigi, a lead guide for Zach's rite of passage nature quest, summer of 2013, and a woman who dedicates her life and work to individual as well as worldwide projects of prayer, action and service, replied warmly and receptively amidst an active and full calendared schedule at the Three Creeks oasis. She invited Zach to write his intentions and purpose for a return visit, and on Sunday, July 13, Zach wrote his response.

I am immediately excited and inspired by this prospect of returning to Three Creeks. It is resonating within me like any genuine faith in hope should. The thoughts of this past year coming full circle with continuity and closure seem realistically attainable, there. I am humbled by the invitation, and continually by myself, I look forward to working the land, seeing and connecting with familiar faces and being applied however else you see fit. I have no concerns, fears or pre-conceived notions. My intent is only innocence and application. I suppose that I am coming innocently, with the intent that perhaps I will be able to leave with further clarity of my purpose. With a furthered understanding of how to both assert myself and allow passivity to coexist.

Discerning time and place, right and wrong, etc. Make no mistake, I am still seeking balance.

I left Three Creeks with a taste of balance, last time this year. Since, I have sought out in myself, and others, ways in which to maintain that balance. Alas, every time I thought I had done my due diligence, I failed. And likewise, every time I thought I could do no more wrong, a positive break through would carry me on to the next lesson. Seemingly, nothing, yet everything, has been sacred. I am at a loss, yet I keep finding more.

I am feeling paradoxical, whimsical, spiritual, intellectual, mystical. All at once. But, this is bigger than me, much bigger. No need to wallow or linger in self-reflection too much, so I will cut myself off with saying that my intention is just that. Intention.

There is a renewed energy within and surrounding Zach, John, and me, as we have a new and inspiring sense of direction. Arrangements needed to be made to prepare for this trip, this quest for recovery and redirection to occur beyond accepted approval. That very afternoon, Zach and I began to coordinate readiness outings around his fatigue and symptom management, likely presenting from both the medications and the aftermath residual of his biological, physiological, psychological breakdown, whatever it was ultimately determined to be named. Immediately, we explore car lots and car acquisition, boost his summer clothing options, and create a travel plan. He had not replaced 'Old Faithful', the Ford Expedition, and he had not even intended to secure a car while hopeful of a return to hoops overseas, while at school in Iowa, and then, of course, while consumed in crisis. As parents, still assisting in the launch to adulthood, we agreed to join him in the purchase of a more practical vehicle. His financial income was stagnant, his savings had been spent in large amount for Fairfield's MUM enrollment and housing, and he had been without any replenishing income for 9months. We would verbally agree to the 'full ride', and he agreed to resume payments when he was well and employed. This mattered to him, independence and self-reliance.

Ford came through again, and we found the 2012 Transit Connect cargo version to match all of our needs. He had leg room, head room, great MPG, and essentially, a house on wheels in the back if he ever needed to camp, haul or store anything. It was a fun exercise, car shopping together, even if he was still quite riddled with anxiety and vulnerability, a shadow of his former confident and well-spoken self. Within a week, we owned this vehicle, and we continued preparations to ready Zach for this renewal trip and the promised hope beyond. The Washington license plate arrived in time to replace the Oregon plate, and its metaphoric representation dawned on us months later. C09112B. We read it as 'care of 911 to be'. Eerie. In the continuation of preparedness and anticipation, Zach was even willing to finally go on a hike with John and me the weekend before leaving to California. He had not done much of anything physical since our Beacon Rock climb in early July, and he agreed he should assess his exertion level following months of inactivity and fitness deterioration. During those same idle months for him in summer 2014, John and I had increased our physical activity, for both mental and physical outlet, as well as a readiness preparation of our own. We had been hopeful to vacation on a 6day back packing trip to the Wallowa Mountains through our church outdoor ministry.

SONFLOWER

Signed up and paid for since early February, before all hell broke loose and uncertainty became our norm, we had hoped our lives would now settle down and allow us this commitment. Originally, we reserved three spots, thinking one of the kids might join us, but we soon gifted the third spot once we realized it might be a miracle if even one of us would get to participate, let alone both of us. That one participant, if it came down to only one of us, we knew would be John. He so loved these eastern Oregon trips, he had shared them previously with his children, he had longed for his wife to finally agree to accompany him one year, and he most desperately needed this vacation in nature away from work and life stressors.

Not unlike our daughter's June college graduation attendance uncertainty, we were aware the dates for the Wallowa trip were rapidly approaching (August 1-6), and our participation was yet unpredictable for either of us. Zach's situation was not resolved, and we remained uncertain about his health and safety. Since February, our frequent evening walks and occasional training hikes held the hope of possibility. A waiting list of eager alternates would seize our spots should we cancel. Serendipity served. Backpacking would prevail thanks to Zach's spontaneous California return and its alignment with our calendar hold. All three of us would soon be mountain bound, requiring a readiness of mind, body, and spirit. So on a sun kissed early afternoon of a July weekend, Zach, John, and I drove out to Lava Canyon near Cougar, Washington, and upon arrival, trekked out into the Pacific Northwest beauty of trails, waterfalls, and mountain valley volcanic rock. We paced ourselves accordingly in the moment, absorbing the glory and freedom of nature, and the glory and freedom of successfully getting Zach outdoors and actively engaged. Zach stepped out with grace and caution combined; fluid motions yet calculated footsteps. There had been many memories of him bounding up and down trails with athletic ease, for a spirited hunger to explore was his nature, and mother nature would always lure him deeper and more comfortably into her embrace. This hike proved different. We were all cautious, uncertain of his neglected endurance and balance, and new anxieties once never in question. John decided to capitalize this occasion as a training session for his wife, introducing the experience of hiking with backpack weight by adding approximately 40 pounds of rocks for me to carry in my pack! Yes, we weighed them! It seemed absurd, but I was willing. Hell, I had been carrying a shitload on my back since Fairfield, Iowa, and John himself had become a load bearing expert beyond compare. Bring it on, I dared!

Balancing the weighted pack on some of the narrow cliff edges was precarious, however, and the exercise garnered proper respect. Turning the trail corners, dodging the hanging tree limbs and overgrown brush, watching the careful placement of my dusty boot, my sizeable foot's grip on the occasional crumbly gravel rock of the trail path, I felt consciously aware of the symbiotic relationship of how imbalanced and uncertain our path, our steps and our terrain had been for months. One step at a time, carefully paced and spaced; one day at a time, carefully paced and spaced. My inaugural efforts and focused attention to the weighted back pack effect seemed to distract us from some of the harsher truths we each silently observed about Zach's vulnerability on the trail. We laughed at me, we encouraged him, and we kept up with John. I was grateful to share this time with both of the significant men in my life, each a rock within my family foundation. Increasingly, it was strange to take in Zach's changed appearance, knowing just a short 10months ago he personified this extremely fit, muscular, vibrant, adventurous, full of energy and life type human being. His muscle tone in the months of bed ridden, mystery hidden illness had now become softer like the days of early adolescence. The formerly taut Laker jersey hung lifelessly from his frame today with the exception of some developing waist handles and a slight tummy pooch. His hard earned athletic definition was succumbing to inactivity and medication side effects. Those medication side effects cycled among symptoms of flat affect (the blank hollow stare), weight gain, skin breakouts, itchy scalp with dandruff, hair loss, and a steady lethargic drowsiness; all were difficult to accept physical changes in his energy and appearance. He had been working with the prescriber to minimize his meds from the moment of hospitalization discharge, for he had been depressed and discouraged by both body and mind alterations. Of course, none of us missed the rage filled, agitated and delusional individual prior to hospitalization and medication either! Unfortunately, Zach's awareness that he presented in this manner before, during, or after his first hospitalization was yet unspoken between us. We were careful to move forward, not backward. Shared awareness and conversation would come.

Whatever was happening to him, his awareness did not seem mindful. He seldom held recall to past incidents, comments, actions, and behaviors. There appeared to be a short term memory loss associated with his ailment. While it remained questionable as to what influence illness had on his brain, the medications also seemed to have an influential grip on that same measure. Too ill, aggressive, and explosive without the meds, too soft, passive, and listless with them. Damn. A difficult to accept values shift when you are trying to live a life of intention, make life choices to direct that intention, nurture your own spirit, while serving a purposeful path. When and what to surrender versus when and what to fight; where would this twisting trail lead? John and I felt uncertain he was bipolar, or that this unique experience wasn't just a one and done type disturbance or breakdown, influenced by many variables intersecting at once. He wanted off the meds and we were wary, but we also understood the developing conflict to his values and principles. What would happen if he fell back into a delusional, isolating hole, we wondered? What would happen if we didn't try to work alongside him, honoring his desire to live without altering drugs and altered states? Was all of this actually a result of excessive meditation, quest severance, dietary reaction, spiritual awakening, his psyche and body catapulting into a personal upheaval of old to new life transformation with volatile deliverance of an erupting rebirth toward purposeful adulthood? Inhale, then exhale. Breathe, Beth, breathe. Were we ridiculous to think he could make this trip to California and then begin to resume a normal life? The questions came rapidly, the answers ever so slowly. There were no certainties, other than the current depressed nothingness day after day in the daylight basement bedroom of our home, in the disrupted vision and direction once so alive in the thrive. Many questions would remain unanswered.

John resumed his travel for work that week of July 21, while Zach and I returned to Stevenson to pack up belongings left behind at my brother's house, the short term housing alternative for Zach post hospitalization. We would treat Rob to lunch as a thank you, and while gathered, receive his impromptu, wisely spoken send-off message from uncle to nephew, man to man. "Learn to love yourself, Zach," he advised gently, imploring with his eyes and luring with a tender tone of voice. Pausing from the sweet and salty first bite indulgence of Pacific Northwest fish and chips ordered by all, Zach looked up slowly and simply responded. "I am trying", he pleaded. The personal pledge was delivered with a sad yet hopeful glance up into his uncle's mellow green eyes, and one could not help but feel the compassion in the encouraging thought which my brother brought. Rob Roy had lived a colorful life, full of his own adventures and outcomes to tell. But in that simple, loving exchange, there was communication spoken and heard between the two of them that seemed to leave each longing to turn up the volume between them, tune in the channel, listen at length, and linger further with each other just a while longer in that comforting and familiar, aging blanket of elder experienced share. There were stories to trade, there was wisdom to exchange. But the lease was up, the rent had been paid, the work awaited, and the travels beckoned. Sage council was finished, in that limited window of opportunity, at that wooden booth in a small town café, during that summer afternoon thank you and farewell. Rather, we changed channels, shifted direction, and said our goodbyes. We returned home once again, the quiet late afternoon drive along Highway 14 westbound, surrounded by the scenic Columbia River gorge to the south. Eager and anxious we both were to prepare and depart southbound and west bound, to California the very next day.

In the year that had passed since Zach's vision quest closure, influenced by my oblivious sage encounter in ceremonial circle, I had acquired some literature about smudging rituals and the healing ways of the sacred sage. Before departing on our road trip, my son and I followed a ritual from these guidebooks and held our own smudge blessing throughout the entire home. Our intention was to clear out the negative energy, cleanse the home for renewed healing, and create a protective shield for our return in the days ahead. The act was a sacred exercise shared between us, the two weariest of travelers within the walls of this home, now willful travelers outside the walls of this home and on into the horizon of a refreshed partnership at play. Adventure held promise in our shared destination of recovery and renewal purpose and intention. We were departing together on a 4day road trip in the recently acquired Transit, nicknamed Baby T, laden with coolers, gluten free food, camping gear, and our overnight luggage for the hotel layovers along the way. Our family partnership had nearly been destroyed in the month of May, restructured in the months of June and July, and now possibly redirected through this July/August quest territory return. We would travel southwest to his destination and part ways in Mammoth Lake. I would fly home, trusting him to arrive and settle with his quest community independent of parent escort, and return home independently unless help was needed. We all agreed to this arrangement. This mother son partnership would complete a rescue mission, once again, and he would hopefully then launch himself toward the next independent odyssey accompanied by a healthy mind, body, and soul.

Blessing, healing, and protection, the gifts of the medicinal sage; these were intentions we sought and hoped to find along this journey. During our mother and son road trip to Big Pine, we encountered these gifts in the form of laughter, soulful music, safe travel, good food, gentle conversation, and fostered forgiveness. On that expansive grand highway of life, this family team continued to journey forward beyond a strange life circumstance of private lane turn around and cul de sac circling. On our wheels, steering toward wellness, we would reconstruct our route, and determine a new direction. There were gifts to be garnered, even though sometimes those gifts would be hard to discover in the clutter and chaos of the unwrapping, in the confusion from all the noise. When Zach dropped me off at the town owned public airport in Mammoth Lake, and mindfully prepared himself to finish the remaining portion of the drive's destination, he lovingly thanked me, sharing that he had not felt as relationally close in too long of a time. While there were many gifts on this travelling trip, my son's send-off was my favorite. Mammoth, it was. My encouraging hug and wellness wishes in return were the gratitude gift exchange of a nurturing parental nudge and a sage mother smudge. We both would take flight.

Arriving Saturday night, I flew home a week before John and I would officially be backpacking in the Wallowa Mountains. With Zach safely out of the home, into the arms of mother nature and friends, and on to a fresh start, we would be on track to backpack. Behind in preparation, John and I foolishly hiked the strenuous Dog Mountain trailhead back up into the gorge the very next morning! This was our ridiculous 'less than a week before the trip, make up the training time mindset' endurance trial of more backpacking prep. That summer Saturday was a hot, dog day afternoon and my feet were soon barking, my lungs a tongue panting. Meanwhile, our Great Dane was liberatingly off the leash. Once we realized that Zach would be gone until the third weekend of August, we agreed we both could now participate in this church organized adventure ahead. Our daughter came home to hang with the cat and care for the gardens while we would be gone. We would soon enough pack her belongings and move her home from Seattle when her lease expired end of August. Long term employment opportunities had not developed for her beyond design contract work with the university, fortunately performed electronically from anywhere. She had participated in this particular church sponsored camping/backpacking trip once with her father in the past, and she knew better than I just what this rookie camper was in for. I believed I was sufficiently prepared for the physical output, but I could not anticipate the extra emotional baggage I would be bringing along with me. A backpack weigh in of 50pounds, my own six-foot bulk, plus a heavy heart so immeasurably weighted; I would scale that mountain soon enough! As we divvied up the meals and divided the weight of shared carry items among the team, how would the leaders assess any extra emotional baggage folks might be carrying invisible to the eye, non-weighable by the scale, and often even unsuspecting to the hiker oneself? The truth on the trail will in nature prevail. Naturally.

John, ever the travelling workhorse, had flown home the night of pack weigh in and food distribution at the church, hours before an early 4:30 am group departure. We had agreed to drive a car load of people and supplies, likely with insufficient rest. He was ridiculously stressed from work and life demands that included a revolving travel schedule managing a turned over sales region, a cycling continuation of his son's mysterious crisis and hoped for recovery, and then the added pressure of planning such a detailed trip accompanied by a novice wife uncertain she would be able or even care to go. Of course, there were the miscellaneous camping supplies still to arrive by Fed Ex, requiring last minute addition, reorganization, and weight added to the already weighed in packs. The coordination and combination of it all were enough for anyone to meltdown. Meltdown happened. While coordinating follow up and coverage for work during his vacation absence, reviewing the packing lists, detailing supply preparation with me to assure we had everything, securing the minute details of fishing gear and supplies, his favorite activity up in the deep lake pockets of our hikes, John's work computer suddenly locks up in the midst of fevered deadlines determined to be met. This would be our turn in lockdown, meltdown, breakdown. The perfect storm. In a frantic state, John panicked and phoned his boss in the midnight hour. Carrying the life overloaded backpack weight of family, work, financial pressure, vacation withdrawal, vacation starvation, all alongside of my own built up anxiety and discomfort about an unfamiliar and frankly now undesirable destination of a vacation; it all contributed to the likelihood of an eventual evening lockdown, meltdown, breakdown for the two of us. CRITICIZE! YELL! ATTACK! JUDGE! ACCUSE! BLAME! RETREAT! John and I had held up so amazingly well for the duration to date. We now had our own personal heightened hysteria in the vacating midnight hour! It was not one of our finer moments, as accusations were hurled, voices were tinged with anger and frustration, and messages were laced in panic and fear. We both had tremendous pressure built up from deep within. Had Zach been home, we would not be organizing around a vacation departure, and our breakdown moment would be stifled further in our dedicated drive to keep him alive. Some tedious moment of an eventual trial would eventually trigger an activation to an altercation. One can only pack the back and wind the mind with so much weighted stress and pressure before some form of release happens.

Our daughter had her hands full witnessing, tending, notwithstanding the parental hour of eruption. Gabby became the nurturing adult, the care giver, the voice of reason, the calming presence, and the mind of logic. She enabled a quick recovery that would at least get us back on track to the backpack which now seemed a stupid choice for a vacation relaxation. Role reversals, and stress rehearsals, just to manifest our metatarsals! The backpacking trip had not been a stupid choice, but rather, a critically needed get away in nature, longed for especially by John. I had agreed to accompany him, and call it our vacation. He had been running himself ragged physically, emotionally, exhaustively and he was long overdue. Doing my best to manage the home front in balance to Zach's care needs and protection day by day, I rarely left the house. I had become a caged caregiver. Escaping momentarily for food shopping and occasional exercise, my daily haunting fear was a return down that dark hole of madness and mayhem. I hadn't realized how depressed I had become. Steadfastly focused on the management half of the support equation. I, too, was overdue. As that pressure laden evening inched ever closer to an early morning departure hour, each of our frayed mental edges were vulnerable. Like fresh kindling near a flame, the edges caught fire. It was understandable we both would break in that wee hour of pressurized preparation for departure. It was understandable our daughter would be confused, irritated, and unfortunately inducted into her parent's situational maddening eruption. But would it be understandable to a boss, the recipient of panic and instability in the midnight hour, who happened to only know a tinted window pane portion of the full Moritz picture framed in life imbalance right then? It would not be, but vacation resumed.

In foresight, the last minute backpacking trip go ahead had not been a good idea, timed amidst such uncertainty and minimized opportunity for proper preparedness. In hindsight, the last minute backpacking trip go ahead had been a great idea, especially for John. He had a fabulous trip as he always would in the great outdoors, releasing work pressure and demands, embracing the rhythms and routines of tent setup and take down tasks, and sharing chores in a group of almost 20, meanwhile guaranteeing himself the ever so needed physical exertion, in the company of familiar friends, worship rituals, and his favored fishing, mosquitos and all. Thank God for this trip that John so loved, familiar, comforting, and liberating. Thank God, I was still thanking God! In foresight, hindsight, and with reflective insight, the trip had become my own near breakdown. The daily physical exertion saved me, but my nights included early to tent retirement, exhibiting uncharacteristic anti-social behavior and exorcising unfamiliar awakening anxieties and emotions. Folding my physical self in half to glide as quickly and efficiently into and out of the lower zippered tent door while attempting to dodge the uninvited entry and bite of mosquitos, I was miserably uncomfortable. Sobbing myself to sleep each night, reliving nightmares of our past six months, and managing fears around what would yet happen, this was not a relaxation vacation. Eckart Tolle did not weigh into my backpack supplies, nor did the principles of his work. While I thanked God for this trip that John so loved, the prospect of this proved too unfamiliar, too discomforting, and too suffocating for me. I loved my husband, but this backpacking accompaniment would happen just once. Thank God! Soon enough, I would even struggle to find His grace.

My martyred misery felt as if I were impregnated and at full term discomfort, preparing to birth an unexpectedly painful delivery, water breaking in the nighttime flood of tears, hearts torn in response to an arrival's pressure and expectation. Maternal postpartum depression presented, for under the same moonlit aura and constellation ceiling as that of my mysteriously ill son, he in the womb of the Inyos, me in the room of the Wallowas, my maternal instincts and pain labored on into the dark of each night. I was overcome with a deep intuitive instinct that Zach was not at all well, and that I was increasingly unwell. Each of us was drifting further from personal grounding, both of us in our respective spiritual and outdoor campground, seeking and searching yet far from healing. While in my own outdoor ministry mountaintop demise, I began to question the language and promise of the church, unanswered prayers, contradictive communications, all the Deity dogma I had so loyally and faithfully trusted. Attempts to baptize myself anew in the icy cold lakes, to fuel myself among the faithful fellowship and fauna, to weather the worn weariness of my whys in the sunrise and sunset of God's great creation were all exercised to no avail. The umbilical cord begged to be cut. My sunrise was setting on a faith finding its failing way to a despairing desert. Our family's unanswered mystery pain and sorrow had hollowed out an insatiable hunger for reasons of what and answers of why. Thirst followed, for my late night curiosity to be quenched and the ongoing viscosity of recurrence to relent. I was birthing my own spiritual wilderness quest in the faith fading forecast of rain and sorrow, pain with tomorrow. The bright sun, blue sky, and mountain air would not rescue me, would not replenish my soul starvation. Meanwhile, jovial John thrived and jived, and that was what mattered most in these moments! He thrived. I survived. Zach took a dive.

Although I was surrounded by God's earthly bevy of faith talkers, hope stalkers, and love walkers, this wandering woman of wonder was possessed by maternal personal pain and fraternal dogma doubt. To engage freely with honesty and trust amidst this fellowship of hikers, Beth would not find the words or the worth. Nothing made sense in our lives right now, and God talk seemed in deep contradiction to our human walk. Sermons sucked. The group had no fucking idea how badly I needed to scream out from the mountaintop trails and vistas, shedding the weight of my worrisome world. I was a caged, frightened animal by night, and a roaming, lost wanderer by day, desperately needing a wailing release and some trusted promise of peace. What has happened to this once faith filled and abundantly active church volunteer, ministry leader, and former employee? Why hadn't the community of worship, the fellowship of faith driven souls, the message and promise of resurrection and redemption been enough to lift us, bless us, heal us, and even protect us from the unfinished, unexplained, unrelenting madness? I kept revisiting the confidence contradictions in my cluttered conscience. Beth needed a sage with some sage to clear up the confusion and bless this mess. Angry, frightened, wary, wounded, exhausted, and radically raw, this disciple was losing her discipline. Within a day or two of trekking the trails and ruminating my trials, a friction blister on my heel would warrant even more distraction. Friction surfaced at night smothered in sorrowful sobs, while friction resurrected daily in painful throbs. Thank God for Grace and her professional first aid mercy. She was my campground angel. And Maria, we would come to learn, was simultaneously Zach's. Could moleskin also be used to heal my blistered heart? August 6th, 2014, was a day I would wake in the Wallowas to trek down and out from the backpacking route, accompanied by a faith no longer devout and a heart and soul swelling with clarification of doubt. A promising, but profoundly intense year later, this exact date would again blister.

Upon our return from the Wallowa mountains, John and I wallowed in the peace, comfort, and quiet of our cherished comfortable home. A lingering sadness prevailed. We had yet to fully realize and work with the personal grief we were each experiencing from the steady witness of our son's mysterious downward spiral. For the first time in four months we had privacy in the home for open discussion and reflection. Zach would return in ten days, and what will be changed? What will we do next, we both wondered. We had heard him reference a Kundalini awakening, a spiritual awakening, a few times throughout this transformative upheaval. Maybe we should research Kundalini. Maybe there is possibility to this awakening. Our check ins with him via email while he was gone were brief, and gave no indication about how well his time at Three Creeks was going. It wasn't until we spoke on the phone with Gigi that we had a better picture, recognizing immediately that we needed to listen closely to her grave concerns, and respond honestly and sincerely with apology and explanation as to what seemed a surprise to her. His condition. It had been a big leap of faith to send him there without their detailed understanding of just how much he had been suffering, how we had been uncertain of what his ailment was, how we assumed this community might understand better than us, especially if it was a Kundalini or a spiritual emergency, an outcome of his quest the previous year. We heard it spoken at the closing ceremony that the year or two following this vision fast rite of passage may be tumultuous, full of uncertainty and life disruption, in so many words. Was this what Zach was going through? My mountaintop intuitions came to fruition.

Apologetically and innocently, we explained ourselves to Gigi and wanted her to know that we would not have sent him if we did not feel a reciprocity of care, a hope that he might respond and rise up, a belief that an environmental change might be key to his healing. We were not looking to take advantage, unload, or wash our hands of care. We were looking for direction, pathway, guidance, and possibility. Constantly. Her warmth resumed, while she emphatically shared that Zach's time at Three Creeks had not gone as planned. He had physically isolated, not eaten, claimed to be in final Kundalini stages, and spoken mystically of a woman he loved in Copenhagen and her antagonistic father. Zach had been too weak to work the land, and overall, he had not appeared well of mind or body. It had been fortunate that a fellow quester named Maria, Zach's campground angel, had been available and attentive to helping Zach get through some rough spells, particularly when he was not eating. There had been a lot of care and support provided, above and beyond what any of us expected, and prior to his departure to return home, they would hold sacred ceremony with him as send off to safety, praying for guidance and protection.

Gigi had created for Zach a document of care guidance that was loving, specific to healing steps and actions, and holistically comprehensive in its scope. We held hope that Zach would honor this resource and its guidance, coming from such a personal loving and healing oriented foundation, unlike the less personal and generic outpatient experience of community health following the recent involuntary hospitalization. This selfless, spirited, shamanic soul not only gave guidance to Zach, but she gave John and me some resources to explore. We were introduced to Michael, a Jungian psychotherapist associated with medication free madness sanctuaries, author of the website, "*What is Madness?*", and affiliate of the Mandala Project in the Bay area. Other resources recommended included Stanislov and Christina Grof's book entitled, "*Spiritual Emergency*", and the writings of Joseph Campbell. Gigi opened her heart to us, extended invitation to continued communication contact, caring affirmations, and plenty of ongoing prayer. We had literally only met her one time at our son's quest closing ceremony. We had then written and spoken a few times in and throughout crisis with Zach, and were now receiving guidance tools to further explore his health and healing. This peace warrior of a woman, along with her winning and wise partner Win, Zach's co-leader guide Will (he is), angel caregiver Maria, and the entire quest community which Zach independently sought out in 2013, would each endear themselves to us forever from these supportive days, moments, expressions and gestures of genuine care. On our mysterious path to somewhere, something familiarly unfamiliar proved to be an ongoing lonely, frightening unravelling. This road we were traveling had been cluttered with dark lit side streets, and ever absent directional signage. Zach's return to his chosen base camp landing, with a welcome sign still standing, had been a green light go ahead following emergency lights flashing.

At this August 2014 crossroad, we had now exercised two presenting opportunities for Zach to heal somewhere other than home, and both had proven unsuccessful beyond initiation. Our son would return home again on the 18th of August, looking fragile and exhausted. His father had returned from LA the previous week, only to turn around and head back out to Salt Lake City, missing the return arrival. John would step right back into the work pace and demands following our Wallowa, one hell of a, vacation play station. We both trusted that we could continue to protect Zach at home base while continuing our search for healing help. After our conversation with Gigi, we held guarded apprehension, for the three of us agreed on the phone that he exhibited continued strange behavior and thoughts, ongoing indications of risk for an end of life choice or action. We would all rally to guide and protect him. I was overwhelmed with relief upon his safe return that mid-August afternoon, but immediately I recognized and regretted the look, the language, and the listlessness when greeting him at our front door. Zach collapsed into his bedroom consumed by fatigue and body ache symptoms, and while sprawled before me, expressed immediately a continued distrust in our perceived ongoing effort to keep him from his loved one. *"Where is she?"* he would demand. "You know", he would insist with a glare. He claimed he would die if she could not come and save him. John and I still did not know if this woman was real, in his head, a psychological Jungian archetype in his psyche, or some other psychotic manifestation. He would sadly sob himself to sleep that evening, resuming an isolation pattern, despite agreeing to schedule doctor and care appointments to explore his many ongoing ailments. We returned to deep sorrow, while hope resumed for every tomorrow.

Beth was housebound for safety patrol and home management, John was diligently working to support his family and appease management, while Zach was choosing his own self-management and care plan. The challenge still in front of us was that we did not know yet if he was in fact, bipolar, in Kundalini awakening, having a spiritual emergence, both, or something else all-together. We had no diagnostics team other than ourselves at this point, and we continued to read books and research online. He was likely invested in the same search exercises while in the daily quiet and isolation of his room. Healthcare navigation is always difficult enough in a clear mind, let alone a foggy one! As an adamant independent, in an unclear, unstable mind, battling delusional demons in the daily dance, he would work at navigating care. With intention to better understand Zach's references to Kundalini, and Gigi's references to spiritual emergence, I read *'Kundalini Experience'* by Lee Sanella, and *'Spiritual Emergence'* by the Grofs. Both were insightful works, offering relevance and feasibility. Zach's psychotic behavior and physical ailments might be attributed to the physical and psychological manifestations of Kundalini awakening. Essentially, I learned, Kundalini refers to a primal energy located at the base of the spine, that when awakened, moves through seven energy centers of the body (chakras) and leads to an expanded state of consciousness and enlightenment. There can be great turbulence in the path to enlightenment, and Zach's symptoms and behaviors sounded aligned with this possibility, other than the skin rash and the angry rage, of course. Once again, John and I were in foreign territory with regard to understanding any of these Eastern philosophies and alternative spiritual practices. We wanted to respect them, but as far as we understood, we knew no one in the practice of these, nor anyone who would locally embrace guidance or care for Zach if this were his circumstance. Furthermore, Zach was not looking for us to solve or figure these presenting problems out for him. He was determined to help himself. We continued to stand guard.

Thursday night of the week our son arrived home, I started the weekly NAMI Family to Family course, accepting that if he was bipolar, we should learn more about mental illness, establishing a better understanding of mental health diagnoses and treatment. John would accompany me when in town, sometimes racing in late from the airport. The two of us were researching every health angle we encountered by chance and by circumstance, trying to become quick studies in the desperate drive to help our son save his life. I returned home carrying a thick white binder packed with 10 weeks of lesson materials. When the house was quiet in the lonely still of the night, I would read and reread, trying to find ongoing relevance and reason. NAMI offered another new world of language to decipher and a targeted search for symptom, behavior, or other markers to help identify illness. To read about the medications and side effects was definitely depressing. To read about how best to communicate with your sick loved one, we would begin addressing. Immediately, we ordered our next resource called, '*I Am Not Sick I Don't Need Help*', by Xavier Amador, Ph.D. We would learn to LEAP with the best of them, listening, empathizing, agreeing, and partnering. There would be ample opportunity to use the skills in the weeks ahead. Good news that first weekend back, was that Zach scheduled an appointment in downtown Portland with a chiropractor who worked with professional athletes. Gigi had referred him, and he followed up. Excellent news!

We did not know it at the time, but later learned he had also scheduled a doctor appointment through Medicaid coverage to address a lingering rash on his left arm. The appointment was scheduled two weeks out, actually considered a quick turn around since local community health appointments were typically 4-6 weeks out, if not longer.

Welcome to public healthcare, my beloved son. You get what you get whenever you can get it! Maddening! Zach had isolated in the home, not leaving once since he returned from California, so when the midweek appointment in Portland arrived, I was eager to see if he would actually exit out the door. I wanted to offer to drive him, and he knew I was available, but I waited in a back room and listened as he paced and paced the floor, clearing his throat, literally pushing himself beyond the mounting anxiety once so absent and absurd for him with respect to any of these kind of appointment and out in the public norms. He finally left the house at 3:15 for a 4pm appointment. I gave thanks to greater powers, something I continued to still do along this frightening journey we had been subjected to, despite my recent faith waning backpack experience. Shortly after 4pm, I received a phone call from the chiropractor office, looking for Zach. I am now deeply concerned, for Zach had refused to use a cellphone in these strange days of isolation and independence, thus I could not reach him to follow up. I called the office back by 5pm, and still no Zach. Where is he? I cannot track him. The haunting and always nauseating lump in my throat returned, serving as cautionary warning, anticipating the stranger and typically some danger.

My imaginary warning light activation switched in a flash from yellow to red, as our front door opened with unusual force, and Zach then entered in a furious state of frustration. Immediately, he grabbed a bottle of opened and available wine from the fridge, something he had never integrated into any previous rage. I learned from his angry outburst that he had circled the downtown address to no avail, driven in stressful bumper to bumper traffic to and from, and felt it all another failure among so many for far too long. Apologizing and attempting to end the office phone call with the embarrassed administrator, she confirmed to me that the address he used was a wrong address. She realized they had not updated their new address on their website. Of course, he had no phone to call them nor the wherewithal to stop and call from somewhere else downtown. He was truly not well, not himself. Our former Zach would have had no problem with something like this. He had navigated plenty of unknown destinations, and utilized cell phones and computers with savvy ease. The regression was too obvious. His brain was not functioning well. The evening proceeded to scare the shit out of me, as I tried to coax him from drinking that wine, unsure of what he might do if under the influence of both alcohol and rage. I began to reason with him, attempting to help him realize the office error and the ease with which we could reschedule.

He screamed at me, "Welcome to another fucked up day in the life of Zach Moritz!" Downstairs he scrambled, screaming "Fuck you!" over and over, exploding in frustration from a repeated sense of failure and inability to right what was all so wrong. I was not mad at him. I was ever so sad for him. But I would not show him pity, as he deserved to reclaim some form of dignity, despite this frightening display of rage. I had witnessed and participated in plenty of setback, plenty of effort to find help, plenty of confused occasion, plenty of perceived failure. Listening while allowing Zach the space to exorcise such emotional upheaval on the stairway while swigging the white wine he disliked so much, I waited upstairs in a back room while texting John. Interestingly enough, the rant on the stairwell did not sound like delusion but rather a collective dump about various disappointments and saving graces that seemed to surface and purge from his psyche. He complained about coaches who had been abusive to him, treatment as if he were a mental punching bag, teachers who had negatively impacted him and labeled him, only to then suddenly hear him exhale out a loud expression of gratitude for a certain coach, a certain professor, a certain teacher. "THANK GOD, THANK GOD", he would praise in recall of those special someone's. He paused from his purge and praise when hearing my text alerts from the back and forth of my fevered electronic exchange with John, innocently laughing out loud and coyly commenting that I could turn that sound off, you know! "You know …. you know, Mom, you can turn that sound off so I don't have to know you are texting!" He had busted me, and it had been classic old time playful gaming with his mom! In the precise moment of that precociously precious playfulness, I knew we would make it through the momentary setback. He could not see me, but I had been smiling. My throat lump dissipated and the red light halt switched green forward. Weary, wily Zach had worn himself out and gone to bed. Huge exhale. What a revealing encounter, and yet not at all in the realm of answering the question of 'what's wrong with Zach?'. Everything, anything, but specifically, something! I ached all over in the traumatizing truth of his situation. THANK GOD, THANK GOD for his humor and our safety.

In the eventual quiet of that Tuesday evening, I proceeded to take all alcohol from the house and hide it or rid ourselves of it, allowing no future challenge of rage on the loose to be mixed with available adult juice. No thank you, said the house manager, care giver, gate keeper Beth. If John and I were in need of an adult beverage, we would go buy one to indulge in elsewhere, and that would be our position for quite some time. Food of great quality and varied selection would be the ongoing bait in this house to catch the big fish and swim alongside him. Mealtime would offer occasional pleasurable connections, so I would explore new recipes and John would fix old favorites. Friday nights, Mom would catch a break from cooking all week, when John would enjoy a favored pastime that helped him unwind from the stressors of work and enabled the flair of his creative expression. On Friday of Labor Day weekend, I drove north as planned to labor the weekend with Gabby. She and I would move her furnishings and belongings out of her apartment returning home the following evening. A welcome escape for me from the intensity cycles of the past two weeks, this also offered a rare solo window of time for Zach and his father. John chose to prepare a Friday night dinner of rare steaks on the grill with sauteed mushrooms and roasted potatoes, their manly favorite, and a best dish to cook when well-done Beth is not around. The evening began as a promising father son occasion until discussion centered around Zach's love obsession and his continued delusion about our collaboration with this woman's father to keep the two apart. An aggressive and escalating tone culminated with Zach directly confronting John in an accusatory manner.

Instinctively, and assertively, John leapt up from the kitchen table, and raced out the front door, separating himself from any possible further aggression and insult. He continued to distance himself out beyond the front field of the property, while his son yelled after him that he was a coward. John made the wise decision to create space when Zach got all up in his face! Upon his gradual return to the front door of his own home, John looked squarely at Zach, who was waiting and looking on in wonder, and in a direct, matter of fact, calm, clear delivery, he addressed his confused but now settled down son. "Zach, I am NOT a coward." His silenced son sheepishly replied, "I know you are not a coward, Dad." They hugged each other in loving embrace, each grasping for what both hungered; normalcy. The manly to mysterious moment passed, and the embrace of their evening ended. Both men longed for what was.

Insert 26 •   2014 Zach with Baby T

Chapter 20: Fall Back Panic Attack

Lean on Me, Bill Withers
Ball of Confusion, The Temptations

John, Gabby and I managed to pack two full vehicles and a small U Haul attachment headed home from Seattle that Labor Day weekend, loaded with her remaining belongings after reducing the haul by a significant Goodwill drop, a steal of a deal sale, and a mattress flat hat secured to the scalp of the Armada. Her father had been eager to join us once we reached out from Seattle amidst our packing and cleaning, requesting additional help and haul. The morning after John and Zach's cowardly connection, John willingly travelled north to help. Within the past seven years, we had become quite the efficient team helping both kids move in and out of college housing and home based housing. This would be our daughter's first and only move home from college, including summers. Her home bound, double load, personal collection replaced some space from the strange cycle of her brother's reduced ownership and dispossession of belongings. Out with the Z's, and in with the G's. Geez. We all made room for her return, intentionally and unintentionally. Her brother had moved his belongings in and out of our home space a few times, when he was vibrant and healthy in post college apartment days, and then again more recently, in these days and nights of mysterious madness. This was her season to return and unload the collections and acquisitions of her life to date, and the only presenting madness was the hustle to unload the U Haul and return the equipment by its due back deadline.

There are cycles in one's parenting life, expected and unexpected, in which you include storage facility to the description of your home and property. Our garage and shed served this purpose, while the kids original bedrooms still lay claim, whether we redecorated or rearranged to lay our own claim. In a 70's house, closets get reclaimed quickly! The expression 'our home' would always mean our family home, despite the kids' intentions to move on. Zach's recent circumstances of returning home we framed as a temporary setback, and now Gabby's a temporary layover. Neither intended for anything more than temporary, each wanting to create their own definition of home and independence. In the calendar of life, we all hoped this would be a fall back, spring forward adjustment to our seasonal clocks. The life window that our young adult daughter would face in choosing to return and live in our home post college life was one that served our family circumstance. John and I were grateful to have her emotional support, as she now engaged on the frontline amidst our ever unfolding saga. She might have chosen to take flight and soar, but rather she returned to the nest, strengthening her wings through local flight patterns, and participating quietly in the repair and recovery of her family flock. This young woman emanated a steady energy of light and balance that would nurture family wounds and further illuminate our troubling trepidations as we adapted accommodations. Household dynamics would shift again, and in time, she would witness firsthand his shifting shroud of shade that would darken our daily light. The house was now full in a way it had not been for 8 years. The house was now full in a way it had never been. Our adaptations lately had been less about the growth in understanding and embrace of emergent adult children or the various intersections of parental, sibling, and family roles. More so, they were painfully about unwelcome deterioration and a resulting reformation from the illness disruption within our lives.

A heightened intention for John and I was to not allow the current circumstances to diminish our daughter's unique spirit and evolving essence on the post collegiate horizon. This would prove to be a consciously clear intention yet continuously difficult challenge to protect and uphold. So much was now oriented around Zach; his symptoms, his behaviors, his illness manifestation. Immediately upon college graduation, her brother had seized the freedom and choice to pursue his post graduate dreams. His sister would postpone hers, at the risk of foregoing them all together, while coming to terms with our family crisis. Gab was brave, patient, steadfast, generous and she persevered. Just over a year ago, she and her brother lived in Seattle together for a short stretch of time prior to his nature quest. Their bond deepened, and their support for one another as budding young adults was obvious. The Zach spirit and soul she had known her whole life, and had come to know deeper as a young adult, had noticeably shifted after Denmark's fall return of 2013 and ever more so since his return home from Iowa in 2014. She was now returning home to a brother struggling to find health recovery and some motivational spark to reignite a reformed life vision. She was also returning home to a family working to rescue itself from brokenness. What would be her developing thoughts and questions as to her brother's behaviors and suffering since she saw him last in July? Likely, she held ideas of influence and concern from summer 2013 forward, but there was much she had missed firsthand throughout 2014. Had she noticed anything strange in Copenhagen when she visited spring and fall of 2013? Had she noticed physical and or psychological shifts in Seattle when together the summer of 2013? How do we mark or measure dramatic changes and what would we link together as influential? We as parents would think dramatically different than she as sibling. What a complicated circumstance her own was, relating as best friend sibling but uncertain ally in an unpredictable war zone once called home. Was this just a case of family once friends but parents now foes? Where did she sit in the situation? At the table of stable, for sure. But also at the window of sorrow, to endure. She would witness soon enough that his friend was now the isolating bed, while his foe proved to be the cycling illness in his head.

Returning from a 6month stretch of living alone in a one-bedroom apartment on campus, and a 4year stretch of off campus living, Gabrielle would compromise some privacy and independence while back in her childhood home. Until a job and independent living situation was attainable and appealing to her needs, home base would suffice. The shuffle and the dealt cards of the grown up, health fucked family reality on deck, was held and influenced by the circumstantial grip of her brother, her parents, and her hand now yet to be played. She thoughtfully transitioned, settling into an upstairs bedroom rather than her previous bedroom downstairs next to her brother. For many reasons, this was a practical accommodation, and we were fortunate to have the spatial options. From our viewpoint, her room choice offered a safety measure in the event there were unexpected rage incidents, intimidating by sheer physical size and then the erratic nature of any witnessed crazed state. She had not witnessed this madness, nor had we described our incidents in detail. When in a well mind, her brother had never been intimidating nor threatening. The room upstairs was a brighter space than the daylight basement cave effect of her own original bedroom, and any noise from her father's office right next door would be minimal thanks to a near weekly travel schedule. Safety, privacy, good light, and manageable noise. Physical transition accomplished. She would find herself busy soon enough, looking for employment while continuing work on existing contracts. Within a month at home, she explored expanding an interest pathway of engaging herself in the neighboring city of Portland, Oregon. Gabby discovered and enrolled in the Portland School of Astrology (PSA) one weekend a month, establishing an astrologer identity and fueling her passion, becoming a feverish student and avid community member. PSA stimulated her creative and artistic wonder, answering a curious pull toward cosmic understanding through academic medium. Thankfully, her avid fascination and commitment became healthy distractions to the reality unfolding within our family fold. PSA would become her safe place.

In response to the weekend's Friday night man date, John and I established our own mandate that we would reach out this month to Michael, the psychotherapist in Oakland referred to us by Gigi, and explore with him the strange eruptive outbursts and behaviors of our son. This outreach would prove to be a peaceful and calming alternate resource guide to the crisis line calls and emergency room drop ins. We would continue to participate in another 9weeks of NAMI classes, exploring and educating ourselves further about mental illness, but also remaining open to a vast array of both alternative and traditional considerations of resources, tools, diagnostics, treatment modalities, any and all avenues of healing possibility for our loved one, Zach. Daily, we were conflicted on how to respectfully, but responsibly demonstrate our love and urgency with this young adult who desperately needed us, who so did not want to need us, who still believed he did not need us, who continued to display evidence of being imbalanced and mind altered. To his credit, we found out by way of appointment paperwork left on the seat of his car, he had spent days in early September pursuing treatment for a skin rash that would not heal, only to secure a prescription for anti-itch cream. This same damn circular rash was identification pursued by Zach, with no complaint of any itch, at every 2014 medical practice appointment. We eventually identified it in October, but continued to witness its medical disconnect throughout the remainder of the year and on into the next from medical records obtained in the future. Landline voice messaging recorded in our kitchen revealed he had secured a primary care appointment scheduled 8 weeks out on October 31. This was the earliest the overloaded, understaffed, community health care facility could offer him in Medicaid primary care, non-emergent reality. While in frequent isolation, our son was clearly trying from behind closed doors to rise up and confront his healthcare, as were we. We had no idea until an eventual season of wellness was upon us in 2015, and a humble conversation was shared between mother and son revisiting illness recollections from each of our experiences, that these same September nights had cycled insomnia, delusional thoughts, paranoia, and suicide ideation. While we were all asleep upstairs, he would sometimes wander neighboring streets in the wee hours of dark morn, contemplating suicide to relieve the strange cycling delusions and demons. Daytime search for treatment, nighttime lurch on pavement.

In that month of September, while Zach sought to quiet those demons and chase more doctors, John and I focused on research, readiness, and resolve. We studied and adopted non-confrontational methods of loving outreach, co-operative communication styles, and note taking strategies for identifying and recording presenting patterns, behaviors, and symptoms. Our notes would build a case for crisis support if needed again, for we knew the pathway to help should we find ourselves in trouble trying to keep Zach safe while seeking some type of health reveal and all types of wellness recovery. The various ways and displays of whatever was happening to Zach were still very confusing, frightening, and not within our skill set or resources to resolve on our own or without Zach's 26year old, willing and agreeable collaboration. We could not do this alone. He could not do this alone. We wanted to do this together. He would not agree to do this together. We were a ship at sea without a captain, and the waters were rough, the direction unclear. His health, and consequent life implosion were not the only storms brewing. Care giver grief was alive and shaking our spirits, as the isolation from friends and family, the disconnection to any validating medical support, and the constant threat of safety jeopardized our own personal health in addition to the family health. To embrace our grief amidst such uncertainty and instability seemed impossible and selfish, for that embrace and reaction might come at the cost of redirecting a priority focus and then distracting a priority purpose. To reach out for our own personal care we believed was too risky, too exhausting amidst constant unanswerable questions and inappropriate projections, and too vulnerable to the immediate threat of losing Zach. John diverted his grief with work, likely showing on the job with presentation as fear, anger, and anxiety amidst pressure, demand, and deadline. Zach's sister diverted her grief with studies, work, and outside pursuits, likely showing in the world with presentations such as guardedness, protectiveness, and compassionate loyalty to those underrepresented, underserved, and unheard. Beth diverted her grief in the garden, in the pool, and in the research. I had little opportunity for my grief to be expressed to anyone beyond John and Gabby, for I held the job of home base security and stability, leaving the house the least other than Zach. I found little safety among friends and family to comfort me, not question me, affirm me, not alarm me. Diversion of grief does not, however, eliminate grief; thus, the diverted grief would repressively spread beneath the shield. Illness for Zach meant illness for us all, and we believed healing for Zach would heal us all. Wounds take time. Scars often remain. Fear hovered daily as this month offered more isolation, no treatment, no medication, low engagement with family, lethargic detachment, constant fatigue, cognitive stares, and a listlessness that dimmed all former sparkle, wit, and enthused curiosity of his supersized self. He could use a friend. Maybe it was about time.

Since Fairfield in February 2014, Zach had not connected with friends other than rite of passage partners. Since Copenhagen in October 2013, Zach had not connected with teammates other than supposed hospitalization healers. Severance to his past and the irreverence of his recent kept us from outreach to local friends. Zach had not been receptive to us, to his hometown, to his health care options, to his sister at home, so how could we expect him to receive and welcome a friend? We did not want to regret neglecting this possible healing modality addition of familiar friendship, a buddy of belonging, a titan of trust. Our son had been so alone, depressed, deflated, perhaps a local friend could convince him to get out of the house, go for a drive, take a walk, reflect on adolescence and adulthood, bitch about problems, laugh about solutions, or vice versa, and basically stand by each other. Begin to focus on life and living, Zach! I chose friend Blake. A teammate and friend from high school days forward, Blake agreed to meet in a café and catch up. To not hear from Zach for 7 months had not seemed strange to him, for they both were finding their way into adulthood, and trusted in their comfortable bond of friendship. 'Soul brothers', Zach would refer to themselves, finding enough commonality yet enough distinction to keep their brotherhood vibe fresh and fathomable. Blake was a big, burly guy who was smart, handsome, and humorous like our son's former self, and together they managed their share of mischief and mayhem, adventure and adversity. To learn of his friend's health predicament, resulting isolation and vulnerability, the update impassioned an admission of his own current choice of isolation amidst life transition that somehow felt relatable enough to trust reaching out and bridging their divide. He felt he needed Zach perhaps as much as Zach needed him in this window of time. The challenge might be Zach's cognitive setback and possible bipolar presentation which Blake could witness directly should they connect and spend time together. I shared Zach's phone update, our landline, and his email currently active and in use. Blake chose to reach out to Zach that month, and whatever communication they had was between them. I just wanted to instigate informed outreach that might result in positive outcome. Friendship as medicine.

In telling the story to Blake, I found myself sharing with him that John and I simply could not bring ourselves to buy in to the mental illness diagnosis in hospitalization as the resolution to the symptom suffering saga of our son. We suspected something more, or something one and done, but the return of symptoms and behaviors left us mystified. His former health, his family history, his previous patterns, and even his consistently unexplainable recurring cartwheel of physical pain and presenting pallor deemed more than a chemistry clash of polarized thoughts and behavior extremes. This was not about a public projection of an 'oh no, not us' type of elitism, arrogance or denial of mental illness consideration, as if to stigmatize that we were above or beyond the perceived as unspeakable possibility. This was about exploring cause and effect, biology of illness, and scope of symptoms as to accurately align the rhyme and the reason of illness presentation in Zach. We assumed all of the many medical professionals and pathways we would pursue and encounter held the same philosophy of commitment to accurate assessment and thorough evaluation of all possibilities for illness manifestation. But you know the saying. *Ass u me.* You know. Never assume. Zach's brain continued to fail him, cycling through stable thought and delusional thought, confusing himself as much as all of us. One of the many challenges in brain injury or infection is that the damage is not visible to the human eye nor sometimes even through the diagnostic tool. A dangerous outcome is the altered brain's influence on one's thoughts, words and deeds. From the sights and sounds of appearances and expressions, any audience might observe and criticize, pass judgement or personalize, and then hold unrealistic expectations in the assumption (ass u me!) that the brain damaged individual can then control, name, monitor or measure their actions. Does the arm function when it is broken? There is no sling to mend the broken mind, no plaster cast to protect the injury, no color pink to signify the illness, nor ID badge to specify an ailment and its impact. Mental illness suffers from significant stigma and can encounter medical negligence through oversight as well as through stereotype. We believed Zach's brain was mentally ill, but that it was systemically bigger than the mental illness alone. A holistic health connection of one's brain to their body, the nervous system hub to the immune system host, warrants a more ethical evaluation and diagnostic depth. Whether in the home, or in medical facilities for assessment and care, Zach's brain presentation visually and orally trumped the multitude of illness symptoms repeatedly spoken, including of that simple, symbolic circular rash ever present. We continued the NAMI coursework, and called Michael.

Our outreach to Michael was by phone and email, introducing ourselves and our story, including the personal referral from Gigi. We read in advance about his intriguing associations and messages for healing alternatives of care amidst madness manifestation. The Bay Area Mandala Project and the Total Health Institute, both mental health recovery intervention alternatives to hospitalization, the Icarus Project advocating an alternative approach to mental health, one of breakthrough rather than breakdown, and the Mad in America website promoting a broadened perspective on alternative treatment for mental health other than Western emphasis on medication all seemed compassionate and dignified care modalities for those in a crisis of maddening proportion. Previous resources we had been open to explore were also referenced in Michael's media links, including experience and explanation of Kundalini awakening and spiritual emergency. All of these resources were rich with ideas and possibility, expanding our scope of what might be options or inclusions for Zach's care, but we were still uncertain as to how to incorporate any of it without Zach's cooperation. And there was always the question of program or treatment modality price tag and affordability. Health care dilemmas any one of us face, especially crises of loved ones, unless we are of extreme wealth perhaps, include the moral and ethical weighted measure of our loved one's sacred value versus our financial means and access. Does one subject greater financial risk to that which might otherwise be stable and balanced in one's life, or even already in a state of risky imbalance, in attempts to save or even improve a threatened life? Should financial cost ever warrant any measure in desperate times? Always, we sought options, for the sake of love, loyalty, and humility laced humanity. There are no guarantees. We would continue to explore and evaluate options for Zach. His illness felt comparative to an impoverished mind, body and soul. Zach's wellness bank account of health wealth deserved more deposits, less withdrawals. But as he withdrew further, engagement with any ideas we brought forward, feasibility and cost aside, he rejected them, reacting angrily and defiantly. Even Michael's constant offer to speak with him and attempt to build a relationship of understanding was an unsigned deposit slip. At least our conversations held almost weekly with Michael offered us as parents a kind, wise, patient soul, with a gentle, soothing voice of wisdom to listen, reflect, educate and affirm us in our unrelenting efforts and explorations. Michael became an additional compass rose to us, like Joanne, and like Gigi.

An early gift of mind manna we received from Michael was a conversation and reference to psychology resources that might help us better understand the constant fixation and delusional myths that had been spoken and written repeatedly through Zach's voiced and typed maddening rants. The cycling reference to a true love, of the father, and his family, were proposed to be the anima and animus in Jungian analysis of personal projection. We had been often overanalyzing much of what Zach would say or write, either receiving it as personal or fervently seeking truth and relevance within its content, so we had little mind about a psyche realization beyond a brain illness consideration. One's brain integrates a vast array of collective experiential input, multi-systemic inter-functionality and holistic energies of influence. There were many factors at play, all in array and on display! We became students of Michael in the science of madness and psyche while students of NAMI in the science of mental illness and meds. Zach would expressively wander far from truths we had lived or understood, and eventually, we would come to know they were far from his own truths and understanding as well, for he would in clear mind on the horizon tell us so. In the occasion of rant, rage or regression, one could hear and interpret threads of truth possibility, but the overall weave would suggest fabrication within the fabric. Absurdly colorful, dynamically creative in pattern and prose, and uniquely suggestive of some reality in delivery, the madness management found guided resource through the help of Michael. We adopted and practiced a very gentle and loving approach to giving Zach time and space for healing, asking little of him, and responding to him with respectful reverence and practiced patience. We missed him so damn much. We would wait, working our way with intention to a wellness return of mind, body, soul for all of us. And there would be occasional rewards.

Amidst the daily darkness of a 7foot shadow, we would encounter a ray of sunshine moment or a reward on occasion that would brighten up the ongoing overcast outlook. The weather within our fall season forecast would spring forth between that of lion and that of lamb! Choosing to join us and engage with us for John's birthday dinner on

SONFLOWER

September 14, Zach's participation was simple, kind, and physically quite present despite the shallow depth of mental engagement expended. He made the effort to come out of isolation, and respond to our invitation. This was John's happy birthday moment of 2014. Quite unexpectedly, and to our delight, occasional flickers of sharp wit and humor would surface. Our recognizable Zach was still holding on to some spunk and some spirit somewhere beneath his mantle of masquerading mask and insanity task. Flickers might become flames, we idealized, for steady warmth and light from him would be ever so welcome. We had been giving a daily dose of this medicine under Michael's encouragement. Give and you shall receive, the faithful believe. But a mere 24hours after the Sunday blessing of a birthday communion, we hear the late night pacing up and down the stairway, the clicking of neck and ankle joints, the stomping footprint of fevered fury, and the red flags of restlessness we had understood to all be precursors to rage or rant racing within the lamb and lurching toward some form of lion outcome. How Gab and I slept that night, I am uncertain. John was already out of town in Sacramento, for when was he not travelling and working in this harrowing, reality based nonfiction narrative! He honored his obligations, both professionally and personally, as best as he could, under the circumstances. There is graduated intention to this steady, consistent father character development of travel discipline and work ethic loyalty toward employer and family in crisis. John's professional payback plan to these priorities arrives not long after his September birthday bounty blessing.

My daughter and I had made eager plans to travel into downtown Portland before noon Tuesday, anticipating her follow-up interview and presentation with a global digital marketing agency. The mix of anxiousness and excitement around the interview alone might have kept us awake, let alone the fearful anticipation of a possible raging eruption. Fortunately, her brother's anticipated evening rant manifested instead in the form of an early morning email banter, with a subject titled:

Don't respond, I'll only instantly delete it.

My throat lump returned, and stomach pain followed suit. They were teammates in synch. Nauseatingly, I opened the mail to meet the message monster. The good fortune of the moment was to not have physical confrontation, but it was the only fortunate element. Despite my heightened fear generated by his elevated madness now evident in his threatening written message before me, and my interpretation of self-harm potential from his peculiar closing sentence, I would choose to leave him alone in the home that afternoon and into the evening. Because, this day, one of so very few of late, was going to be a day of attention, care, and support for Gabby, dammit. He could not rob us of this. Was it a threat of psyche purge or a possible threat of action proportion to be taken more seriously? She could have driven to Portland on her own, but I selfishly wanted to be with her, and we were with one car to use between the three of us currently. I wanted to be in the presence and spirit of her young adult hopes, to celebrate with her something positive, so alive and so vibrantly healthy. To lift her up, to be in the excitement and anticipation of a great opportunity for her, while in the midst of such nonstop, exhaustive focus and energy around her brother. Was that so unreasonable for a mother to desire? Perhaps. She was willing to share this moment, with all her excitement and enthusiasm, and I was so grateful to accompany her and seize a reprieve from what I grieved. But also, I felt very alone and afraid, regardless, for the email from Zach, sent to mother and father, was the most bizarre written rant we had yet to receive. Angered he was about the father of his true love, about strange and unfamiliar references he made to a global community of psychologists and spiritualists, including a random mention of unspecified superiority complexes, and global efforts against emancipation, as well as court proceedings and politically incorrect politicians, these were words and expressions of his own design. He seemed to have truly gone mad. Again. His closing words read:

Congrats on making the fearless fearful for his own life. And since spelling it out is apparently necessary, I mean that both literally and figuratively.

Now, from whom should he fear his life, I wondered? Himself, I jumped to conclusion. And why was he blaming us, and attacking us? Remember, Beth, to not take the madness as personally directed, to trust that there are circuitry problems, and that the messages are not representative of intentions or actions. Maybe. Exhale.

Needless to say, I was gripped in fear all morning and all afternoon. I had been keeping this from his sister so that she could move rightfully into a focused headspace for her own eager pursuit. But meanwhile, I was texting John since he had been in the email address as well. Mother and daughter had planned to dine out in SE Portland following the interview, and even considered catching a movie. This was a welcome day off from my home care assignment, and an opportunity for me to spend time with my daughter. To get out of the guarded house, to inhale then exhale the gift of some fresh air, I was long overdue. What would Zach do in my absence? While waiting in the car, I read. Not a garden or home care magazine, either of which would have been more mind distracting, but in true Beth form, NAMI literature to study, the Amador book to practice LEAP principles, and a book about breaking the bipolar cycle. John and I were regularly practicing Amador's LEAP strategy of **L**isten-**E**mpathize-**A**gree-**P**artner, so as to minimize furthered aggravation with Zach when he was agitated and irrational. We continued to be sponges in expanding our knowledge and exercising guidance to fresh ideas, but I was often a mess of a mop in a bucket full of tears and fears, wringing myself late at night in the privacy of my bedroom, into the reliable receptacle of a pillowcase rinse. While in the presence of my adored daughter this special day, however, I would reserve the tears for late night and focus on a leap into her moment of joy, carefully timing what and when I share about her brother. After eagerly listening to her interview feedback and thorough assessment of her performance, I chose to share with her the Zach email content and situation. We agreed to leave it alone, let it rest, and hopefully avoid stirring any further rage or resentment. I was traumatized, however, from past events, and I could not seem to let it go. My mind and heart were distracted deep within. There is just so much she has not witnessed nor been directly privy to. Could she understand my trauma? Certainly, she had been traumatized, no doubt, but much had been filtered.

By 3:20pm that afternoon, I emailed Michael for emotional support and any Jungian or Michaelian reassurance. I truly feared the 'what ifs' to Zach self-harming or who knows whatever else in a crazed or rage induced mindset. Kind Michael ever so carefully guided me through some basic check in questions as to Zach's sleep patterns, his eating patterns, any possible disturbances that might be resolved to help him settle down. Michael helped calm and quiet my fear monsters. John also engaged in this email exchange that evening and shared with Michael how just the day before, Zach had made breakfast, cleaned the kitchen, come upstairs clean shaven, and spent the day in warm spirits as he joined us in celebration of John's birthday dinner. The flicker of hope in that birthday evening had shifted to a flame of hostility so soon after. Michael sent an evening sign off to John and me that once again provided the nurture so needed when under such duress. He wrote, *You and Beth and Gabby are wonderfully caring and devoted to Zach, and those family bonds will help him greatly as he finds his way forward.* Exhale. Relax. Affirmation, so calming and assuring. Scented like a rose, compass rose that he was. Like the soothe of the soft ocean breeze and warm heat of the sun's rays when you lay still on a sandy tropical beach, momentarily free of all cares and worries; you let go and allow affirmation warmth to heal you. The long deep exhale outcome is medicinal cure to one's wearied soul. Michael then offered to Skype on the computer with Zach at any time he needed or wanted someone to listen and work with him; if only we could convince our confused son to receive this generous and supportive offer of care. He refused.

Honoring our commitment to make a full outing of the day, Gabby and I devoured some Thai food and caught a quirky comedy/drama movie at a small historic movie-house theater in SE Portland. I was still uncertain and wary of what we might return home to, so maintaining a relaxed vibe was tough. A movie might be helpful for distraction, and we thought the promo of *Frank* sounded right up our movie lane. A British pop group of the 80's (true story) had this band member who adopted an alter ego, wore a large paper mache head in performance and often within his daily life. The story of the characters and their musical pursuits unfolds. There would be music, it was artsy, and it was definitely not a mainstream movie. Perfect escape it would seem. We would not know that the authenticity of both the band and the specific alter ego band member's true story would be altered in the script of the movie. The band member in real life actually died of throat cancer, but the movie built a story line around a suicide ending, and we were wickedly caught off guard late into the movie. The choice happened to play to our vulnerabilities in this particular window of seeking relaxation and escape. I felt sick, nauseated again by the irony of the intersection to our get-away art movie moment, the circumstances of our son at home, and my recurring PTSD symptoms from May madness on. The moment was maddeningly surreal. Frankly, our drive home was eerily quiet, reflectively anxious. Our hesitative entry into the home was greeted visually by a lingering, empty glare from our zany Zach seated at the kitchen table, slowly and very methodically eating his meal. No greeting, no words. A silent sigh of relief and prayer of thanksgiving from me was then followed immediately by a melatonin induced crash into bedroom escape, pillowcase sponge wringing included.

The next morning, I rose early to take a walk and shop groceries before the household awakened. Returning home and entering the front door, Zach towered by the entryway space holding the house phone, and looking at me with the most tender and vulnerable of eyes. Margaret Keane '*Big Eyes*' came to mind. I was uncertain and wary of his intentions in the moment, not fully recovered from the hangover angst of the day before, when he longingly asked, "Can I have a hug?" WHAT?!?! Lowering my groceries, I responded immediately, without hesitation. I hugged him with a grip that spoke forever. "Yes, of course, anytime, any day, anywhere, Zach! I have been waiting and hoping one day you would ask again or even allow it. I believe you have so needed touch and familial love that is both physical and emotional in its contact. We all so want to help." I pleaded and preached to him. Until then, a hug was never so precious, so meaningful. While in the spontaneous doorway moment, I shared with Zach that his outpatient case worker from the June hospitalization had been trying to reach him, probably intending to close out his case since the 90day outpatient duration had passed. The phone still in his hand, he responded that he had received and even returned the call. He seemed clear headed, responsible, capable, like old Zach. Perhaps, I thought, this is why he is hugging me. He is elated to have the monkey off his back of hospitalization and medications. No matter, I will take it for whatever the inspiration! That May/June chapter would now officially be behind us. I email Michael, thanking him and sharing this gift of the morning that followed the rant and the fear of yesterday. From harm to hug, the moment was monumental. Everyone is elated about this morning glory of a bloom, which climbs its way into further bloom throughout that day and on into the following week.

But our morning glory bloom became swallowed up with nightshade doom when John returned home the next evening. He entered the home laden with luggage and briefcase, and some additional baggage tagged with uncharacteristic gloom ready to be revealed. Gabrielle and I sat down with John, while Zach hovered in the kitchen listening and petting the cat Napoleon, who himself hovered among all of us, absorbing the vibe while scanning our faces. John spoke slowly and methodically, while sipping his medicinal pour. The household pillar shared that he had been caught off guard with management, uncertain as to how or why he had not been forewarned or specifically how his work had suffered, but that the company was choosing to place him on a 90-day plan to prove his merit and worth. WTF!!!!! He looked dazed, and rightfully so. We were all dazed and disordered from this heartbreaking juxtaposition of our struggling son's completion of 90day sentence to our juggling John's initiation. Juggler he had become, handling whatever crisis was at hand. Work, home, family, health, he pushed himself to support it all, only to be pushed back in return. John was all too familiar with the gig, the 90day plan routine, for he had been asked to utilize the very same tool for some employees he had inherited that were underperforming when he had been assigned a new management position. He felt blindsided by the gut hit to himself, without any warning or waved yellow flag. Other than our son's May/June hospitalization knowledge shared among his employer human resource team and management team, the company and his many contacts had no fucking idea just how deep the level of stress and pressure John had still been self-managing for weeks while performing multiple transition and training responsibilities and amidst the ongoing health crisis of his son. Would it be assumed that a family crisis of such magnitude would simply dissipate, having no lasting effect on a historically accomplished employee? What the hell was going on here, and where was any human resource support?

In management's measure, this dedicated human resource, of a now 'Dear John' status, was expendable within a 90day moment, within a corporate scheme of profitability goals and objectives, within a behind the scene personal conversation subjective? Just what were the measures of failure accuracy and missed intentions to warrant this plan, anyway? It would not be unusual if he were distracted or distraught in the juggernaut of this juggle. He had been travelling and working diligently throughout our family crisis other than the two weeks around the traumatizing breakdown and hospitalization of his 25year old formerly successful and healthy son in June and then a week vacationing in the Wallowas in August. Would there even be a heads up conversation prior to the slap of this 90day threat to losing his job? The madness came in new forms. We were outraged, but our backs were against the wall, and engage in the dance we must. We all needed to process this news. There had been no human resource outreach extended to us throughout our crisis, including any mention of Family Medical Leave Act or other resources of legal rights. Instead, a 50point list of defined procedures, reports, and actions that John must now respond to and report on each week. This was the compassionate corporate hand extended. A weekly travel requirement completed the mandated specifics, despite his regularly tracked insane travel schedule the family experienced him to maintain throughout the suffering of a huge crisis on the home front. I was furious at the disrespect, the false assessment of it all, the added pressure now carried for John and his family. John deserved better. For reasons not ever understood by us, they had the grip and they were twisting the balls of confusion while the band played on. Temptations taunted, but there would be no room for additional anger actions from this house. There would be no allowance for an overreaction of emotion to further damage our spirits when we had worked so hard to steer a steady course of recovery to saving our son, holding up our daughter, maintaining our marriage, reforming our family, honing in on our homestead, only to now jeopardize John's job. John deserved better. It had been enough to encounter and manage the random anger and illness of our son that had yet to be explained, let alone allow a new anger into the management scheme of our household, our lives, and our progress all because of a 90day plan that was yet to be reasonably explained.

We each agreed to do whatever was necessary to help John survive this new nightmare. His family would stand by him and with him while he proved his merit to the company. He had invested himself in developing a respectable, dedicated and proven history of performance, and now was presented as irrelevant and on someone's motivated chopping block. This slam made it hard not to suspect that the company management or human resource team was disturbed and influenced in some way by our hospitalization medical expense, and perhaps even the sensitive nature and subject matter of our son's situation. Or was Zach's paranoia just rubbing off? We spoke to friends about various legalities, our Family Medical Leave Act (FMLA) rights and responsibilities, the employer's FMLA rights and responsibilities, and while there were likely violations of negligence and privacy rights, we felt it best to take the high road and prove the mistake of this damnation. It was one more mystery we could not presently solve. We would keep calm and carry on. Thursday, September 18, 2014, was another date among many in this crisis stage of our life we would not forget. The day after Zach's release from a 90day outpatient plan, John would enter into his company's impatient plan. Like the morning previous, hugs healed in a wounded window of whatever and why. As Gabrielle and I listened and comforted John that evening of evolution, Zach looked quietly at his father and slowly departed to his downstairs camp of isolation. I felt in that moment of caught observation, that Zach may have wondered about the possibility of his influence on this outcome, directly or indirectly. He appeared saddened and helpless. And he was. What trial and purpose is this new mess, oh Holy One? The shitstorm seems to keep flying in our face. Boy, we are obviously falling far from our former grace. Did God actually believe this was what we could handle? All too often, we are told it is so. Bullshit! Never utter those falsehood claims.

We began to consider that Zach's isolation might be his own effort to attempt some means of control toward the strange outbursts, to protect what he could in keeping us and himself from its delivery and its wrath. That evening was the first time in a long time that I felt I saw empathy reflected in Zach's increasingly catatonic expression, other than the fleeting moment of the requested hug the morning before. Perhaps, his soul can yet still be stirred. Throughout John's working career, our family lived up close and personal around how long and hard the hours were that John worked, and the extra efforts he would regularly employ to serve the company, the customers, the coworkers, and the unpredictable calamities of doing business. We would rally strong, but it would be hard to recover from the inflicted trauma of this wicked wound. I had secretly begun to research jobs for myself, for our daughter, for weeks prior to this doomsday deliverance, sending design leads her way, without regard to how irritating that likely was for her. She was capable and busy doing her own searches and applications, so she did not need me pushing and implying. I think it was a way that I felt I might be helpful to her since I could not seem to be helpful to my son, nor to my family. In the quiet evening of the computer job searching hour, I would fantasize about how I might hold down an evening job, and yet still care for and protect Zach, care for and protect John and his work demands, care for and protect Gabby from this undeserved role and its setbacks, and then maybe even care for and protect myself in the mix! Many men and women must do so to survive, I reminded myself. The idea of securing work outside of the home felt strangely therapeutic, somehow, as I imagined a life outside of this spinning cage, this round and round and round we go, where we stop, nobody knows wheel of misfortune!

A job away from the home sounded like quite a naïve concept of escape at this point, but then, an extra paycheck would always be helpful, especially if Zach were to incur more medical expenses and increasingly be unable to generate income, or if John were to lose his current job. I wanted to run away from the critical responsibilities inside the home through the fantasy idea of a paid job eliminating our reality. To have an assignment that I could actually manage and influence outcome with success through my work ethic and dedication sounded gratifying, unlike this job at home that I increasingly experienced as failing. I had even tried to pursue a part time school district gig in late August, before Zach returned from California and again exhibited his recurrence of madness. That idea was quickly dropped, as were all of the job searches within the weeks to come. I had to accept the significance and privilege of my 'stay at home' caregiver and life stabilizer role ever more so under this new pressure poke from John's employer, and I would. Protecting John from the unpredictable challenges on the home front, shielding him so he could literally go to battle weekly and defend himself in his job, proving his worth and his keep, all the while behaving as if undistracted from his son's cycling emotions of rage, madness, and death speak looming over us daily with lingering possibility. This was complicated for all of us, and hard not to feel that even our daughter was as trapped in the circumstances as our son was in his mind. While she searched for full time employment and her own personal launch, she was witness daily to her brother's life meltdown, her parent's life disruption and the exhibition of responding behaviors and emotions due to the ever increasing weight and pressure of it all. Siblings subconsciously suffer silently in situations as such. Gabrielle was wearing hats and putting on pants she had no business adorning in the wardrobe of a young woman about to embark on her adult life. It was what it was. Project Run*a*way, season 2014.

A week into John's plan, our next upset presented. The four of us shared a weekend highlight of homemade pizza, a rented comedy, and healthy conversation. But the very next Thursday, Zach's late night pacing returned, which came to signify an email, a rage, or a random mad moment. John had returned from his travel late that evening, and already, I could not protect him from events happening in the home. Exhaustion allowed sleep, but the morning offered evidence of disturbance. We found couches and chairs flipped over downstairs, a camping knife on the end table, and some broken glass just outside the sliding door of the TV room. In a future well mind, Zach shared months later that he had walked barefoot through the neighborhood and local park in the wee hours, distraught at some sporting event on late night TV, stirred by delusional thoughts and ideas that came to him through the TV, struggling out of control. He was so often tortured in his mind. We wondered how we could continue to keep him safe. In the immediate morning following his late night mind flight, we had no knowledge as to what happened and why. The camping knife discovered was kept by us and hidden from him. This incident was the first time since the June hospitalization that caused us to wonder about knives he had access to and even used frequently in the preparation of food in the kitchen. Do we rid ourselves of those too? Are we making silly assumptions or safe assertions? How the hell did we know!? Who was this uninvited guest fucking with his head? After this incident, he again isolated, while we tidied up the morning after disarray, and held the unusual disruption as another fear fueling mystery for months after.

I took the liberty of reaching out again to psychotherapist Michael after this strange discovery, for paralyzing fear revisited and I did not want to disturb John with additional worry. Our home strategy of lovingly listening and waiting for Zach to mend whatever his ails were would rapidly wear thin if more acts of aggression occurred. Michael was wise to remind us that a local and active professional should be engaged with Zach, especially if safety becomes a threatening issue. Michael had been kind and supportive to us, but we each knew he could not advise ongoing in a responsible or ethical manner long distance, especially if Zach's behavior turned physically aggressive or unsafe. That truth was as clear as a compass in its directional scope. His care was immeasurable as this dedicated advocate of care for those who suffer in madness and crisis, never refusing to respond or listen when we sent our emails, which were typically sent in heightened times of desperation and discernment. John and I felt a debt of gratitude, and frequently relayed his significance to us. Affirmation in return. We realized, increasingly so, that we too were in need of professional therapeutic care, but neither of us felt that the ability or means to leave our respective responsibilities and tend to our own personal emotional care was feasible. It is the ironic nature of American culture to just work harder, work longer, risk further health implosion to all involved in crisis so that a whole family can break down as ill, thereby increasing society's medical care needs, medical care costs, and medical care services rendered. To minimize that looming possibility of getting physically sick while breaking down emotionally, we focused on eating right, exercising when we could, and research, research, research. The many ongoing prayers offered from so very many friends and family had to be what helped keep the three of us from falling apart. We would have time for that crash later.

Zach mentally crashed again, the morning of September 30, when he stomped up the stairwell, searched our master bedroom and bathroom, and demanded to know where the noise was coming from and where 'her father' was. He adamantly claimed that I was working with 'him' to make the noises of intention to disturb Zach. The three of us, mom and children, were cloistered vulnerably close in the hallway corner at the top of the stairwell where he continued more aggressively to release his maddening rage, screaming, shaking, spitting, and pacing the hallway floor. The father figment of his imagination, was a fragment of his mind deterioration, furled forth in flagrant accusation and frequent mention. I recall a sudden mind memory moment of the senior staff member at MUM in Iowa telling me he had never seen anything like Zach's implosion. That recall resonated in this reality, for I had an almost out of body experience, watching the face and the fury of my enraged son, possessed and distressed, sick well beyond anything normal. Were we going to need an exorcism? Where did all this evil come from? I implored our vulnerable giant to agree to get help. He called me 'a fucking selfish bitch' and went on to rage about his doctor appointment in early September, how he was sure the man was the father of his lover, and that all of us were collaborating with him to taunt Zach with expressions, noises, and constant disruption. He spoke of fighting off daily thoughts of suicide, of emptiness, of no one listening to him when he was asking everyone for help. He let out a scream of frustration, punching his fist into the wall to the left of my face, cussing and breathing heavy. That punch was the first time I personally feared the uncontrollable monster within my son. Maybe it was the tight, intimate, physical proximity we three had to one another. I did not know this possessed person. Somewhere from deep within, the words came out clear and concise as I looked directly at him and emphatically stated, "Zach, you are going to shower, calm yourself down, get dressed, and we are going to the hospital to get help." He did, and we did.

I waited 3 hours while ER did intake and assessment of my son. When the social worker came to speak with me, I let her know that I had been asking him to voluntarily hospitalize and she informed me that he was not asking for that choice. She said he was asking for pain treatment, because he kept complaining of pain all over his body, that his joints and muscles were in severe pain. Why, then, was no one concerned about the root of this pain? Fear? Stigma? Previous notes of bias? The hospital notes retrieved well after the occasion of this intake revealed that he was documented as suicidal and in severe physical pain. These notes further recorded that he simply appeared agitated but not psychotic nor responding to any type of internal stimuli. In other words, just another hissy fit for the spoiled advantage-taking young adult is how I experienced the entire intake response. Why can't anyone interpret what is wrong? His physical appearance and reasonable presentation, once again, was misleading, and how were they to know the madness in its fullness without valuing and trusting our parental front end feedback? I asked for a DMHP which was all that I knew to suggest, but the social worker believed he would not qualify for involuntary hospitalization. I did not want him coming home in this state, vulnerable to suicide, vulnerable to something happening that he could not control, but the medical experts perceived him to diagnose simply with a mood disorder resulting from an argument with his mother! Blame the mother, the messenger, the deliverer, the caregiver! And so, the narrow minded skill set and training of the social worker's suspicions went to work, negotiating with Zach around whether he had any money to put himself up for the night, or whether he would welcome a drop off at a homeless shelter instead. He would not come home, and they would not shelter him in any holding facility. He chose a local hotel, and we agreed that together the very next day, he and I would explore a residential mental health treatment facility across town that the hospital staff informed us about. I was grateful to learn of this alternative facility option, having never found it or heard of it in our previous searches for local help and care. Seemed like an insider's secret! Even if this facility was currently full, an opening might come about and offer a next option of possible treatment and care in this continued search for help.

Terrified when I dropped Zach off at the hotel, I feared for his safety. Should the hospital have discharged him knowing his record? Is he really as stable as he would have them think? Would he attempt to take his life at the hotel? Were we safe with him at home? What should I tell John, or not tell him for now? How do I possibly hold all of this in faith that something will awaken and turn this all around? The hospital staff deemed Zach not at risk or gravely disabled. I would beg to differ, but my begging meant nothing. From the parking lot of the hotel, I called the residential facility and introduced our circumstance. Of course, there was protocol to securing a space, and it would not include a mother speaking on behalf of her grown son. Medical referral would be necessary. In fact, medical referral would have likely gotten Zach hospitalized. Procedures and protocol, where is my guide? Thank you. Click. By 1pm the next day, I had called the hotel, spoken with Zach, and arranged to pick him up. Again, I encouraged him and even asked him to voluntarily seek hospitalization and treatment. We agreed to drive over to this referred facility together, attempt to meet the manager, and then visit the corresponding mental health agency affiliated with this facility to arrange for therapy. The silence of the ride together was immediately broken as we pulled into the parking lot of the residential facility. "You fucking selfish bitch! I am asking all of you for help and this is what it looks like? Everyone is spinning me in circles, and I know 'he' is behind all of this, working to make me so sick! Why is he doing this to me?" Zach raged on. I turned the car out of the parking lot and drove directly toward the mental health agency, as I had no idea what to do at this point. "Please, Zach, ask for voluntary hospitalization." I begged. Zach ranted and raved while I drove along busy streets contemplating another emergency room visit rather than the unfamiliar agency offices. It was in this pocket of care that I finally erupted.

The months of standing by my son, working with him, protecting him, researching for him, advocating for him, and all I could hear was 'fucking selfish bitch'. And then there was the haunting reminder from the NAMI classwork that kept asking us if we were creating clear enough boundaries with our loved ones, if we were letting our loved ones know where the line could not be crossed in their mentally ill behaviors. The line had been crossed, and I mirrored his outburst. I screamed, I ranted, I wailed, and I wept floodwater, all the while now driving directly to the hospital. My rant seemed to calm him, in a strange way, and I resented that. I had worked so hard at holding up, not succumbing to the power of whatever had this grip on him, and then I broke. 'It' (the father?) won. I, too, was sick. Sick of it all. In his calm, and my quiet after the storm, we agreed to return to the hospital, specifically ask staff for help toward bipolar treatment on record and not just the pain management interpretation. Perhaps we were to accept this diagnosis after all, we agreed, and get after some treatment that would resolve these outbursts and cycles of pain. We had no idea still of what we were managing other than pain, illness unknown, and no medical team of support. It was October 1, and once again we headed to emergency care where he was admitted for evaluation of need, and I was left behind to wait and wonder for 3hours in the emergency room entrance seating area. When the social worker eventually came looking for me, she proceeded to discuss Zach publicly in a crowded ER, and I suggested we should be talking privately about such personal mental health questions. She looked around and emphatically stated that this was the only space we had and it would have to do. Rather than look for accommodation, and address me with concern and respect, she instead suggested I head home and they would call me. I recall feeling like I had been a bother, perceived as part of the problem, another irritating parent in the scheme of irresponsible young adults and their absurd family conflicts. I will never forget the pathetic treatment of this insensitive and possibly overworked medical professional, nor the presumptive manner about my son and me, when in fact he was ill, not well of mind. Where should we be going for help in these circumstances? No one seems to know. So the helpless and the hopeless become ever familiar with those to them who are heedless, and then possibly even influence a path to homeless. We can do better.

No one called from the hospital. I called 4 hours later, around 10 pm, and spoke with a different social worker, who informed me that the hospital team had run tests, found nothing, tried to secure a bed at the residential facility but it was full, so they released Zach to the same hotel. The hospital records acquired long after this visit, reveal a record of his expressed pain in his ankles, knees, shoulders, wrists, neck, and lower back. The records suggest a referral to rheumatology. The team ran alcohol and drug panels, and in the UA bacteria measure of the urinalysis the comment RARE appears. Does this mean there was presence of bacteria? Clearly, this hospital was not equipped to help us in our quest for care, whether he had mental illness or perhaps an undetected virus or bacteria. But then, who was equipped and how were we to find them? Where were we to go for legitimate help? Diagnostics found nothing. Medical wisdom was lacking. The next afternoon, I called the hotel to check in with Zach. John and I had spoken the night before, and we agreed to a weekend plan to get our son into a hospital across town that might be better equipped to handle this mental health case with less callous. My job was to keep him safe, even if at a hotel for one more night. It would be more difficult to get him out of his isolation success within the house if he returned home. When Zach and I spoke, I apologized for my own break down the previous afternoon, while he acknowledged his own poor behavior. He went on to speak of how 'the father' kept coming into the room at the hospital the night before, pretending to be a caregiver, so he basically attempted to placate the staff, he continued, to keep himself from going after 'the father figure'. I began to worry about him hurting someone, possibly a male that he sees as this delusional figure, in this clearly psychotic state. I had begun to wonder if a perfectly nonviolent person could resort to any form of violence based upon the madness of thought, in a diseased brain. What do we know about anyone's uncharacteristic brain dysfunction, uncontrollable thoughts or actions? Not enough.

Still, I asked Zach to stay another night at the hotel, to think hard about hospitalization and professional help, and informed him that Dad and I would pick him up at noon Friday. He was clearly still having delusions. Although, in a less delusional moment, and more so a disappointed moment, he shared that he walked over to my physician's office to get his rash looked at that afternoon, and was turned away. No longer a patient of theirs they responded. In his own able attempts, Zach kept trying to find help. Urgent Care offices, managed and owned by my physician, were right next door, presumably taking patients with universal healthcare insurance much like the local hospital their office was affiliated with. Hmm. He had Medicaid. Hmm. Why hadn't they referred him next door? He likely looked scary, sounded scary, and was scary, just looking again to find help. That damn rash found no love. In preparation for our Friday pick up and deliver plan, I proceeded to call ahead to the crisis line Thursday evening and report the fall back of Zach's behavior since May/June previous records. The two recent trips to the hospital seeking help, the rage events at home, and our ongoing work at home to wait out possible healing had each activated renewed fear for safety, and fear of suicidal ideation actualized. Documentation had begun. I then called the hospital to report Zach's delusional comments, and I indicated I would return again with him if he was aggressive when picked up the next day, as it was the closest hospital to the referred hotel. At this point, the social worker from the nearby hospital asked me why I wasn't going to the hotel with the police or a DMHP to check on our son right now, as if I knew at all what to do in this situation! I feared police involvement and had no reason to feel I should be protecting medical caregivers from my son. Should I have feared this? What route of community support was I to seek? I asked her why the hospital kept discharging him in this vulnerably delusional state, not calling in a DMHP for assessment. Who was responsible for the measure of his health and safety in an unwell state, I wanted to know? The police? Jail? I was confused. Who could empathically guide me and not empirically guilt me?

The hospital and its evaluation and diagnostic tools could not determine Zach's health crisis as having any physical health foundational concern, no internal stimuli, despite the repeated record of rash and multiple body pain points. Apparently, I was to seek police care if his health issue was diagnosed as mental illness, despite his consistent presentation of multiple physical health issues simultaneously. There is an obvious diagnostic and treatment care problem gap within this client case. How was an average citizen to know when and how to differentiate the health care proceedings of their loved one if there is not an established and trusted physician in their corner fighting for their cause? The hospital responded to my challenge by calling the crisis line to confer, and we all activated a chain of support and guidance. No one seemed to know what to do with Big Z. He was an anomaly, once again. Worried about Zach, and wondering about the hospital worker comments regarding the police and DMHP suggestion, I called a new member of my compass rose society. While in the NAMI coursework at our local chapter, I had befriended the executive director, and learned that she frequently placed herself into the outreach and care of families in crisis, especially with mental illness crisis at the core, and the potentiality of police involvement. Peggy was the definition of mental health advocacy, and she was a personal safety oriented mentor who could advise us and willingly walk with us through the various mental health supports within this community. She took my call, listened, offered to stop by the hotel, check for his car, and check at the hotel desk, just to help put my mind at ease, simply ascertaining if Zach was at the hotel and ok. Perhaps he would isolate in that room as he did in the home. Her barely 5foot frame defied her stature of strength and might, looking out for the vulnerable like my nearly 7foot son. That was the short and tall of it. He was determined safe. We agreed to not involve the police.

We would seek DMHP (designated mental health professional) involvement again at the alternative hospital the next day. Peggy was yet another tool in our toolbox, the aid in the lemonaid when life gives you lemons, the voice of reason when you are in madness season. Our son was safe and secure at the hotel, and she would avail herself again to us the next day if we needed her. A night of rest beckoned us all, including for busy traveler John, arriving home from week two of the 90day plan, home on his weekend parole, and already engaging in a new plan of protection for his son the next day. Our daughter, thankfully, was travelling north to Seattle to spend the weekend with friends. She could steer clear of any association to the family's decision to again involuntarily hospitalize her brother, our son, should it prove necessary. Hopefully, it would not be necessary. Hopefully, Zach could and would speak up for himself. At noon on Friday, October 3, John and I ordered some lunch for the three of us, picked up Zach and his few belongings from the hotel, and proceeded to drive down the roadway to Vancouver Lake on a blue sky, sort of on the sly, not gonna lie, mission possible we had schemed up. Each of us were silently suspicious for different reasons. While eating our lunch in the wide open space of the park, we broached the topic of getting professional help for something bigger than any of us had been able to tackle. We admitted we intended for him to voluntarily go in and get help today, and that we would accompany him as soon as he complied. He was furious and erupted into swearing, accusing trickery and teamed involvement on our part with his continued delusional male nemesis. He stood up briskly, took his shirt off and said he was going for a swim! Shit! Would we need to call help to come down here? Why would he go for a swim? Would he try to drown himself? I was so fucking paranoid, drowning in my own fears and obsessions around this crazy, upside down world of ours.

Zach returned from the lake edge shortly, however, and continued to speak aggressively toward us. We insisted he get in the car, and miraculously, he did, while demanding us not to speak as we drove off toward the alternative hospital as planned. His breathing rapidly accelerated once in the car, and his agitation presented more like rising fear than raging anger. What we then witnessed, was both terrifying and revealing at the same time. He shifted from an aggressive, foul mouthed, mad speak angry impression to a whimpering, child-like cry of such frightened expression. Impulsively, he grabbed at the passenger seat door handle implying a leap out of the car door. He wanted to escape something, and it did not seem to be his parents. This heightened moment spoke to the vulnerably violent potential impact of illness meeting action. John and I shouted out to stop him, coaxing him that we were getting him somewhere safe, somewhere with help. He manically thrust his 6'10" body across the seat tops into the very back womb of the Armada belly, size 16 feet flapping across my head space and face while back seat bound, his lithe body of nonstop pain curled up in a fetal position upon landing. Again, I had never seen anything like this. He appeared possessed. "Take me somewhere safe, take me somewhere safe", he pleaded in a quietly quivering voice. His body was trembling feverishly, he was trying to exercise control of his breathing, and he was weeping. My entire maternal instinct was punished with helpless pain, not able to hold him, stroke his face or neck to calm him, or 'pet his back' as he used to call a back rub when a young child. John was steadfast in his focus and clarity of purpose, driving safely fast while speaking calmly slow to his loved son. LEAP was asserted while leap was averted. We transported our Z to the other hospital in town, he was assisted from the car with a wheelchair, fragile and shaking, and then he was admitted and secured into a safe room for evaluation. Exhale. We went home to collapse into each other. Our homework had been done with the crisis line documentation, our plan had been executed, and a gravely disabled qualification was soon determined. Round two of involuntary hospitalization.

When John spoke to him the next day before his transport to the evaluation and treatment (E&T) center, Zach told John he had intended to kill 'the father' whose avatar image continued to haunt and taunt him. Choosing to destroy this nemesis and his control over Zach, he felt he must jump out of the moving car. But within that same conversation, he shifted from fear and anger expression to a sudden practical and organized thought of concession. He casually asked if we would bring him a pillow, some specific books, and some sweats to E&T. Shifting to thoughts of deemed necessity, practicality, just like that. This fall back, panic attack would lead us to believe we might need to accept that he was, in fact, mentally ill. Against all that he hoped for, stood for, worked for, he would probably have to be medicated ongoing for stability and safety. We still did not know or understand any other alternative to explain his symptoms. We had done what we could to hold off pharma road, but truth be told, we still weren't fully sold, and the thought of pharma power made our blood run cold. I wrote both Michael and Gigi to update them about our week, our hospitalization, our status. We needed to affirm them, as they had been so instrumental in loving us, loving him, no judgement, no irrelevant questions, no pressure. And to think, we were only three weeks into the 90day plan for John. He was a rock. He would not fallback. In fact, he would spring forward. He did not have a panic attack. He would move onward. Together, we would.

YOU ARE WHAT YOU DO

WORKSHEET

I want to be _Physically healthy_ .

Act _Daily ~~exercise~~ routines, rest, treatment, sustenance_ by doing this:

1. Take care of my body
2. Eat appropriate to my chemistry
3. Avoid triggers, environments, people who bring me down

I want to be _Emotionally stable_ .

Act _~~Expressively~~, genuine ~~and their own creativity~~_ by doing this:

1. Speaking and owning my truths
2. "Find the similarities" between others
3. Allow and nurture vulnerability

I want to be _Relationally satisfied_ .

Act _with compassion and empathy_ by doing this:

1. Honesty
2. Integrity
3. Understanding

57

Name: Moritz, Zachary C.
Medical Record,
Birthdate: 06/06/1988
Date of Admission: 10/04/2014

Insert 27 •   2014, October, E&T document

222

Chapter 21: Bull's Eye!

Time Has Come Today, The Chamber Brothers
Tick Tick Boom, The Hives

The date was October 5, 2014, and our son was involuntarily hospitalized for the second time in four months. We thought we knew the drill after round one. We expected a court hearing after the 72 hour hold to determine the length of his hospitalization stay for continued evaluation and treatment, followed by a discharge game plan established once treatment strategies were employed and responsiveness was measured. Once again, compromises were made to get him out of the house, into professionally directed safety precautions and assessments of care, while still trying to discern a comprehensively accurate diagnosis to drive treatment. Thankfully, earlier hospital records and correspondences that stereotyped Zach as substance abuser were finally removed as exaggerated misuse of intake facts, not useful or purposeful within any of his ongoing health measure tracks. His recent diagnosis would be coded as panic attack with chronic pain. Medical notes from this round of care revealed that Zach received Trileptal for mood management and Ativan/Lorazepam for sleep and anxiety. He refused antipsychotics and pain medication. Records noted his admission of marijuana use as an attempt for pain relief to no avail. A description of his named ailments included throbbing pain with sharp intensity throughout his joints, especially in his back, neck and knee, insomnia and poor sleep, and 4 months of severe migraines. No mention was made of the ever present rash under the left arm. His intake lab work included a complete blood count, comprehensive metabolic panel, urine analysis, thyroid and drug screen with negative results. Zach shared with staff his continued delusions, auditory and visual hallucinations, as well as an ongoing suspicion of conspiracy involving his parents. These admissions, his extreme presentation upon emergency arrival, and the inclusion of parent notes describing behaviors and symptoms from the past 3months all contributed to a gravely disabled hold for further determination.

Our September attempts at a faith, hope and love home care triage had been as ineffective as the non-medicated healing strategies employed, because after all, madness still roared. Zach continued to reject our assistance not unlike how he commonly rejected much of what hospitalization would offer. The care team was already familiar with Zach at the E&T facility from the previous stay. His physical presence, accompanying story, and unusual behaviors stood out among clientele. Within their daily routines, he again received nursing care, medications, psychiatric medication education, social services, and rehabilitation program engagement. His participation this round was immediately more agreeable for he was motivated with greater clarity about a rapid discharge intention. E&T medical records tell of his immediate refusal to pain medication, quoting him as stating, "I need acupuncture, massage or physical therapy, not drugs. I do not want Western medicine!" The aggressive arrogance was out of character to our healthy Zach, but the staff would never know how a healthy, pain-free Zach would behave. Hot towels were administered for his back pain, as he stubbornly suffered in silence. His personal goal sheet completed at October intake offered a reasonably simple yet clear statement as follows: *"To be healthy, to be happy, to be doing what I love with the person and people I love. To feel good. To understand."* Now this was the spirit of the young man we knew. To understand…. this was what eluded us the most, what eluded him the most, and seemed to continue to elude all his care teams to date. He projected an ability to be in control, to speak with control, to participate with control, yet his mind and body altered his control. This team among others had no comparison, nor any month long observation to witness a full cycle of the out of control behavior he would display.

Three days after intake, I attended his court hearing in which the length of his stay would be determined. As I joined the roundtable of decision makers and legal shakers, I was immediately silenced by the same judge that oversaw his first hospitalization. Zach's parents were not to actively participate in this round, other than to offer our notes regarding behavior patterns and healthcare efforts since June. This decision projected an attitude of arrogance, a play upon power, a measure of manipulation. But also, it may have been due to his adult age, the resulting disconnect to parental healthcare coverage, our role as loving and desperately concerned parents but not legal guardians, or any number of legal justifications for which we had no knowledge. The emotional despair and resulting confusion ever present in the preliminary round of court proceedings was now further infused with secondary concerns about Zach's broken allegiance to the original prescribed treatment plan. Following mandatory court room procedural legalities, the judge summarized, speaking directly to Zach in an agitated and seemingly intolerant manner. Her terse message and assertive delivery insisted that he should take control of his erratic behavior, get a job and become a productive citizen. She had reviewed the notes and highlights of his personal life story and his previously healthy credentials, and her message implied that he should get on with his life and stop with all this foolery. The judge judged. The absence of any medical diagnosis or legitimate health concern other than the mental health presentation was interpreted as treatable, manageable, and within control of his choices. Simply one more shame game frame to his name. This hearing was different for all of us the second time around.

"Such potential!" I heard her exclaim this but in a tone of disgust, not encouragement. That instigated a reactive glare from Zach. Her tone and comment seemed a taunting tactic, a subtle yet accusatory strategy to perhaps guilt him into owning his behavior and instituting change. If I hadn't felt without options in this silenced situation, on behalf of the dignity and demise of our very vulnerable adult son, I might have defended him. One more professional among many who had misjudged his unfortunate predicament, I would have claimed. But I had no actual idea of what the current circumstantial truth was other than that the man I once knew my son to be, and the life he once led before illness took over, was now consumed by our family's desperate search for some system of wellness care. We felt trapped in this present reality, presumably not unlike the trapped nature of pain permeating Zach's aching body, disturbing Zach's delusional state of mind, and necessitating Zach's lockdown from the very freedoms he so feverishly sought in his post collegiate independence. Zach was gripped with a strange illness internally manifesting, both physically and mentally. Unless one was present to witness the outward expressions of rage or panic induced madness as we had, one would not know just how sick he actually was. His handsome and reasonably well groomed appearance combined with his ability to speak and deliver attentive engagement would mislead outsiders to assume and expect capable, functional behavior. While in the silence of my own restricted courtroom participation, I witnessed Zach dare

225

to speak up for himself, despite his own contained participation and imbalanced mind struggle. To this somewhat sassy and personally presumptive judge in her moment of stereotyped reprimand, just before her announcement of his 14day hold, he glared, dared and bared a defensive response. In court, like on the basketball court, defense was often his strength.

"Don't patronize me!" Zach challenged back at the judge's 'so much potential' statement, speaking directly to her. "I am trying to get well so that I CAN contribute. I don't know what has happened to me, and why everyone is against helping me get well. This is no place for me to get well! And for the record, I have never harmed anyone and I never would." He saw right through her words and mannerisms, he understood the treatment modalities at the center to go against his personal ethics, and he heard clearly the stated definition of gravely disabled in the assessed determination of an assigned stay. Gravely disabled up at bat again, strike two. I knew we needed this judge's determination for another treatment stay. Zach had been in danger of serious physical harm throughout September when he indirectly messaged safety concerns with his camping knives, and then again in route to the hospital with us, when he attempted to jump out of a moving car. We believed we needed to keep him safe from himself, that much was clear. But I did not expect the decision making judge to address him as she did. She suggested that she saw right through his believed to be controllable behaviors, as if he were just another master manipulator, choosing some selfish shenanigans at will! Not unlike many and most, we judge on what we behold, sometimes by what we are told, and often without proper consideration of other influential possibilities yet to unfold. It was not her job to evaluate the fullness and truth of the presiding circumstance, or to find answers to our questions. It was her job to discern the safety and oversee the legal proceedings for the here and now authorization of hospital stay, and that she did. I was grateful for that. However, as a silent observer in this court hearing, I was surprised and curious to hear and witness Zach speak up for his own dignity within this court room battle round. To witness his spoken delivery to her without the type of venom we would often receive in the home was of great relief. Because of that courtroom exchange, I felt a successful stabilization would again occur for him, much like we had experienced during the first hospitalization. The shift seemed more feasible, given that we had already witnessed some cycles of kindness and cooperation sporadically throughout September despite the cycling symptoms of bipolar blip or schizoaffective trip. I would leave the court room and my son in lockdown, saddened by the notion of another involuntary hospitalization for Zach, but greatly relieved we secured professional help again and that he was safe.

Meanwhile, in the land of the free and the home of the brave, a weekend furlough formalized. John returned from his weekly travel late afternoon on Friday that particular week, and we agreed to escape once again for a weekend away out into the scenic allure of the *Columbia* ever so *Gorge*ous canvas. I picked him up at the airport following his flight arrival and the completion of his dutiful 2hour weekly phone call of 90day plan review with his boss, mining every detail of a 50point improvement plan. I referred to it/him as the ball squeezer, and I did not mean the stress relieving kind. It was one more gripping version of insanity for us to endure each week. As the blue screen of his computer finally shut down and the buzzing ring tone of his phone actually turned off, we drove out beyond the traffic standstill and city suburbia frenzy toward the simplistic, congestion free welcome of White Salmon. A quiet weekend at sister in law Marta's cabin oasis beckoned once again. Seasonal change was evident in the array of orange, red and yellow leaves framing the evergreen backdrop of state highway 14. We would allow ourselves the freedom this weekend to fall into fall, relieve our stressors, and seize a worthy break. Our burgeoning astrologer would attend school all weekend, while our burdened athlete would attend lockdown and treatment. Extended family and nature would attend us upon arrival. We bubbled over without restraint into the conversation of each other's weekly update and review, driving east and bathing in the glow of Calgon caress to such en*Gorge*d encounter. The weekend escape would soothe away the cycling insanity of our lives and ease the pressure buildup from each of our seismically shaken stories of scale. Family embrace and warm hospitality would blanket us, cradle us, and rock us to sleep throughout the nature of the weekend's nurture. Rest, recuperation, and reflection accompanied by uncaged personal freedom to do as we chose would be medicinally curative and temporarily normalizing.

The return drive home on Sunday evening held a casual yet anticipatory edge sharpened by a conversation of mutual decision to call the E&T center and inquire if Zach would accept a visit from us. Our desire was to initiate intention around his upcoming discharge with an effort made to include conversation about boundaries and expectations. We both vowed to each other that he would not be allowed to return to our home without a commitment to 3months of consistent medication and therapeutic work as the mutually agreed upon foundation for supporting recovery. This was influenced by our NAMI training. We would work a little harder, work another way in managing mental illness as his possible true nemesis. Maybe we had been in denial, and the judge was right. But, still, no one else lived day to day with the patterns and postures of pain and presentation. We had been NAMI coached for weeks and Big Pine mentored more recently to employ boundaries and expectations as reasonable and necessary guidelines to healthy collaboration in the home. Ultimately, we had been ineffective 'waiting on the sidelines' for healing initiative and action over the past three months, giving him space to self-evolve or problem solve, frightened by the threat of self-harm, but harmed each of us nonetheless without a shared agreement of proactive health care and respective home share. I suppose one might call this our "tough love" moment. We were sick to our stomachs about the confronting choice, but we were equally sick about the paralysis of no choice and it's resulting likelihood of regression back to where we had been. Sick is the key word here, and we understood how much we all needed professional guidance and care managing his sickness. To imagine him rejecting our firm position for home stay frightened us, for he had nowhere else to go in such an unwell state. Easily, he would be a 7foot target for unnecessary trouble out on the streets or in a shelter, options he had been coached to consider by hospital social worker crisis experts in response to his behavioral health. More than once, the message had been implied that we, the parents and caregivers, might actually be enabling these erratic behaviors, 'allowing them' to occur in our home. That blame game gave a whole new meaning to parental allowance! There seemed contradiction in these care tending suggestions for we interpreted them to be messages of 'shame on him' and 'shame on you'. That shame train had a destination nowhere healthy. Shame on any misdirected message aiming to lay blame, then medicating to tame, only to misunderstand the legitimate name of the game. Lame!

The rules of our game changed immediately on Monday morning following our Gorge get away. When I called to inquire about our hoped for rules and regulations visit with Zach, I was informed he had been discharged. After 5days, he had been cooperative, he was no longer acute in his care needs, and he had called his friend Blake to ask if he could and would come to pick him up. "Well!" ….. I paused and processed, dumbfounded in the shock of receiving this information without any prior consultation. "Where will he be going?", I ponder out loud. "Will he be living with Blake also?", I wonder curiously but quietly to myself. After all, we had been Zach's shelter, safe haven, support crew, and coordinating collaborators with the various evaluation and treatment center staff, or so we thought (ass u me d?). Is he just going to arrive on our doorstep, expecting to resume where we left off? As an adult of 26 years of age, with Medicaid insurance, and no longer in a state of acute crisis, I suppose the professionals felt Zach would make his way, and his way happened to be a phone call to friend Blake who had reached out to him in September. Blake would be caught off guard, innocent and naïve to his friend's full vulnerability, and the recent panic attack circumstance that brought on this second hospitalization. Of course, Blake would innocently help his friend out, for he happened to be accessible and available. John and I were stunned, confused, curious and yet concerned about Zach's choice and action. This was going to force our hand to exercise immediate boundaries. By early afternoon of the day of release, our curiosity was quieted. Blake had picked him up, they had gone to lunch, and immediately following, Zach and his few belongings were dropped off at our address. In through the front entryway he walked, or rather, he ducked, after the twist of neck and the glide through the door finish, his trademark entry. In that same doorway, he had been escorted out by officers 4months prior, he had stood on the front porch and crowed about cowardice to his father the month prior, and he had departed the home with his mother just two weeks' prior, headed to the hospital for help following a frightening rage hysteria and fist pounding panic attack. What would be next in this miniseries mystery unfolding?

John and I greeted our son in the living room, cordial but clear as we asked about his intentions. We expressed our expectation of commitment to 3 months of medication and professional outpatient care, and we reviewed with him his discharge paperwork and new prescriptions for mood and anxiety stabilization. Zach casually responded that he would think this all over, and began to meander toward the hallway, as if to retreat downstairs to his bedroom space. The tough love moment arrived after months of accommodation, adaptation, and attempted collaboration. The here and now truth of the moment was that we must all move forward and not fall back. We could not return to isolation and seclusion, the threat of madness and returned delusion. "Where are you going, Zach?", I assertively demand, knowing full well John barely has the emotional energy necessary to survive his current 90day management manipulation, let alone his son's current 90second parent manipulation. Our opportunity to regain control in our home and protect against any possible regression back down into the bedroom cave and its accompanying monsters and muses presented. "Unless you agree to our terms, our contract, you cannot stay here. We will not allow you to continue to go without treatment while in this home." Exhale. There it was. I was micromanager and dictator all in one. This was a necessary territorial claim to stake, so terrifying to express, to verbalize out loud, as it had potential to be divisive at a time we had feared division, to subtract at a time we had even been fearing subtraction. Not unlike the math discipline and math homework demands Zach had so procrastinated around throughout his schooling years, he hoped to put off this decision of the presenting equation. Mandated medication and therapy did not yet add up to contractual recovery steps in his mind, and his mind was still showing signs of imbalance.

Our minds were clear. It felt empowering to stand up for ourselves, for our household, for our livelihood of a job, for our emotional and physical health, for our parent intentions to drive home proper and timely care and commitment. Equally, we wanted to empower him to recognize his own well-being and the necessity for collaborative next steps. There was, however, an accompanying sense of self-imposed shame that paralleled the empowerment. We knew he was not well, not fully capable of using good judgement, not himself. The stand had been a vulnerable line to draw, but had become increasingly necessary. I stood firm and spoke loud with clarity and decisiveness. "You can leave and stay in a hotel again until you accept our terms. Take your car, pack your belongings. We will be here ready to work with you if and when you are willing." He then gathered an overnight bag and left, duck, twist, and glide. Despite old familiar moves, a new dance would now find its groove. Within a day, I emailed Zach and invited him to work with us. He wrote another bizarre note in response unleashing randomness that was increasingly becoming less unusual. According to the written rant, we were all creating this struggle, he felt ongoing hate for a purportedly twisted and abusive father in law figure also at fault, his faith in any survival continued to uphold one woman and himself, and he made mention of an endless evil we had continued to project onto him. Son! Sigh. Sickness indeed. He went on.

You've left me no choice but to come back to the house. I will be there tomorrow. I will pick up my meds today. And I can't wait for whatever hell you'll have prepared for me upon my arrival. Do your best,

I've got plenty more walls to punch and pain to purge. I look forward to having my parents back, someday. Until then, go to hell, because trust me, it's found on earth.

Ouch! Yes, son, we have found hell on earth alongside of whatever ails you, but we refuse to succumb to it. We had accomplished new directional opportunity this second time around, and collaboration would again be critical. Hope resurfaced in the possibility of expanded healing teams that might possibly bridge the divisive factions of Zach and his demons versus his parents and their 'compass roses'! Where do we travel next on this constant medical highway of caregiving choice and action?

One would not likely imagine our resource reference map for immediate directional assistance to be a magazine from the American Association of Retired Persons. AARP! Excuse me. AARP? Was that a belch, a hiccup, or an ah-hah moment sourced from delayed discovery? Ah-hah! The find was one of lightning strike literary luck, and its jarring jolt was shocking and sobering. John, Gabby, and I had been seated in the living room following dinner Thursday evening of that discharge week, and Zach had just returned home Wednesday from his hotel contemplation vacation, having filled his prescriptions and resumed a reasonable attitude considering the strangely familiar yet still very hurtful email exchange. The family foursome was reconcilably reconvened. Father and daughter were engrossed in computer screens, while Mom Beth was consumed with an October/November 2014 AARP magazine article entitled, *Scary Superbugs in the News – Are You at Risk?* I proceeded to read about Chikungunya, then MRSA, and next, Lyme disease. Light bulb moment. Circuits connected. Electricity pulsed. Halo happened. As if the moment were a divinely destined intervention, an astoundingly angelic awakening convention, Zach joined us in the living room, proceeded to lie on the floor and hold his left arm up, wondering out loud why no one had cured this circular rash on his arm. This was exactly how the Lyme discovery and home diagnosis happened! '*While some people report fever, headache, fatigue, and a circular red bull's eye rash, others have no symptoms at first*'; I read this revelatory sentence first to myself and then immediately insisted on reading out loud further to each of the Moritz angels conveniently so conventionally gathered, loyal and loving family members all. We were serendipitously thrust into a sudden enlightenment toward clinically diagnostic self-assessment! Transcendence transformed us! Let us be mindful of the needs of ourselves! Hallelujah! Amen. The article continued on with a description of experiences familiar to us. '*If left untreated, Lyme can cause chronic muscle aches, joint pain and neurological symptoms'.* While gathered together following essentially 8months of hell erupting and eroding this loving and evolving family foursome, the startlingly simplistic, merciful message of ultimate here and now essence, would be the grounding gift we had been praying for, hoping for, begging for, working toward.

Zach looked up from the floor at all of us, stunned, yet more attentive than we had seen him in far too long. We met our opponent today. A European nasty nymph bite bacterial boil on the left arm it was, not a Fairfield faulted swollen lymph node and sore throat that initiated his hazardous harm. Our struggle had been the result of a tiny bite from a poppy-seed sized, bacteria transporting tick. Suddenly, we believed we would find answers to the what and why questions ever present. "That's what it is", he spoke softly yet assuredly within his own ah-hah moment of actualized association. Immediately, we recalled and revisited the carbuncle/black headed pimple pustular presentation while in Copenhagen, connecting further association as we calendared from January 2013 to October 2014. Had that infection and his long term health eruption aftermath been in fact, the result of an infected tick bite transmission? Was this fading red bull's eye rash near the infected entry point related to that incident? Had the tick delivered bacterial infection that could cause such full body/mind disruption? The wonder wheels spun rapidly in each of our brains, furthering analysis of the theories, the rationale, the increased likelihood of a Lyme living room diagnosis. A puzzle sitting on the table of our lives, with pieces that had been difficult to find and to fit, suddenly connected together to reveal an infectious image of tick borne truth. "Have you seen the documentary, '*Under Our Skin*?", Gabrielle asks us all, delivered in a deeply concerned tone with a guarded facial expression. "It is frightening!". I sit in stunned silence, wondering how it could possibly be any more frightening than what we had been living. I had never heard of the disease or the movie. Soon enough, I would find out. Computers shift focus, as we each turn our heart hunger and soul starvation to researching Lyme disease. We could not satiate the hunger, searching further and further for diagnostic tools and pathways, disease symptoms and manifestations, and treatment protocols with resources for access. Thus began the painful truth gathering twist of Lyme disease. Please bring us the gin and the tonic. Following the recent fall back, we would now fall forward into the remainder of 2014. Lyme, the 'great imitator', was our new found foe. Immediately, we found that research of information on tick borne disease was conflicting and confusing. Determining an effective care plan for this disease and activating confident steps toward healing would not be the smooth water following stormy waves these captains at sea hoped the journey to now be. Computers navigated us to multiple frayed threads of Lyme narrative that included treatment and diagnostic controversy, leading Lyme support organizations embattled, medical providers and infectious disease specialists at odds, insurance coverage conflicts and denials, and worst of all, the expectation of prolonged and recurring patient suffering and caregiver helplessness in chronic stage of illness. We did the quick math and Zach was chronic. Where was the healing tonic?

The search to discover and the ongoing reach to recover continued to be a strange and unsettling experience for us, even in the light of such new found clarity. So much about Lyme was unclear, unknown, uncertain, unsettled, uninformed, uneducated and unexpected. Unbelievable! Determined to conquer, we would not allow ourselves to be further discouraged. In that living room moment, it became obvious the missed opportunities an astutely observant medical professional should have recognized and associated, clinically speaking. Zach had been a knee surgery patient who had unusually prolonged knee pain following successful surgery with very disciplined rehab. He presented with multiple severe Lyme symptoms and a circular skin rash at the medical facility in Iowa, he suffered 2 involuntary hospitalizations and multiple hospital intakes locally, presenting each time with the circular skin rash and easily 10-15 dominant Lyme symptoms without any suggestion, exploration or consideration of this disease. No lab pointed the direction, and clinically speaking, ignorance had not been bliss. These truths mattered. Personally, we had never known or encountered Lyme disease ourselves prior to this moment. We did not associate the possibility or likelihood of a tick bite unleashing European bacterial strains during that perceived carbuncle moment in Denmark. No random personal encounter or acquired knowledge of similar suffering in the last year and a half of our crumbling lives suggested or presented the idea of Lyme and tick borne illness as a bacterially driven possibility. Mental illness trumped bacterial infection, when in fact, we were learning that bacterial infection pumped mental illness. These truths mattered. Education and awareness were severely lacking. Diagnosis and treatment held similar truth.

Regardless, what seemed to matter most was this great gift of discovery. We would now pursue legitimate diagnosis, a treatment plan, and a recovery. Cause and effect logic had arrived, and with it came renewed hope! Finally, hope could be restored, for faith in it had been so fucking forlorn. Zach's illness and the elusive chase to pursue logical and legitimate medical cause and effect were thieves robbing faith vaults from what once had been wealthy spirit banks! Church, worship, prayer, meditation, mindfulness, yoga.......one by one these previous tools of strength and support for any one of us had been faithfully and hopelessly worn down throughout the family's extended search and rescue mission series. Our spirits were broken. But while faith and hope dwindled, love always remained the core strength and an endless source of resilience. The family foursome finally arrived to our Lyme awakening thanks to an alarming magazine article wakeup call clock. Rise and shine, Moritz family! We would shower ourselves with furthered fervor, facing our found foe, following proven and purposeful pathways to diagnose, treat, and eventually conquer. This would be our redirected recovery intention on wellness road. I was eager to transport our living room discovery along with such profound proclamation to NAMI class that same evening. Within the two weeks remaining of our 10week course, we found our true mental health diagnosis and it was Lyme! I believed this clarity had to be shared with our trusted teammates, for we agreed we must educate others with what we had serendipitously learned about this disease and its mental health affectations. My innocent and naïve intentions were not prepared for the looks of skepticism and the eyes of doubt, delivered by group members as well as class leaders. A previous lesson had mentioned the 'not me, not us' syndrome that families, especially parents, tend to adopt when a mental health diagnosis is determined for a loved one. The family joy I had been overcome by earlier that afternoon was now glaringly absent among our newfound mental health bound friends and families. There were questions and stares, and some shifted uncomfortably in their chairs. Perhaps I needed to be more sensitive. An implied disclaimer for our son Zach's behavior and hospitalization outcomes resulting from mental health disturbance was not to be the intention. He battled mental health symptoms, there would be no denial. But we had also been conflicted sitting in those seats for weeks, trying to fully fit the provided description of each mental health diagnostic to Zach. None seemed to fully align. He did not have a history or family history, and the antipsychotic medications did not relieve the multiple ongoing physical symptoms nor the depression and anxiety. The mystery had not seemed sufficiently solved in 10weeks of avid attendance. Nonetheless, the class, its contents and the relationship connections, had proven to be meaningful sources of safe support. No judgement or shock value, until now, when confronted with alternative mental health influences exclusive from the provided education material.

Maybe the shock and stunned reception were actually internalized reflections about their own loved ones, their own possibilities, their own doubts, and their own wonder. Could there actually be others among us diagnosed with mental illness, but in fact be suffering with Lyme disease? It was and is a fair contemplation in this particular scenario of share out, or in any illness absurdity we are wondering about. Zach had the rash and at least five primary symptoms, therefore he was worthy of a clinical diagnosis. In fact, we counted at least 20 indicative symptoms. Joint pain, neck pain, back pain, joint and neck cracking, extreme fatigue, severe migraines, blackouts, tremors, light and sound sensitivity, anxiety, rage, insomnia, swollen glands, stomach cramps, facial twitching, tingling sensations, tinnitus, balance issues, brain fog, mood swings, delusions, hallucinations, depression, and a bipolar diagnosis. His completion of a clinical diagnostic checklist obtained online that assessed symptoms experienced in addition to measures of frequency and severity proved to be overwhelmingly obvious. How had we all missed this? How had the medical community missed this, time and again? While sharing in class that evening, the sudden suggestion that our son's diagnosis might define him differently from their own loved one's mental health truth was not a welcome proposal. Gathering for weeks, safely sharing and delicately holding each other's life struggles in balance to each of our own loved ones' very painful mental health weekly challenges, we developed a sense of belonging and oneness. The feelings of isolation and loneliness within our respective communities would quiet here. Week after week, I had openly shared and willingly participated, finding comfort and helpful tools from this sacred source of networking care. Refraining from a separation of myself, my son, my story might be better served for all. The connections, the work, the concerns shared as individuals and group, remained relevant regardless. There would be no denying Zach's behaviors aligning with bipolar and schizoaffective mannerisms and features. But the question left unspoken among the share out that evening, was whether underlying illness such as Lyme or other, could or would present with severe mental illness. Lyme and tick borne illness would not be cause of all mental illness, but for just how many cases would this in fact be causative?

Skepticism of a Lyme diagnosis for Zach would shadow us for quite some time, well beyond that evening and group encounter. Establishing credibility to the disease symptoms and diagnostic criteria were repeatedly painful experiences for Zach, for us as parents, and for most sufferers of this disease. This unfortunate truth would be a dominant theme of conflict our entire journey battling this disease. Lack of education and awareness about Lyme disease and tick borne illness particularly within the medical professions, but also among the greater global public, was appalling to us. We were appalled to never have found this direction in all of our own desperate research while amidst recurring bacteria based behavioral battles. Arguments between and among national and international medical resource and policing organizations of infectious disease dueled conflicting constructs to patient credibility and care. A practitioner's professional pledge and protocol might lack motivation to even look for tick borne illness symptoms or to confidently treat patients presenting like Lyme when a clinical observation is not backed legitimately by easily accessible nor accurate diagnostic tests, proven conventional treatment plans, or protected medical practices. How dare a practice overprescribe antibiotics unless, of course, to perhaps manage pimples that present profusely!! Medical board reprimand versus 'Hippocratic Oath'? Ignorance and impudence can and do prevail. Who monitors the balance of health care system directives that challenge practitioner 'Hippocratic Oath' objectives in this arena? Meanwhile, victims of this disease suffer and struggle seeking proper assistance and care. This 'great imitator' disease has not been universally recognized as chronically legitimate, has no updated universal test to accurately diagnose, and has no simple nor single strain universal treatment path. Tick borne illness has the ability to financially destroy a patient amidst insurance coverage denial and question, alternative out of pocket treatment expense, and disability consequence to the daily functioning of one's life. But it can also destroy a medical practitioner, financially, legally, ethically, professionally, and perhaps even morally. Ignorance and impudence leads to apathetic acceptance and adamant avoidance. The very real and present dilemmas we continued to discover had yet been unresolved and embattled for decades. The uncertainty of proven navigational pathways to health and wellness for late stage Lyme, combined with our experiences to date of the Lyme symptoms not being recognizable or diagnosable festered new concern for locating knowledgeable and willing professionals to help us after that illuminating October of 2014. We had to find informed, educated, available help, and find it yesterday.

Lyme disease is an infectious disease caused by the bacteria spirochete Borrelia Burgdorferi, which is transmitted to humans via a tick bite from an infected black legged tick or deer tick. We read this baseline definition first on a health line website which offered us a picture of an Erythema Migrans (EM) rash that looked eerily like Zach's rash he had been inquiring about at almost every medical stop along our journey thus far since May 2014. The EM rash is diagnostic of Borrelia Burgdorferi infection, and yet it is not always present with infection. We would ultimately come to recognize that the rash and its presence on Zach's left arm below the bite area was a gift that should have been a direct clue early on to assessing more accurately the many other symptoms Zach had been battling for months to then align with Lyme. He was fortunate to have this mark, as it gave credibility to the likelihood of Lyme, clinically speaking. Given that his other health symptoms were perceived as generic health afflictions related to either mental illness, substance abuse, rheumatoid arthritis, chronic pain, or depression, to name a few of the various diagnoses recorded, the rash should have redirected. John and I printed off a copy of '*Advanced Topics in Lyme Disease*' by Joseph Burrascano, a well-recognized Lyme disease specialist and researcher, subtitled '*Diagnostic Hints and Treatment Guidelines for Lyme and Other Tick Borne Illnesses*'. This article would begin our collection of evidence, and an ongoing exercise of educating ourselves. We printed an informational brochure from the Lyme Disease Action of the United Kingdom which introduced Lyme Neuroborreliosis, Lyme affecting the nervous system. Because this source and its research was from Europe, it was one of very few resources we found relevant to the fact that our son Zach was bitten by a European tick. Bacterial strains would differ. Zach's central nervous system had certainly been disturbed and warranted consideration of European tick bite impact.

The tool that became our first action initiating resource, was the two tiered diagnostic testing decision tree for Lyme disease available on the CDC website as of October 2014, updated previously in November 2011. We knew we would have to secure a formal diagnosis from lab testing results to gain legitimate credibility despite clinical evidence we were confident about, so a few guides were printed. Perhaps the most reassuring, albeit more frightening, article and research we found initially was a response to web searching Lyme and psychiatric disorders. The Holtorf Medical Group out of Torrance, California, had reprinted an article on their website titled, "*Lyme Disease the Cause of 1/3 of Psychiatric Disorders*". This article spoke specifically to our experience with Zach, especially in referencing neuroborreliosis or Lyme encephalopathy, often compared to neurosyphilis. The infection of the spirochete bacteria in the brain penetrates the central nervous system and can create mimicry of any type of psychiatric disorder as well as cognitive dysfunction. This find gave us credibility at a scientifically researched level, stating further that the severe neuropsychiatric behavioral symptoms could be reversed or ameliorated (improved) when a multi system treatment program specifically targeting Lyme disease was used. We felt reassured and encouraged by the factors of credibility, reversibility and improvement. But we were also frightened by the researched realities of this disease. There was a global absence of widespread common knowledge, and legitimate resources and pathways for securing care were limited. The depth of impairment and disability that sufferers confront for possibly an entire lifetime was some pretty edgy truth to swallow. In 2014, it had been common for us to find that most of the research resources were dated and informational websites were few, sometimes offering conflicting information. A predominant conflict among various alternative sources was the credibility of a chronic stage Lyme diagnosis (beyond 30 days of the tick bite) versus an acute diagnosis (30 days or less from the tick bite). At the time of our immediate research in October 2014, two leading research and advocacy organizations were embattled around the above mentioned diagnostic and treatment legitimacy. ILADS (International Lyme and Associated Diseases Society) and IDSA (Infectious Diseases Society of America) were at odds around diagnostic and treatment guidelines, and thus their competing narrative confused us as to best first steps for the patient and their caregiver. We tended to lean to the frontline of patient and caregiver voice.

Friends in the medical profession recommended we pursue an infectious disease specialist appointment for Zach, the obvious pathway they had been trained to trust. Yet very credible Lyme resources of patient and doctor success stories we researched and read about recommended naturopathic, multi system, holistic approach to care. Initially, we would sadly continue to navigate independently without expert guidance face to face, at a time when we had finally established collaborative agreement with Zach. Well, hell, we had done independent search and rescue for the last six months or so in learning to navigate the mental health psychosis stabilization pathway. We would now map our way through this system as well, encountering new compass rose members along the way, still engaging originals as needed. Compass rose gratitude grew. Shifting from a mental health lead to a Lyme lead, we had to build a new toolbox and we began with the pursuit of a physician referral for a Western Blot laboratory test. We would skip the recommended Elisa that the CDC guided you as first step because we read it might be a false start. The Western Blot offered more precision, we read. Truthfully, we had fallen back, and we wanted to act fast without further setback. We wanted precise and accurate information, and we wanted fewer delays! By the Monday following our bull's eye revelation, we were at a local lab seeking a credible positive result for a Lyme disease diagnosis. Momentarily, we had a fairly stable Zach in our corner. Ever alert we were, however, to the tick tock that might suddenly accelerate the caregiving clock. Elated to discover a cause for Zach's health disruption, we were yet again, however, thrust into social commentary, suggestions, and opinions about the tick topic, reminding us of a continued necessity to shelter ourselves from ill-informed or outdated gestures of perceived help, advice, or opinion. If you hadn't encountered Lyme, we learned, you were not a valid resource to us. There was enough conflicting information out there to misdirect or misalign ourselves with. We found the public, the professionals, and the private opinions all too often revealed offensive ignorance as to the true crisis and crime of Lyme. Underplayed and underestimated, Zach and his tick borne illness would remain a far cry from understood.

The wake-up call research realities of Lyme so insatiably read and understood early on in our discovery were also spoken of in shared sisterhood week one of our Lyme diagnostic pursuit. An honest and forthright warning was given to us by my new friend, NAMI executive director Peggy, a scientist by career background, also nuanced in mental health science through NAMI work and leadership. Enthusiastically, I shared with her our newfound discovery. Peggy's candid response to my eager revelation haunted me for a long time. "You are in for a very difficult and long haul," she asserted cautiously in direct delivery as if to allow for the impact of the honesty, while still comforting me with her sorrowful yet loving set of eyes. No enthusiasm, no celebration, no bullshit! Compass rose Peggy would give it to me straight, thorns and all. She and her family had been battling Lyme disease within their family tree for far too many years, and her daughter's local acupuncture practice cared for far too many suffering clients of Lyme. This diagnosis was not necessarily an easier, more treatable trade off than bipolar or mental health, she made quite clear. In fact, it's complexity might prove to be burdensome beyond local resources available, I further learned. But we were initially determined to prove otherwise. To learn this from Peggy was disturbing and disheartening. Yet, to find someone familiar with the illness felt strangely comforting to the lonely waves of isolation we socially surfed while in long term crisis care, now a-wakeboarding in Lyme. John and I had already come to value and appreciate a meaningful and supportive relationship with this brilliantly resourceful woman. This tick illness informed encounter felt serendipitous, to learn of Lyme's unfortunate touch within her life and our own, and to welcome her most fortunate touch within the life our own. I had developed a kindred spirit connection with Peggy minutes into our initial acquaintance at NAMI, and I trusted that her knowledge and familiarity of this disease would prove helpful to Zach and our family. I valued her instincts and her judgement. Anticipating Zach's need to build an army of Lyme literate teammates, a meeting to introduce Zach to Peggy was arranged for the following week. The two reflected on this shared Lyme discovery and initiated a relaxed, relatable relationship. She too became someone he would trust to understand. Within days, we scheduled lab tests, acupuncture, and naturopathic care to explore effective treatment options for Lyme.

Only a month into John's employment disciplinary plan, and not even a week since Zach's 90day deployment discharge, our spirits were lifted by this ah-hah moment of discovery. We rallied around Zach with less fear and he seemed to soften, releasing previously agitated energies of antagonistic action. He was finally willing to allow us to help, to team again, and we all needed this boost. He was still very sick and vulnerable to the manifestations of the illness. A new goal was to secure antibiotic treatment ASAP, but to accomplish this we had to locate a Lyme literate doctor, secure an appointment, and still prove Zach's presenting predicament. We were now urgent about finally activating a legitimate treatment plan to treat the legitimate source of illness. Not unlike his Copenhagen return, our Fairfield return, and his hospitalization return, I would again become my son's travelling advocate and chauffeur to all doctor appointments. Individually, he would pledge to honor and participate in outpatient therapy, medication, acupuncture, and his own ongoing self-care. Together, we would micromanage and dictate as teammates in this new world order. Lyme kingdom come, treatment together will be done! To further encourage family trust and collaboration, John, Gabby and I had discussed bedroom placement in the home while Zach was in recent hospitalization. We each agreed to offer any room in the house to him upon his return, hoping to accommodate light and sound sensitivity, minimize aggravation from neighboring noise and construction, and encourage a departure from the room that held negative energy from more recent associations. The mother and son blessing of sage in late July was up for evaluation, now subject to our current interpretation. Perhaps this new room placement decision along with Zach's readiness and acceptance to change suggested the actual gift of this sage, the blessed wisdom of that smudge. Because for months, he just would not budge!

Zach chose the smallest bedroom upstairs that had been his father's office space, and John willingly accepted the change and choice with graceful gratitude. Our weekend oriented itself around cleaning, moving, and establishing new functionality of switched furnishings and belongings. Other than Zach's physical pain and bacterial symptoms to manage, there was a resemblance to a former family rhythm. He would claim his personal living space down the short narrow hall from our bedroom on the main floor, a more active and accessible pathway within the home. The only floor creaks he would now deal with would be those he created, not those he heard overhead which stirred his paranoia from the basement bungalow down below. His sister would counterbalance the privacy shift, reclaiming her larger former bedroom space downstairs in exchange. John inherited a larger office space than the space he volunteered to Zach, and everyone seemed to redefine their individual personal living space according to their own needs. Now we would refocus on conquering Lyme. The week ahead took shape with post hospitalization outpatient therapy, my physician's referral for an initial lab test for Lyme, NAMI visitation with Peggy, acupuncture scheduled for pain relief, and an appointment with a local naturopath on Zach's insurance plan to further address Lyme diagnostics and treatment. Zach also had his long awaited primary care appointment on October 31, which he had independently sought out in early September through his community health plan. Waiting two weeks for that seemed risky, so we initiated additional steps. We would seek help around every corner, no longer waiting for a Kundalini awakening to clear the chakras, a non-medicated madness holdout, or young adult emergence of new life from old. Lyme had us behind the eight ball already, and ping pong had always been our game of choice. Every day was preciously delicate and deliberate around our new focus. We had experienced enough calendar cycling patterns with Zach to begin to anticipate how and when this disease might respond. Fending off a madness meander was likely to reoccur, but at least we now understood the behavior to be reflective of bacterial blood brain barrier invasion. Still, he would need to be kept safe until Lyme treatment stabilized him. The two medications he continued to take from recent hospitalization were not antipsychotics nor were they antibiotics. They reduced anxiety and induced sleep. A nasty email, an accusation, a rambling delusion, an unsafe choice were all possibilities if we could not initiate antibiotic treatment soon to hinder the bacterial impact on his brain and resulting behavior. This is what we read and believed.

While in the work of trying to establish an integrative care team beyond just the post hospitalization outpatient care, we were also faced with the reality that Medicaid coverage would only cover few of the treatment options, particularly the alternative care necessities of Lyme treatment protocol. Our finances would quickly feel the added stress and strain of navigating and adopting various uninsured treatment paths for a recommended Lyme recovery approach. Managing finances continued to be paramount in the expensive care of this disabled, unemployed, low insured adult child battling a disease of such controversy and complication as Lyme. We read of this truth and lived it soon enough. While we benefitted from employer insurance in hospitalization one, and Medicaid insurance in hospitalization two, the out of pocket medical expenses were going to leap, and not be cheap. There were far too many treatment unknowns and uncertainties, most of which we understood to be uncovered within existing health care systems. Our research on successful healing in Lyme treatment emphasized a broad balance of holistic care, which would align well with our son's own personal ethics. Much of what we read about insurance support in Lyme treatment emphasized lack and limitation, resulting in significant monetary strain. We certainly were not financially positioned to say yes to everything, and yet we were family positioned to desire yes to everything. Zach deserved every effort to get well and we would do whatever it would take. We were willing to empty our savings, mortgage our home and tap our retirement if it meant healing our child. Unlike far too many in health crisis, we at least had the equity and liquidity at the front end of this financial drain. I read how quickly a household's position can change in the pursuit of chronic Lyme wellness. Sometimes, I held fleeting thoughts about future use of fundraising websites such as GoFundMe if our personal financial well ran dry. When your loved one faces a medical crisis, you don't ever want funding to be the reason or hesitation from providing them the best of care. That 90day employer grip still squeezed fear from all of us, but increasingly we developed indomitable resilience, fortitude, and perseverance despite the disease and employer squeeze. We would rally.

The fact that we had identified tick borne illness did not reduce his symptoms. He rallied daily, but the pain and the process exhausted him, confused him, and still controlled him. When his brain cognition would allow, he began to research, attempted to take notes, and cooperated willingly with us in this consuming and driven health care pursuit. Books I ordered as further resources on Lyme began to arrive, and I was determined to become well–informed, micromanaging as necessary the navigational path we would need to follow. John would help, often guiding us to scientific articles of validation or treatment success. The first four books I consumed in fall of 2014 included *Insights into Lyme Disease Treatment* by Connie Strasheim, *Confronting Lyme Disease-What Patient Stories Teach Us* by Karen Yerges and Rita Stanley, Ph.D., *Cure Unknown – Inside the Lyme Epidemic* by Pamela Weintraub, and the more recent 2014 release of those four books, *Why Can't I Get Better? Solving the Mystery of Lyme & Chronic Disease* by Richard Horowitz. Strasheim and Yerges and Stanley broadened our case study knowledge, but Weintraub and Horowitz's books were incredibly helpful. The science, the depth of medical direction, the examples, and the overwhelming truth thorn prick of a warning spoken by our rose Peggy would all find credible validation within the message and content of these books. The Horowitz book became our baseline bible, travelling religiously with us to appointments, quoted from as a primary source and guide to Lyme scripture and medical care passages. We would become confident at speaking up for our Lyme life, educating others with evidence wherever and whenever necessary. These resources gave us tremendous credibility when challenged. The *Cure Unknown* stirred some fear sauce in me. The narrative tells of an entire family afflicted with over a decade of suffering, exploring treatment only to 'get better' but not get cured. The author's last sentence in final chapter 56 of the 2013 updated addition to the book first published in 2008, addressed a painful premonition I came to eventually understand at a depth I would never have imagined. Ms. Weintraub wrote, *"But for patients on the ground, for the ones who fail treatment or get diagnosed late, life in the Lymelands remains a difficult, often devastating affair."* Peggy's message was affirmed once again. In chronic Lyme, and sometimes even acute

Lyme, one must embrace treatment and a measure of recovery for the long haul. No cure, only containment.

Devastating it was then, to receive our Western Blot results and read negative on the front page. The blood test was to detect the presence of antibodies (blood proteins) produced in his body responding to specific toxins or harmful substances like Lyme bacteria or other co infections present in his blood. Should the test reveal various protein bands, it would indicate the presence of Borrelia Burgdorferi. It might also explain the many symptoms presenting that would appear to be his body systems affected by bacterial invasion to cells, fluids, tissues, joints, all as immune system response. Our first lab test specific to Lyme, attempt one. Negative. We had been warned that tests often are false negative, which discourages the credibility battle a Lyme sufferer continues to wage while already health weary. Zach had a 41 band test positive on the IgG Western Blot. Not enough. Positive. To understand these tests and the corresponding medical jargon, I had to research medical term definitions, and revisit Horowitz's book, so well written for the layperson. The mailed lab results don't come with a medical dictionary, and we had not yet worked with the naturopath or a community health primary care practitioner (PCP) to assist us with interpretation. While digging through the pages of *Why Can't I Get Better,* Horowitz's book, I found a helpful fact on page 62 to assist me in explaining the Western Blot test limitations and its failure rate. Item #5 toward the bottom of the page stated, *"There are multiple strains of Borrelia present in the United States (approximately 100), and there are over 300 strains worldwide. Blood tests often do not cross react between these strains, and consequently can lead to false negative results."* Well, of course, Zach was bitten overseas. His strain of *Borrelia* and any other co infections would be defined by the geographical strain of his bacteria. We would test again, reminding medical folk of the obvious clinical diagnostic truth of EM rash and easily 20 symptoms of suffering, and we would continue the challenging course of treatment pursuit. Zach was deeply discouraged time and again, and left the lab printout out on the kitchen counter with a scribble down the front that read, "same shit, different day". Shitstorms, yes there were plenty.

To ease his pain and frustration, both physically and emotionally, and to support continued attempts to engage him in spaces beyond medical office appointments and his new bedroom barracks, we bought Zach a 2hour float. Helpful and calming, he still was quite setback physically, so the benefits were fleeting. Each day, each night, I would bait him with hope on a string, luring him into the belief that acupuncture would help, the next lab test would be positive, the naturopath would treat us for Lyme, the upcoming PCP appointment would help us with further treatment, an infectious disease specialist referral would happen, and all would accumulatively help him get well. We were fishing, and patient persistence was mandatory. Our local naturopathic appointment was promising, but she focused on ruling out other immune system concerns and health issues, testing dietary allergies, exploring various homeopathic remedies for his psychiatric features and the multiple pain issues he suffered. She did not comprehend our urgency, new to this client and his crazed cycle of problems and presentation. She followed proper protocol as a professional in her field, but we became borderline pushy. Not a Lyme literate medical doctor (LLMD), I realized we could not continue to lose time in this practice. There was an LLMD in town, which was miraculous in itself for Pacific Northwest options, but he was not taking on new patients, nor was he covered by Medicaid. Our initial choice of this naturopathic doctor was influenced by health care coverage and availability. Commonly, we pleaded for urgent attention and accelerated action. Within a week of care, we convinced this naturopath to send Zach's blood in for analysis to IGeneX Labs, a well-known among Lyme circles, highly qualified lab service with precision accuracy in determination of tick borne illness and its multiple strains. We were advised to expect a 4-6 week wait for response. Tick tock the spirochete clock.

Zach had managed fairly well these first 2weeks home from hospitalization after his terrifying episodes of late September early October. We had yet to accurately discern if triggers or patterns played into his cycles of rage, but after reading about bacterial spirochetes and their reproductive cycle of 28-32 days, we began to chart the heightened delusional outbursts of rage. Finding pattern, we then had reasonable concern that he might cycle again through rage or rant very soon without a medicinal assault on the bacteria. He had erupted in Iowa the end of March/early April, he had shifted into isolation at home the end of April/early May, he almost took his life with a knife the end of May/early June. Medication tamed the months of June and July, but by the end of August after the return from Big Pine and the missed medical appointment he again erupted. Early September on Labor Day weekend he cowered alongside his father. Zach then punched a wall in rage and nearly jumped out of a moving car the end of September/early October. The end of October/early November neared. Would we fall back again? The evening of Tuesday, October 28, John was out of town, and Gabby was having dinner at a friend's home. Zach and I finished dining together before he began to speak out about a Copenhagen woman and her evil father, two avatar type delusions we were still unsure about as to any reality base other than his sister's vouch for the Copenhagen woman's name familiarity from conversations with her brother during healthier days of pre Lyme awakening. His facial expression turned catatonic, and his voice shifted to an assertive, angry tonality. Zach's spoken content then wandered into strange stories of unknown Danish relatives of this woman, of her father, of an abusive past, of the family's extensive power and influence, of the father's repeated attempts to destroy him. His tone and agitation took a trip down a familiar crazy lane. The content was equally crazed. I casually left the table, clearing plates and attempting to mask my rising fear. Creating some space between us in the neighboring room but within sight of each other, I proceeded to speak to him using practiced LEAP strategy to listen, empathize, agree, and partner. Fear was contained.

Amador taught us that no matter how strange a deranged person is in the telling of story or conversation, accept that their belief is present in their mind and therefore feels very real and true to them. Challenging them with logic and denial only creates increased agitation and potential rage. Allow your loved one, our Zach in this instance, to talk the madness through, as long as there would be no immediate or potential concern for safety. Words and thoughts are one thing. Actions are quite another. Allow empathy and find agreement compatibility with your loved one, I would remind myself. Help him plan healthy decisions and choices that divert away from false delusion and direct him toward a safe and reasonable alternative of thought or action. In doing this, Beth, you will create partnership. I self-coached, but mostly, I listened in wonder. Repeating phrases and clarifying thoughts, the strangest shift eventually happened almost two hours into his crazy talk of old delusions, new delusions, accusations, and exaggerations. Zach stopped, looked at me with imploring eyes, and spoke to me in a hushed tone that reflected cautionary confusion, now absent of agitation. He questioned the moment but also defined it. "I just did it, didn't I? I just spoke about these people again and got angry, and then rambled on and on. It all just felt so real." He caught himself, heard himself, and was able to name it rather than just buy into it, be possessed by it, or even respond aggressively to it. Rage that would previously rise up from within him, or down from within his mind's whim, was suddenly intercepted! WOW. This was shocking and yet very revealing of what we now understood to be bacterial mind alter of influence and control. "Yes, Zach, you just did that and the things you said were bizarre. It was not unlike written emails and spoken anger you have exhibited during psychotic mind rage manifestation previously witnessed." I risked volunteering this truth in response to his quandary and query. We moved from LEAP technique to a hop, skip, and a jump into teamed analysis. Distracted from our dazed dismantling of his delusional dance, the front door suddenly opened directly into our kitchen karma kinship. His sister entered bright eyed and energized, casually sauntering over to the table near Zach. She entered that mesmerizing moment of revelation and sat down to listen. "You missed it, Gabby. You missed me in action." Zach shared, looking helplessly at his sister, attempting to regain some form of crazy clarity from this voluntary admission of crazy charity! He acknowledged that he lost himself momentarily in a random brain burst of out loud jabberwocky, but then came full circle to self-recognition and awareness admission of what had happened, even mockingly speaking of it freely to his sister. I was overwhelmed with awe by his level of aware but also felt cautiously forewarned by the awake. Another wake-up call warning had been alarmed. Tick tock, so goes the crazy clock.

Friday's primary care practitioner (PCP) appointment could not come quick enough. Zach had waited almost two months to get in the door as a first time client not identified with critical care need. Zach's goals for that Halloween afternoon appointment were clear, for we had been spooked in disguise for too long. Seek credible proof through lab work, receptive response to the disease diagnosis and referral to infectious disease for activation of antibiotic treatment; these were the goals to accomplish. Arriving at the clinic early, we were eager to address current concerns, and advocate for advanced care. Prior to the appointment, I read online about this particular community health care network and found no direction or resources for clear channels to the care pathway we felt Zach would need. I expected a challenge today. We would have to promote our position and push back against any mimicry we might encounter from the claim of clinically diagnosed Lyme, despite evidence and research we were prepared to defend. Actually, that I would prepare to defend, for Zach was not in a position to advocate for himself, and I understood this. He understood this. It would be a team effort, and I would do what I could to allow him to initiate, to speak for himself, to feel capable, but I would not quietly allow this long awaited, likely debated, possibly jaded meeting of the moment to simply pass us by. In our back pocket, costing out of pocket, we had IGeneX lab testing planned, acupuncture care scheduled, and naturopathic explorations going on, but this PCP care offered a potential path to antibiotic treatment care covered by insurance, and possibly with immediate effect toward upending an impending implosion. Zach was present and presentable, but he was lethargic, in pain, and cognitively dull. He was withdrawing more lately, I noticed, so I was prepared to speak up today should he not respond clearly or reason effectively. In a healthy Zach mind, these skill sets he would ordinarily employ with grace, kindness, and intelligent discourse. I had witnessed enough times in this year of madness and mayhem, when medical professionals at intake would assess, assume, and assert, while unstable Zach would regress, resume, and revert. I had become conditioned to anticipate and respond. Depending on the need and the circumstance, I would fight for my son, my child, and my family, not allowing a continuation of bias, judgement, and stereotype to occur any longer in this drawn out, past due, diagnostic mishap and misunderstood treatment trap. I would begin the appointment listening, with respectful engagement and collaborative enthusiasm, for teammates were critical to gather. I would respond accordingly.

Escorted to a patient room, a young nurse practitioner arrived late and introduced herself as his primary care professional. She was distracted and in a hurry, responding indignantly and irritatingly from the get go to our eager and exacting introductory message. Lyme disease? A circular rash? With a record of psychiatric hospitalizations? Her facial expressions and body language fully offended. The smirk, the denial of Lyme feasibility, the suggested diagnosis of ringworm, and the mockery of our daring and ridiculous request for Zach to feasibly receive a community health care insurance referral today to an infectious disease specialist was enough to shut Zach down in retreat, and ignite some Beth bitching heat! I had humbly, and very vulnerably at the time, witnessed the doctor in Fairfield do this, a hospital social worker do this, the judge do this, and now this nurse practitioner attempt to do this. All had been condescending and arrogant to the patient/client credibility and character. These professionals held the degreed power of their own diagnostic suggestions and insistence above any credible evidence or evaluation request of a more holistically comprehensive narrative presented. False assumptions prevail and ineffective prescriptions fail. Why can't we collaborate to find truth and build trust in search of wellness? This scenario was all too commonly the plight of the ever so vulnerable Lyme patient, we were told, and now we again watched it unfold. Unfortunately, we hadn't previously understood that Lyme was our plight, and once we did, we expected collaborative professional support, not contentious professional rapport. Looking back, it was atrocious the way we were treated, all the while under the influence of spirochetal flare. We had to somehow prove our illness and its merit. Demanding to see the clinic manager, I reminded the PCP the ways in which she had violated the very objectives of this clinic so clearly promoted on their website, and I suggested she do some homework on understanding Lyme and spirochetal presentation. We waited while she frustratingly fled the room, and Zach turned to look at me like I was the mad one. Mad, I certainly was! Mad, sad, and determined not to be had! Shortly, we were escorted into the manager's office, once again describing our story, offering our proof, finally receiving proper care and support, and even given a pledge to either secure an infectious disease referral or a pain management referral in follow up to today's blood lab work up testing for Lyme. This Michael, the clinic manager, was on his game, just as our other Michael, the panic manager, had been on his. Compassionate, respectful, and validating, we fought for a medical teammate who listened! Our care was actually practiced as primary. Another blood lab workup was performed to test for the bacteria, to identify the antibodies, to seek the bands present in his blood. Home we went to weather another weekend of waiting, while continuing plans of next step care, including a plan for this caregiver's care. I needed a break.

A fall visit to the Boston area to spend time with my sister Joanne had been planned ever since we discerned his Lyme diagnosis, and the gift of this upcoming 4day weekend for me was approaching quickly. Other than the early August backpacking adventure, and trips to the grocery store, to the community indoor pool to soak away some pain, and to the neighborhood park to walk off some stress, I had been primarily a homebound care giving adult coordinating support and protection for Zach, and for all of us. This early November get away initially seemed the right time for me to seize a respite, to exhale into a safe alternative surrounding, to release some accumulated pressure, and to refresh for the work ahead yet to be done. John would manage the Friday through Monday extended weekend that I would be gone, with our daughter available for support as well. Zach would attend outpatient therapy and acupuncture just days before I left, and his blood lab draw would be mailed out to IGeneX the actual day of my departure. Bases were covered, even though Zach retreated to his room the night before I left without a farewell or verbal contact. We all held it as insignificant at the time. Both John and Gabby were unaccustomed to the constant vigil I had practiced for months, for they both had preoccupations with work or school or home projects. My absence would be a trial for Zach, for them, and for me, for the two of us had been directly available to each other daily since that living room diagnosis. A certain measure and reliability of safety and trust had been established and exercised. Each of us would need to now trust in the shifting freedoms this long weekend would present. John and I agreed to communicate daily, and he welcomed the opportunity for a more engaged connection to his son. Gabrielle's presence and participation these past two months at home continued to be deeply meaningful for us. We understood her compromise and the personal sacrifice of a delayed launch into her own independence and self-sufficiency. Our day to day situation she graciously adapted to without fully compromising her continued efforts to seek and explore employment opportunities for herself, all the while nurturing her astrological interests and education. The three of us knew how to rally around Zach and each other, and we would. Newburyport and sister love beckoned, even though I would not stop fearing eruption for a second, because his next calendar round might soon be reckoned. Late October/early November, we seemed to have things under control for now. Bull's eye, that would prove to be a lie!

CHECK LIST OF *CURRENT* SYMPTOMS: This is not meant to be used as a diagnostic scheme, but is provided to streamline the office interview. Note the format- complaints referable to specific organ systems and specific co-infections are clustered to clarify diagnoses and to better display multisystem involvement.

Have you had any of the following in relation to this illness? (CIRCLE "NO" OR "YES")

Tick bite	N (Y)	"EM" rash (discrete circle)	N (Y)
Spotted rash over large area	N (Y)	Linear, red streaks	N (Y)

SYMPTOM OR SIGN	CURRENT SEVERITY				CURRENT FREQUENCY				
	NONE	MILD	MODERATE	SEVERE	NA	NEVER	OCCASIONAL	OFTEN	CONSTANT
Persistent swollen glands			X				X		
Sore throat	X					X			
Fevers			X				X		
Sore soles, esp. in the AM	X					X			
Joint pain				X					X
Fingers, toes			X				X		
Ankles, wrists				X					X
Knees, elbows				X					X
Hips, shoulders				X					X
Joint swelling	X					X			
Fingers, toes	X					X			
Ankles, wrists	X					X			
Knees, elbows	X					X			
Hips, shoulders	X					X			
Unexplained back pain				X					X
Stiffness of the joints or back				X					X
Muscle pain or cramps				X				X	
Obvious muscle weakness				X					X
Twitching of the face or other muscles			X				X		
Confusion, difficulty thinking				X				X	
Difficulty with concentration, reading, problem absorbing new information				X				X	
Word search, name block				X				X	
Forgetfulness, poor short term memory, poor attention				X				X	
Disorientation: getting lost, going to wrong places			X				X		
Speech errors- wrong word, misspeaking			X				X		
Mood swings, irritability, depression				X				X	
Anxiety, panic attacks				X				X	
Psychosis (hallucinations, delusions, paranoia, bipolar)		X					X		
Tremor		X					X		
Seizures		X					X		
Headache				X				X	
Light sensitivity				X				X	
Sound sensitivity				X				X	

MANAGING LYME DISEASE, 16ᵗʰ edition, October, 2008
Page 9 of 37

Insert 28 •   2014, October, Lyme checklist Pages 1 & 2

| Vision: double, blurry, floaters | | | X | | | | | X | |
| Ear pain | | | X | | | | | X | |

	CURRENT SEVERITY				CURRENT FREQUENCY				
SYMPTOM OR SIGN	NONE	MILD	MODERATE	SEVERE	NA	NEVER	OCCASIONAL	OFTEN	CONSTANT
Hearing: buzzing, ringing, decreased hearing			X					X	
Increased motion sickness, vertigo, spinning			X					X	
Off balance, "tippy" feeling				X			X		
Lightheadedness, wooziness, unavoidable need to sit or lie				X			X		
Tingling, numbness, burning or stabbing sensations, shooting pains, skin hypersensitivity				X			X		
Facial paralysis-Bell's Palsy				X			X		
Dental pain		X					X		
Neck creaks and cracks, stiffness, neck pain				X					X
Fatigue, tired, poor stamina				X					X
Insomnia, fractionated sleep, early awakening				X				X	
Excessive night time sleep				X				X	
Napping during the day				X				X	
Unexplained weight gain				X				X	
Unexplained weight loss				X				X	
Unexplained hair loss				X				X	
Pain in genital area		X					X		
Unexplained menstrual irregularity	X				X				
Unexplained milk production; breast pain	X				X				
Irritable bladder or bladder dysfunction	X					X			
Erectile dysfunction	X					X			
Loss of libido	X					X			
Queasy stomach or nausea			X				X		
Heartburn, stomach pain		X					X		
Constipation	X					X			
Diarrhea			X				X		
Low abdominal pain, cramps				X				X	
Heart murmur or valve prolapse?		X					X		
Heart palpitations or skips		X					X		
"Heart block" on EKG	X					X			
Chest wall pain or ribs sore				X					X
Head congestion				X					X
Breathlessness, "air hunger", unexplained chronic cough			X				X		
Night sweats			X				X		

Chapter 22: Holiday Hostage

Trouble, Cat Stevens

Please Come Home for Christmas, The Eagles

The week prior to Newburyport travel to visit my sister and escape for a long weekend away from the routine of constrained living and constant caregiving, our family had established some positive steps forward following our Lyme awakening. Zach had been home from his second hospitalization for 3 weeks, in compliance with our mandated guidelines and cooperating as a teammate in the now very focused and intentional pursuit of diagnosis and treatment for Lyme. Tuesday before my travel week, he had acupuncture treatment, and an appointment with his meds management outpatient clinician. Wednesday, he had a morning appointment with his psychotherapy clinician, followed by an afternoon appointment for a blood smear submission to IgeneX lab in Palo Alto, California. Our new naturopath agreed to support us in the test pursuit, hoping to secure positive results that would 'legitimize' our living room clinical diagnosis. Credibility in chronic Lyme would be a never ending battle. The three of us sat in her office reading descriptions of co infection possibility from the lab website, comparing Zach's symptoms to those described for Babesia, Ehrlichiosis, and Bartonellosis. We were essentially playing guess and go with some attention to escalating cost. We selected a panel of 4 specific blood tests in search of tick borne pathogens other than Borrelia Burgdorferi, neglecting to specify the priority of a Western Blot. Given his neurological symptoms and dominant psychiatric features, we reasoned co infection was likely, but all three of us were novice in that notion. From this 'learn as we go' exercise of reading about the lab panels together, that afternoon before my Massachusetts morning departure, I suspected our dear doctor, not unlike all too many in the complexity of tick borne illness diagnosis and treatment, was kindly dedicated to helping Zach, but clearly too inexperienced and ill-informed for optimal and expedient care. Unfortunately, this had been proven a recurring reality within our healthcare community and certainly beyond. When Zach heard mention of the out of pocket expense for our test choice, he timidly commented, "Merry Christmas to me." I acknowledged with an optimistic response. "Yes, Zach, Merry Christmas to you, and ideally, to all of us! It will likely take 4-6 weeks to await test results, so I suppose there is the possibility of positive results celebrated as a holiday gift." His humility was appreciated, for his vulnerable fragility could easily have given way to vacated futility. We were students without an instructor, making educated guesses, preparing to test on a challenging and controversial subject, and hoping to pass. Failure had become familiar. A positive lab test seemed to us that measure of success.

The trip would now take precedence. Bases had been covered in the week's appointment care and the weekend's preparation for care. I had hoped this new caregiving rhythm and the teamed welcome at home would carry over a sense of reassuring confidence into the trip, but the idea proved to be naïve. Distance from direct responsibility and day to day management were without question appreciated breaks, and my sister host was gracious, comforting, and of utmost understanding. Still, I checked in day and night only to confirm that Zach was, in fact, showing signs of a shift in behavior. Unaware that he had purchased two non-pharmaceutical Chinese herbal remedies from the acupuncturist the Tuesday before I left, one an herbal analgesic for pain relief, and the other a Calm Spirit for anxiety, he then began to replace his prescribed medications, 300 mg of Trileptal and 1 mg of Ativan. Independently, he decided to choose and use an alternative medicine that weekend without coordinated consultation among the various teams. I learned about the herbal remedies the night of my return, while I learned about the discontinuation of his prescribed medications from John's discovery two days into the weekend of my absence. The collection of recently filled prescriptions sat as empty containers on the kitchen counter set aside for recycle. Tactically unspoken but tacitly understood, his message was all too familiar from actions in the recent past. By the third day of my absence, Zach had begun to skip meals and not show for shared dinner, indicative of the former isolating behavior and now suspected as symptom regression. My Massachusetts medication and Newburyport nuance in response to these long distance discoveries were privately predictable. Prayer, I would still keep, melatonin I popped for sleep, and the nightfall trickle of tear drop sorrow, I would woefully weep. There was yet no miracle in the mix of a Lyme tomorrow.

Straight to his down the hallway main floor bedroom upon arrival home Monday eve, I knocked softly on his closed door, and curiously peered inside. He lay quiet under the covers of his king size bed, receptive to my returned presence as indicated by the gentle welcome he offered. Whew. I knelt beside the bed and inquired with as low key a tone as I could dial into following the marathon travel day and the foreboding fears kept at bay. "Zach, what is happening with you that you have begun to push away your medications and supplements, that you have not been eating?" In a dazed and dreamlike state, with eyes half closed and attention drifting in and out, he informed me in a whispered delivery about the medicinal herbs he bought and their perceived effect on his Lyme bacteria. He continued to tell of cramps and diarrhea following their use, inspiring the belief and intention he then held of personally killing off his spirochetes singlehandedly. He had remained in bed resting throughout the purported die off only to then follow up any urge of a bathroom purge! The belief in self-healing had once again returned, voiced in a much less aggressive manner that particular evening. "I have been shitting those bugs out daily since you left, and I think they are leaving my body. I need to rest. I am exhausted and weak", he mumbled. His long, lithe body cocooned up into the sprawl of the smoky blue comforter, his once vibrant blue green eyes glazed without sparkle, and his groggy but gentle delivery sounded disarmingly delirious. Always there seemed to be truth mixed with delirium when infection would fester, as he struggled between clarity and confusion, reality and delusion. Other than the gentle versus angry tone and the delivery of his 'tick shit and die' mind twisted mantra, Zach's current behavior signaled careful caution in the tick tock alarm clock of active Lyme still in spirochetal stock. After all, this was the first week of November and our haunting calendared cycle of bacterial reproduction and symptom display aligned once again with previous patterns tracked. "Zach, you need to eat to maintain your strength, hydrate to replenish lost fluids, and you have appointments this week to keep. Do not allow yourself to fall back into the unhealthy patterns of isolation you exercised previous to our awakened knowledge of Lyme!", I pleaded desperately. He simply smiled with his eyes shut and drifted off to sleep, oblivious to the obvious, subliminal to the criminal we now knew as Lyme.

Progress notes recorded by his prescribing clinician during this stretch of October/November outpatient care were obtained in 2016, and they gave clue to the struggles Zach continued to face in this timeframe. He had notified her of his family's living room diagnosis, as well as the family's efforts to redirect treatment to be inclusive for Lyme. Also tracked and recorded were his frightened confessions of experiencing cycling cognitive loss, word retention loss, inability to read and comprehend, physical pain, and recurring suicidal thoughts of up to 3x a week. The notes tracked his growing concern as to whether these multiple symptoms were a result of the prescription drugs or the Lyme bacteria, or both. He was trying to resume meditation without success and had attempted medicinal marijuana without success. The clinician made notes to recommend a Lyme titer and a rheumatology referral for his primary care practitioner to follow, but neither ever transacted beyond these notes. Uncertain of and disconnected to any urgency of his presenting Lyme getting proper treatment protocol, she had not identified any connection of Zach's psychiatric features for which she was treating to this recent clinical diagnosis of tick borne disease. Same shit, another day, as Zach liked to say! Meanwhile, without access or knowledge of these records in real time, we continued to work at home with Zach without any awareness of his confessed and recorded ideation and fears.

The day after my travel return, a mailbox delivery offered us some great news that I hoped would assist us in our November slump. As a result of our October primary care appointment, and the clinic director's support, a referral to see an infectious disease specialist had been approved by Medicaid. The notification indicated that we had from November through February to utilize these services without any out of pocket expense or further authorization required. Hallelujah and Boo-yah! I could not wait to share this with Zach, and yet when I eagerly did, he remained convinced of his irrational belief that he was just fine taking care of the Lyme himself, not needing any more providers or supports. That was a high low moment of exchange. Tick shit, and sigh. "Go away", he would grunt in response to my enthusiasm, my urgency, and my determination to seize this opportunity of infectious disease treatment care. I called the office despite his disinterest, and scheduled the first appointment available, which happened to be the week of Thanksgiving. Thanks I was giving. I had convinced myself that I would somehow motivate him by then to value the importance and significance of this referral, attend the appointment, and push hard for antibiotic treatment ASAP. This difficult to acquire appointment seemed imperative to pursue as well as any other wellness pathway we could access and try. Otherwise, then what? Lyme was mischievous.

Later that same week of early November, the lab summary arrived from Zach's community health primary care appointment, with blood test results negative for Lyme, again. This created in the records accessible to all of his local medical caregivers, a circulating diagnostic shut down now messaged as *'medically cleared'* of Lyme. The accompanying letter and lab result sheet gave no descriptive or explanation as to the what and why of their testing process nor an interpretation of the negative outcome. Who would we challenge for explanation and interpretation? The previously assigned primary care professional had since left the community health practice, so now Zach again remained without a caregiving relationship in primary care practice. To explore an infectious disease referral, despite researched information indicating attitudes of disbelief about chronic Lyme among this specialty, was practical and prudent. All pathways would be worth consideration. Increasingly, I became suspicious that we would have to utilize repeat pathways to help Zach stabilize this next oncoming cycle of Lyme affectation – crisis line, hospitalization, mandated meds, mental health diagnosis and outpatient care. We had yet to secure professional validation of his Lyme diagnosis. Securing tick borne illness validation and care should not be so evasive. *'Medically cleared'*, the medical records would read, despite overwhelming evidence, clinically speaking, and multiple scientifically researched sources we found referencing the high probability of false negative lab results to occur in Lyme disease diagnosis. Add to this the European bacterial strains likely not measurable in standard American labs, we were possibly screwed for local lab test validation. We awaited our only other outstanding lab results, hoping that IGeneX would be the golden ticket. Meanwhile, the spirochetes multiplied, and the symptoms stirred.

November of 2013 had been a life altering year ago, when we were oblivious to the surge of infectious disease symptoms, and full of optimistic opportunity for each of us. We had scheduled a commonly successful knee surgery for Zach, anticipated an exciting career shift to management for John, welcomed a much needed career shift from school counseling for Beth, and prepared to celebrate college graduation for Gabrielle. As a family facing such dynamic shifts, we shared among us a variety of thought provoking conversations about life, love and ongoing learning opportunities for growth and discovery. Tick borne illness did not make that list, despite an already unwelcome, unprovoked penetrating presence of spirochetal residency sheltering somewhat silently in the deep tissue and blood brain barrier of Zach's body habitat at the time. In the very much awakened now of November 2014, a year later, the teasing transcendence of tick taunting trauma all year long offered new perspective. John approached the 2month marker on his employer 90day improvement plan, our daughter had been home near 90days continuing her search for full time work in her field, and I would manage the infectious disease specialist's 90day option of an appointment referral. What was up with these 90 day terms? We grew accustomed to looking for patterns and cycles, trends and timelines, so as to possibly drive educated decisions rather than react to unexpected challenges. Education and prevention rather than intervention or retention, so said the school counselor program developer! But the truth is that life presents it all, and we must deal. As November and December months of 2014 arrived, escorting us toward the end of our family's most difficult calendar year, we each had much to personally balance. Zach remained our central priority. He did not need a daylight basement bedroom to find his way back to the isolation and strange behaviors the disease would manifest once again just down the hallway. Increasingly, he fell out of balance, requiring all of us to work that much harder within our own balancing schemes, while remaining sensitive and cautiously aware of his understood imbalance. My next intervention strategy would be a pleading visit to the one and only local Lyme Literate Medical Doctor (LLMD). I would beg for a new patient exception, for Zach needed primary care that would treat his full breadth of disease.

Within a week of Zach keeping himself hostage to his idea of healing with herbs at home, various personal belongings began to appear on the floor outside of his bedroom door or on the kitchen counter, followed by bed sheets and towels left out daily. The bed sheets and towels were a first, and I interpreted this as his desire to wash away any dead bugs, since he believed he was killing them off, shitting them out, perhaps even sweating them out onto the sheets and towels...... a mad mind can be creative and imaginative! I willingly washed these items as unspoken participation in tag team care, leaving him clean, folded sheets and towels in return for some kind of hoped for effort on his part. It was a mysterious game of exclusive exchange symbolically signifying mutual surprise, support, and survival. Nutritionally balanced plates of food in the fridge were set aside for him, hoping he would find his way to their bait in the middle of the night. I would hear the hallway floor creaks and his noisy aching joint cracks as the lanky shadow would ramble down the hallway past my slightly cracked bedroom door. Food and sustenance were the baited bounty out into the kitchen as my perceived act of preventative care. Enabling, maybe. Accommodating, definitely. Lifesaving, probably. Healing Lyme, not at all. He avoided all of us by rising from his room in the wee hours of early morning while we slept. I would finally fall asleep upon hearing his sounds, seeing his shadows, and then trusting in life and the living versus death and the dying. Hoping and praying for the current madness cycle to safely pass, I would eventually drift off in slumber. He was significantly less aggressive this round of isolation, but increasingly and accumulatively, his regression detoured any determined defense against the deepening effects and influences of the disease. Occasionally, he would not touch the balanced meals set aside for him, so I began to purchase healthy prepackaged 'backpack' foods that either would be left at his door or found by him in the early hour pantry rustle. November's cycle at least now owned the knowledge of what and why, and the closer proximity of down the hall shelter felt less removed and inaccessible than the basement bungalow of May through early October.

Lying in bed at night, waiting for the life affirming footsteps that would typically forewarn with ankle and joint crackle pops around 2 or 3 in the morning, I would binge watch *Madmen*, a show my sister introduced to me while cozied up together in 'Mass'. The intro theme music with its accompanying artistic graphic visual, timed in synch with the creepiness factor of Zach's manifestations and his 6'10" willowy wobbly frame meandering down the hallway at night would momentarily mesmerize my own mild manner of madness! I would fast forward the creepy introduction, transitioning more quickly and consecutively into the entertaining time warp of the 60's and 70's, inviting a visual recall of childhood tapestry, and an elusive escape into the fictional fabric of some other fragmented life. When the image of the character spiraling downward would sync with the theme music, I would experience a wave of nauseating fear, for our own world within these household walls was spiraling downward once again. When I heard my son's footprint in the hallway, I would spiral off succumbing to sleep after repeated succession of consecutive seasons and episodes. The sound of his shower in the late morning, a glimpse of him in the hallway to and from the bathroom, a flushing toilet, a door opening or closing, a pantry rustle, a seal suctioning sound of the refrigerator door grip; all of these sounds were indicative of his engaged movement and thus motions of life. The silent stillness to the closed door, a walled off barrier indicative of illness, was ever symbolic of the unhealthy, immobile, inactive shutdown in the makings that would setback any healing. Zach was curled up for hours in his bed while stirring dysfunctional cognition in his head. At what point do I again confront him, I wonder. I did not want to waken the angry giant we had stirred in the past. Tony Robbins may encourage the giant to be awakened within, but not necessarily the angry giant within intentionally closed doors! I dared to poke and pry, and immediately sparks would fly. Tony, I awakened the giant, and he was a tiger.

Less confrontational, I next chose to write Zach a pleading email. I wrote of *my* constant back and forth communication with his naturopath, *my* efforts to secure an appointment with an LLMD, *my* scheduling of an infectious disease appointment next week, and *our* ongoing love and commitment to him. My, my, my, our; not much teaming in those efforts. When I referenced the influx of so many loving prayers offered so very often for all of us, the tiger roared in written return.

"I've never trusted you. My brain is fine. My body is healing itself. I don't want your help. Stay the fuck away from me with your attempts to indoctrination. Faith, hope and love, huh; go away. Deaf ears are unable to listen. Don't reach out anymore, I'd rather let you watch me suffer. Hear that."

Zach was back on attack, and once again, strategies needed to be established to prepare ourselves for a third round. I cancelled the infectious disease appointment, letting them know we would try again when he was well enough to get out of the house. I called and left messages with both clinicians, letting them know of our predicament and seeking next step guidance. And then, I received crushing news within an email from the naturopath novice to tick borne determination that his IGeneX lab results came back negative. Devastating. On the night before Thanksgiving, we left Zach a loving message about the gluten free meal we prepared for him, how we would love to have him join us, and how much we missed him. In the morning, we found on the counter an intricate Lego creation on display. He had obviously spent the evening mindfully constructing it. Beside the build was a handwritten response at the bottom of our invitation note. *Everything is NOT awesome!* he scribbled as if it were a third grader writing it, typical of his penmanship skills while sick this past year. Unsteady and trembling hands would further reveal Lyme neurological affects which I first noticed when reading activity sheets he completed during hospitalization. We were tenderly touched by the memory this Lego display triggered for us. Year after year, the holiday and birthday Lego purchases inspired the creative building frenzy that Lego construction would instigate. Those occasions were especially bonding for father and son. Awed we were, even though the situation was not awesome. The movie song lyrics resonated recollection of our February Lego movie outing prior to his Fairfield departure. His clarity then versus that of now, and the laughter among us so liberatingly lavished early on in this very same calendar year. Maybe everything would be cool if we could all be a team again, living our dream. Everything might be awesome then. Lego lyrics, plastic bricks, please do help us find his fix!

Our familiar threesome faced the November holiday weekend without Zach, hostages all to the disease and its influence. In the shared loneliness and longing for our son, brother, and family life of past, we offered the comfort and companionship of each other as mutual care. We puzzled, we scrabbled, we cooked, and we baked. Sadness draped our table, our home, our holiday, our spirits. How long before we can get help for Zach this time around? How do we even get help for Zach in this disabled but not too gravely state of his current being? The holiday weekend came and went, and the three of us resumed our work and our lives, despite our growing fears. By Tuesday of the following week, I ventured forward to knock on Zach's door, in an attempt to encourage him to resume doctor and clinician appointments, and make another urgent plea to get up and out of the house for pursuit of treatment. His response was to scream at me how he hated me and how he wanted me to disappear. He vehemently claimed to be curing the disease himself, feeling better every day, and blaming this entire conflict as my own doing. I challenged back by speaking truth of this illness and the unhealthy, personality transforming impact it was having on him. I stressed ongoing urgency to get help. The quiet house then erupted into a verbal shouting match, causing his sister to race upstairs in response while the cat Napoleon raced downstairs to avoid the haunts. The verbal assault accelerated. "I hate you! You should go away somewhere for at least five years! And you, Miss 4.0! All of you, I don't need your fucking help! Go away!" he screamed from his doorway, towering and crazed. My intention to communicate, to collaborate, and then to even concentrate proved unsuccessful. I fell easily into the bait of the hatred and anger vitriol the madness delivered and responded with defiant proclamation, as if I were addressing a logical, rational being. Amador's LEAP had left my toolbox. "I, we, will not be going anywhere! This is our home, and you are violating our agreement. Wellness will not happen for you behind these closed doors! You must get out into the world and engage in supports! You are the person who needs to go somewhere!", I assertively yelled back. My back was literally, and figuratively, up against the wall, as Gabby helplessly stood by, stunned by his outrage and wounded by the 4.0 verbal insult intention directed at her with no logical point of reference at least within this moment of delusional debate. "Zach, that's not fair", she calmly and confidently responded to her confused brother.

Remember Gabby, the fair is in August. I could not help but think of John's smug response to any family claim of something not being fair, for the fair is in August, a reference to our county fair, and it was a sarcastic play on the bigger truth he wanted to convey, which was that LIFE IS NOT FAIR! And life was certainly not being fair to Zach or anyone in this household during too many days of darkness and too many months of madness. Life had not been fair. Lyme and tick borne illness were not fair. She and I retreated to another room, while Zach retreated further into his room. Nothing but more pain and separation had been accomplished. We were all hostage this holiday season, in one form or another, and soon enough, 90 days would once again be our ransom. In the here and now of early December, I would resume a familiar strategy of phoning the community crisis resources and sharing our latest regression. I began outreach to his recent teammates, the informed and engaged clinicians. Wednesday, I called his psychotherapy clinician, asking how to involve crisis care for involuntary hospitalization if I cannot get him out of the house. We had successfully gotten him out of the house the previous two hospitalizations, fortunate to land on weekend hospitalization entry points which proved convenient to John's work schedule. Zach's recent isolation, his lack of self-care, his discontinued involvement in basic life skills such as food preparation, laundry, engagement with family, and any departure from the house were noted. His therapist listened and encouraged me to call the crisis line to relay this information. Speaking with his med management clinician, we then clarified examples of how gravely disabled his behaviors and actions could be measured for qualification of hospitalization versus a continued recline and decline at home.

Brooks, his outpatient clinician, insisted that action should be taken, affirming that he would continue to dangerously regress further without help. I needed this professional backing, an outside opinion of credible clout that we could trust. This particular clinician, who was previously Zach's nurse practitioner at the evaluation and treatment center during both hospitalizations, and now treated him in outpatient care, was one of Zach's very few caregiving angels. She held the care thread of continuity that stitched together hospitalization and outpatient care to the present decision making necessitated by his recent return to madness of mind. Her commitment and sincerity to all of us earned immediate honorary membership into my compass rose society. When she empathically but emphatically recommended John and I consider securing professional therapeutic care for ourselves amidst this life upheaval, her support and care extended beyond her client Zach. She affirmed us in our dedicated and devoted care to Zach, but she also encouraged us to prioritize a more dedicated and devoted care to ourselves and one another. This advisory angel, this riveting rose, recognized and helped remind us that we had nearly exhausted our capacity to sustain this work, advising wisely that individual therapeutic care was past due. The menu of these harrowing months offered a sick and perverse steady diet of spirochetal rotini and bacterial bologna, both of which we could no longer swallow or digest in the 'life isn't fair', caught unaware, huge serving size portion of care. The first weekend of December was now upon us, and John was home and available for discussion of a family plan to team around another hospitalization for Zach. Our daughter was away at astrology school all weekend, so again, she could as best as possible refrain from unnecessary participation in decisions and choices that we as her brother's parents and caregivers would need to face. In the midst of discerning next step strategies during that weekend, a wee hour of Sunday morning encounter at the hallway thermostat with a stark naked Zach seemed to 'seal the deal' on fears and suspicions of declining health. We were wakened by the tinkering clicking sounds of thermostat adjustment noise outside our bedroom door. There he stood, frighteningly scrawny, nakedly naughty in all of his angry outrage and physical display.

"You all are trying to freeze me out of my room! I just know it! I come out each morning to change this fucking thing, and you keep changing it to freeze me out!" he raged at us from the hallway corner. No one had previously touched that thermostat, but we jump out of bed and open the door in zero seconds flat! Well, hell, Zach, it's winter, you're naked, and it's cold, I am thinking sarcastically to myself. He looked skeletal, and I was deeply disturbed by the reality of our situation. My son stared at me with a hateful glare, for recently, I had become the enemy of target. John was able to step between us, calm him and suggest he put shorts on to move into the kitchen and speak. From cold and yet uncured, to hot headed we endured. Ultimately, a cool down was responsibly lured, by our love and warmth again assured. Temperatures fluctuated while spirochetes situated. Climate change would improve. His father implored that Zach agree to return to treatment and expressed how concerned all of us were for his health and safety, but Zach denied any need for help and refused any gesture of help. Both men found their way back to bed without resolution but averting revolution. These encounters were always quite revealing. Thanks to the naked spiel and the skeletal reveal of our thermostatic shock fest, we now felt we could offer proof of grave disablement. This would become evidence that further enabled the necessary justification to another round of stabilization care. Without stabilization there would be no Lyme treatment realization. Preferably, Lyme treatment stabilization would be our wellness realization, but we were too far down the blood brain barrier bacterial backlash to trust a Lyme treatment to resolve these presenting symptoms of psychosis. We needed to secure a professional who understood tick borne illness. Time for me to beg.

Monday morning, before calling crisis and developing a strategy to transport Zach to the hospital, I visited the local Lyme literate medical doctor's (LLMD) office of Dr. Daniel Newman and proceeded to tearfully plead our son's case. We learned through continued research, without guidance or direction from local health care, that a legitimately trained and experienced Lyme literate doctor would be our best source for authentic and knowledgeable Lyme treatment repair. Regardless of closed practice or insurance coverage absence, we would at least try. Mental health hospitalizations could not be the only outlet for help. While waiting to speak to the LLMD staff, I witnessed Richard Horowitz's book for sale on display in the reception room, among several other indicators of Lyme attention and mention. What I did not realize in my hour of plead was that the doctor would not take on additional patients because of his own recent health care battle with cancer. The notice was printed and posted in the office entryway. This tick tracking treatment provider was now personally tackling cancer, while continuing to faithfully tend his loyal list of existing patients. Dr. Newman was a medical doctor, a naturopath, an acupuncturist, and local educator in the practice of advocating for Lyme patients and their families. How had I not found him prior to now? I burst into tears explaining myself at the counter to the staff, who quickly guided me to a private room, and listened to my story, my plea, for desperate care of our Z! Would the doctor make an exception? Would he even simply consider a consultation with John and I to help us navigate away from the local Lyme illiterate path of care toward a treatment plan of intentional Lyme literacy and legitimacy? No one yet, beyond Zach's own family, believed or accepted that our son had Lyme. I was grateful for their promised consideration. They would ask the doctor. Within a day, the office staff called and John and I were scheduled for an information gathering appointment the following Monday. We informed the staff of Zach's impending hospitalization situation, for we could not convince Zach to join us until he returned to a stabilized mindset. They understood.

In that second week of December I finally began to see a therapist. I had researched local Psychology Today listings, read about the candidates in close proximity to my home and those covered on our insurance plan, sorted out my favorite by description, qualification, and serendipitous availability, and then secured an initial intake appointment. We had now endured a year of severe emotional crisis, and we would all eventually employ psychological professional support. I knew I had personally crossed over into the emotional danger zone myself, when I would experience frequent outbursts of random crying spells no longer just into the pillows of the night. At any time throughout the day, every day, I was unable to nourish or nurture myself. I could not clear the darkened fog of my upended existence, increasing in diminished value to myself from the self-assessed failure to protect my son and my family in this continued cycle of troubling times and desperate measures. I was losing my sense of self. Formerly so solid and sovereign, I was losing my strength and my spirit. The recent hallway clashes would break me. I had handled the 'fuck you' along the way, but the personal and spoken hatred was foreign, leaving me forlorn and forsaken. I was finally defeated. But the war raged on. Personal care was primed but still it positioned secondary to the weight of the week. The psychology of today prioritized securement of help in creating a plan to get Zach out of the house and into his own therapeutic return to mental health care.

With the help of the county crisis team, a designated mental health professional (DMHP), one who encountered Zach in his past two hospitalizations and now successfully secured a current court order, a crisis trained police officer, the receiving hospital mental health team, and our compass rose Brooks encouraging us and guiding us, we would strategize a plan to allow mental health and law enforcement personnel to enter our home and resume the rescue, round three. Thank you, rose Peggy of NAMI, for instituting crisis training as an important necessity for local police officers who confront mental health crises. Thank you, crisis line support, for securing a legal court order, and bravely guiding our vulnerably disturbed young man safely out of the home and back into hospital care. Our intention, of course, was to get Zach safely into one more hospitalization so as to stabilize him for tick borne treatment, but no one could be certain of what might happen when working with an unstable, unwell adult male in response to his unwanted, upcoming attempt at convincing him otherwise. At least he was unarmed, although the officer was not. John would be the liaison to Zach and the rescue team this round, for Zach was no longer speaking to the women of the household, expressing hatred for us both, even refusing to speak or look at us. The plan would unfold on a Friday afternoon, when John had completed work responsibilities and travel demands prior to the yearend stretch of December vacation. He had successfully earned his reprieve of the 90day plan, just in time to direct a third hospitalization for his very sick son. No corporate human resource help would be extended, but our community human resource chain of help now comprehended, even though ultimately, Zach would have to be apprehended.

Within a day of this unspoken to Zach plan of attack, this well laid plan to get him back on track, a winter storm swept through the neighborhood. Severe winds swayed the backyard giant evergreens back and forth in a violent dance threatening to snap and land on the roof with their whip like movement and damp ground instability. The power outage flickers teased a temporary shutdown of our electronics and taunted a possibility of all night darkness, both inside the home and outside on the streets. The storm was symbolic of our plight, as if the Gods were reminding us or warning Zach of what was to come. The morning after the storm, Zach had placed his beloved basketball shoes and post collegiate uniforms, those which survived the many purges of belongings these past several months, outside of his bedroom door. The message we interpreted from his separation severance was a type of surrender proclamation to never return to the game or maybe even a giving up on his once purposeful vision. I wept at the thought of a final divorce from the material outsourcing of his first love, basketball. He rejected any attempt at reconciliation. More darkness, more storms, more fear. I wondered how the physical and mental symptoms of Lyme he so suffered with were further impacted by the storm's added vibrations, sounds, and stirrings. Could we get help here soon enough? Would this storm somehow awaken the Lyme rage tiger before we could stage our holiday hostage release? Would we remain ever hostage to Lyme? How long would it imprison us? Could he ever leave its prison? Fucking Lyme. Fucking luck. Fucking fuck!

December 12, 2014, and the storm cleared only to present the next one. Gabby and I sheltered downstairs cuddled up to each other, while John courageously attempted to speak with Lyme zombie Zach in his bedroom barracks about a return to hospital care. Zach refused, asked his father to leave and John did. Instead then, as planned, John allowed a police officer and a DMHP to enter the home, to enter Zach's room, and begin negotiating with Zach while in possession of a court order to remove him from the home for transport to the hospital. These type of police trained circumstances are nerve wracking for all involved, for safe outcome was uncertain, and unexpected violence had potential. We knew Zach was in a weakened state, unlikely to be physically violent but likely to be verbally aggressive. Cooperation was what we hoped for. But he resisted, argued against going, and the officer called for backup just in case. The afternoon event turned into a bit of a neighborhood shitshow, as a police car arrived followed by an assisting fire truck with a number of firemen in uniform now all attending the deemed hostile Zach, handcuffing and escorting him out of the home, off to the hospital. Zach was not violent, but at 6'10", safety precautions were wisely employed. The hostage release occurred at 3:30 in the afternoon, when local school let out. Our home school had been in session, for we were students, once again, of the resources and methods necessary to safely secure help for our frightened and angry sick son. Was this the help we really wanted, or what he actually needed? It was the help that we found and all that succeeded. To know your adult child is extremely sick and in need of treatment and care, and to accept that the authorities must handcuff him to secure a safe journey to healthcare repair, this was added trauma to our drama. Within days, John's employer improvement plan handcuffs were released, and Zach's Lyme improvement plan handcuffs were secured. What an irony and twist of fate. We were up at bat once again for either a third strike, or a hit and a hoped for homerun. The bases were loaded, and by now, we wished we were loaded. Could we just escape this insanity? In a bottle, in a blanket, in a playlist, turn it up and crank it! Take the bat and swing it at Borrelia. Hit the ball and strike out Burgdorferi. Lyme disease was on first, Zach's previous mental health diagnosis from hospitalizations on second, and our own family's health and fragility on third. If we struck out here this third time swinging, the loss impact could be huge. If we got a hit, some runs could come in, the score would go up in our favor, and we might win this insanity game. Successful Lyme treatment would be our championship dream! Zach was now at the medical hospital, and evaluation and intake assessment had already begun to further discern and deliver E&T placement for this third round of psychosis stabilization.

Our tracking notes of the days since he was last hospitalized were provided and they included our clinical diagnostic discovery of Lyme. The updated medical notes now at least acknowledged the Lyme, despite earlier lab results on record indicating he was '*medically cleared*'. The intake team was open to explore this further. Zach, however, in his psychotic and physically exhausted state refused the staff's suggested spinal tap or lumbar puncture. He was quite hostile, agitated by pain, discomfort, and distrust. The intake diagnoses included psychosis, cardiac dysrhythmia, bipolar and anxiety disorder. Hospital notes indicated he complained of painful urination, painful joints, the rash on his arm, and stomach pain, for which he was given Prilosec and probiotics. His approval and placement processed quickly and he was transported to the same treatment center a third time in 7months on the 14th of December. Despite the Lyme, he still had to do his time. From the E&T notes obtained well after this third admission, the intake recorder wrote that Zach was delusional about a diagnosis of Lyme disease. On several daily progress notes during his stay, he was referred to as 'lacking insight', or having the condition of anosognosia. We had learned all about this big word in our NAMI class, and apparently, the E&T team had just completed a training on this mental health mindset phenomenon. They then discerned he appeared perfectly qualified as lacking of insight. By now, we knew that far too many medical professionals were lacking of insight to this very real enemy called Lyme! Pretty sure they all have anosognosia! On the initial intake paperwork, Zach would be asked upon each admission, what his understanding was of the reason for the admission, and his third time around answer offered plenty of insight. *Well, I don't have one, an 'understanding' that is…to be taken from your home, handcuffed, and into an environment like a hospital, one can only assume that they will receive healing. That assumption quickly merged into hope and said hope only gets crushed. So, to try to understand something that doesn't want to be understood is pointless. I am here, I don't understand why, and I don't have faith that I will know soon.* Zach wrote a clear and honest truth. Insightful it was. Anosognosia, kiss my ass. When asked what he would like to work toward while in treatment, he wrote, *the pot of gold at the end of this rainbow ride.* My smile, I had to hide.

For two days upon arrival at E&T, Zach did not eat or drink, noted as crawling on the floor of his room, complaining of severe stomach pains and joint pains, and labeled as hostile while waiting for the court hearing to determine the length of his stay for treatment. We learned specifics from progress notes obtained afterwards, but of his health flare ups from my immediate phone calls on day one and day two to inquire about when his court would be scheduled. Instead of court, he had been transported back to the medical hospital of original intake. On the second day of his recorded isolative and ill behavior at E&T, dizzy and unable to walk, complaining of severe stomach pain, someone there had made the wise decision to do so, but did not notify us. At the medical hospital, he received IV fluids and IV Haldol, he was diagnosed with gastritis, and he was tested again with a blood test and a drug screen, and supposedly a Lyme serology was drawn, per hospital notes. Outcome, we don't know. Not in the records. He complained to staff of painful urination, stomach cramping, joint pain all over his body, and of a pink circular patch, 3cm x 2cm, recorded in the hospital notes as observed on the inner left upper arm, AGAIN!!! Hospital notes indicated he was found crying and moaning in his room, writhing from nausea and pain. We knew none of this prior to reading notes obtained in 2016, for he was an independent adult with no signed papers authorizing our involvement or notification. I ache about this reality for a very long time after. This ongoing inability to procure accurate diagnostics with compassionate, validating patient care was cruel and full of hippocratic harm. Zach would miss his court hearing this hospitalization due to his weakened and severe condition, but was assigned the full 14day hold on Wednesday, December 17, as witnessed by his father, and represented by an attorney who revealed that Zach refused to speak to him. Axis I, the primary mental health disorder diagnosed as schizophrenia. Now they would name him schizophrenic, or at least they would use the code and qualify insurance payment. Whatever......please just stabilize him. Respect my son, do your job, get it done, before I consider further the Lyme lawsuit smoking gun. Should I? You are all killing him.

The morning of his court hearing I spent in my third therapy appointment, a place of comfort now, where I was welcomed and safe. I knew I would not attend Zach's hearing given the hatred expression and my extremely worn down, vulnerable state. It was, however, not lost on me, that 14 days from his hearing on the 17th added up to December 31, 2014. Would my birthday celebration be one of avoidance or welcome and inclusion? For sure, there would not be a pink martini, and unsure, the greeting might just be birthday, not Happy Birthday! I think I will pour myself a black and blue martini. For now, Zach was safe, our family was given a 14day respite, while Lyme and the spirochetes partied on. Monday, December 15, John and I seized the hour granted to us from dear Dr. Newman, the LLMD in town, and we were eager to find proper direction for the 2015 new year addressing our son's ongoing tick borne illness battle. We shared with him the fullness of our story, our version of Zach's story, and we finally felt Lyme validated, including the psychiatric symptom presentation. Despite his own stage IV cancer battle and the resulting reduction of hours to serve existing patients, Dr. Newman offered to take Zach on as a patient in the event that Zachary would personally agree to the relationship and the treatment work upon discharge from hospitalization. We openly wept with joy. This was our first holiday gift of the season. Finally, we would not have to argue credibility, or accept mental health disability. Rather, we would follow the path of Lyme literacy and trust in this LLMD's competency. This generous gift would be wrapped and placed under the imaginary holiday tree this Christmas season, along with John's imaginary handcuffs, finally unlocked and removed following the accomplished feat of his infamous 90day plan completion for employment approval. The holiday was still hostage, so celebration was yet wary, and not at all merry.

John was home for the holidays, and able to visit Zach at the treatment center. He visited him on the 17th, 18th, 19th, and 21st of December, until Zach told him not to return. On the 17th, their visit was a phone call, following Zach's medical hospital reboot. John heard plenty of psycho-babble, as he called it, but amidst it all, his son told him he loved him, which was John's holiday gold. On the 18th and 19th, he brought his son favored foods, and shared some meals and careful conversations encouraging him to soften up his continued talk of anger toward his sister and me. But by December 21st, John was told to leave upon arrival for visitation. I had heard the words spoken all too often at home. "Get out. Leave." At least Zach didn't dress John's message in fuck, as he had many a time with caregivers and me. "Get the fuck out!", he would swear toward any and all, and quite often. His anger and hatred had resurfaced, and John was the latest recipient. The shift back to this behavior and expression gave us concern about discharge planning. What if

Zach wasn't just projecting with regard to his expression of hatred, I challenged John and the caregiving staff. What if he could not get past this strange anger and hatred he spoke of particularly toward me but also directed at his sister, and now even his father? If we are home caregiving and household managing while John travels with his job, are we safe? How can we allow him to live with us upon discharge and trust our own personal safety if this hatred behavior and thought process continues? The questions and doubts mounted. Now I was finally able to value my own fears for personal protection beyond the fears I always held on behalf of his protection. In just three 50minute therapy sessions, I had already regained some courage and clarity to valuing myself in the mix of all the decisions, commitments, and sacrifices. I would have plenty of work to do in that category! Our concern at present was that Zach would need to get beyond his frightening positions of hatred and anger toward us before we would feel safe having him return to the home. Exhale, shoulders down, release. We despised holding him at these functional facilities, but we relied on them to return his functioning faculties. Balance beam, Libra scale, the yin and yang of this teetering tale. This is where the meds which he truly hated either succeeded in their effectiveness or didn't. The meds softened him round one at bat in E&T, and now in round three, he was prescribed the antipsychotic drug Risperdal again, previously successful for a short spell, but with added side effects of hell, so soon time would tell. Christmas was known to be a season of miracles.

It was not a miraculous season, however, for the family of a friend who had been battling for her life throughout my rough months of struggle at home with Zach. Her cancer battle had been recently lost. On December 22, three days before Christmas, her husband and children, along with her dearest extended family and friends would say farewell in tribute. In attendance at the funeral, I struggled for focus throughout the service from the flush of my tears and the hush to my sobs. So raw, I was, from my dates with death several times this past year, and recently from the current uncertainty of my own son's health situation. To observe and listen to the sorrow and loss of this family, the lock securing my own caged grief and loss broke open, unleashing months of restrained personal sorrow. Perhaps it hadn't been a good idea for me to have attended this service, but I loved this woman, and it felt necessary and right to pay my respects with my presence. Missing the opportunity to visit her while she was ill at home during her dwindling days, I now wept for her, for her family, for my son, for all of us. Exiting the church ceremony at its conclusion, I looked for a quick way out to avoid the crowded hallway, hardly discreet with heels that had me towering, a distraught and weary expression further souring, and a focus on escape that was quite empowering. There often were times I understood Zach's inability to hide, and this moment felt like one of them. His towering spirit lifted me in the moment. Swept into the departing crowd, my easy to spot weeping willow of a physical presence rewarded an encounter with Zach's friend Lindsay's mother. Hello Sandy. My tears are not just for Judy today. Our conversation immediately focused on an inquiry about and a message for our loved but locked down Zach. No one but very few intimate friends and family, and my recently informed therapist, knew that Zach was involuntarily hospitalized. At that grieving funeral exit, I would grant her a gracious entry.

Zach's first high school girlfriend, Lindsay, a lifelong friend since high school days, had been feverishly trying to get ahold of Zach. She could not find him on social media, nor reach him from previous phone numbers. She was determined to visit him when home this Christmas holiday from Wyoming, according to Lindsay's mother. Sweet, spunky Lindsay, the friend who Zach and his pack went to visit in 2012, and now two years later, in the massive crowd of a funeral mass, Lindsay's mother asked me how Zach was doing and how Lindsay could reach him. Sigh. More tears, beyond those for Judy and her family. Where to begin, in the crowded hallway of a church sanctuary following a funeral service amidst moving mass of bodies and wounded hearts seeking out the presiding family of grief? I chose full disclosure of Moritz family grief. I told Lindsay's mother all that I could in that fleeting moment of afternoon mourning, encouraging Sandy to invite Lindsay to come visit us when she arrived home. Then I could share more, answer questions, and encourage an outreach to him once he was stable. Her mother, my friend, wept with me as we held our own private ceremony of loss and pain. She understood my fear and despair and she promised Lindsay would visit. A meaningful hug would seal the sacred bond of trust shared in the gift of that connection. I was at peace with the personal choice to attend my friend's funeral, honoring her and her family despite my unstable and very vulnerable emotional state at the time. I also found peace in the unexpected outcome of the funeral exit, gifted with the compassionate care and respect of Lindsay's mother. I knew that Lindsay and her mother loved my son, and all those who loved him would be devastated to learn of his predicament. That serendipitous encounter was a holiday treat for the Moritz Christmas of 2014, a Christmas that consisted of no wrapped presents, no holiday meal, no Christmas tree, no holiday cards, no carols to sing, no winter wonderland, and no merry amidst the wary. But we were alive, and that in itself felt a miracle. R.I.P., Judy.

Lindsay arrived on Christmas Day, and Zach's full story was shared. She was determined to visit him, and we forewarned her of his rejection of us, his request for us to stay away, and the potential of rejection even toward her. We reminded her he was not well, not himself. But she longed to make a difference, to at least try, and we could not deny her that loving intention. We hoped she could make a difference too. So we called E&T to notify the staff she was coming, we gave her directions, and off she went in hopes to help her friend Zach. Oh how I had missed his friendships of meaning, people who knew him as opposed to nurses, clinicians, doctors, social workers, crisis line workers, police officers, emergency care professionals who just were acquainted with the madman who came into their care. His friends and teammates would tell you of the insight he did not lack, nor his humor, his wit, or charisma, as a matter of fact. It had just been such a lonely year for all of us, but especially for him. He worked so hard, as each of us in the family had, to confront and overcome this mystery. Could we ever catch a break? The phone rang within the hour that Lindsay left the house, and she was sobbing on the other end. Zach told the staff he refused to see her, and she could not get in. She felt helpless, full of sorrow and sadness for him. I wanted to hold her in my arms and promise everything would be alright, but I could only comfort her over the phone that I cradled instead, encouraging her to write him what she would like to say and he would receive her message when his mind was clear. For now, my sad and sorrowful Lindsay, go find your merry in Christmas and say hello to it from the Moritzs. Our family celebrated many a merry in the day, and while this isn't one of them, there will be a better day ahead. We have to believe. We love you, Lindsay.

John's last week of the holiday vacation at home had arrived, and he would soon travel to Arizona the first week of January for a mandated corporate meeting of forecast and review. The confidence and loyalty to his employer following the management ball squeeze, and the absence of support throughout our personal collection of crises, was in question. Thankfully the benefits of employment went beyond management grips and human resource gaps, for our health care benefits, among many great features, included solid coverage for therapy. Each of us would finally tap into professional care, working long and hard with therapeutic care to heal the deeply imbedded wounds from this war. John was finally able to initiate his own therapy support on December 29, and while much of his therapeutic healing would focus on the crisis and trauma of his son's health and battles, he would equally work on recovery from the still misunderstood trauma inflicted by management. He survived an absurd trial, refusing to compromise his own dignity and self-worth, nor his devotion and dedication to family and future. John is a durable gemstone, meant to last. He had confronted perhaps the most difficult intersecting challenge of his family life and career life to date in 26 years as a father, 30 years as a husband. He deserved a fresh start in the new year, as did Zach, as did this entire family. Hopefully, 2015 would bring peace. There were just a few days until Zach would be discharged, and his peace light had begun to shine. John received a phone call from him on the Sunday after Christmas. Zach was kind and loving, desiring a return home to embrace and work with us all. He would rebound within the fourteen days of treatment, despite a steady barrage of staffers telling him repeatedly that he had been medically cleared of Lyme, that he did not have Lyme but rather that he should accept his mental health disorders diagnosed. They continued to kill his spirit. Wounds were inflicted, and scars would remain.

Written notes of hospitalization record repeatedly mocked Zach and questioned his inability to be honest about what is going on with himself. Mental illness, not Lyme, staff would constantly remind. Where was the honest attention and care forthcoming to his complaints of continued pain in his joints, his stomach and even his testicular area with urination now a painful process? For this information was found in the later obtained records as well. Despite the discouraging doubts Zach dealt with from caregiver notes on record, the enforced drugs worked their mellowing magic, necessary in the wave of our wand toward receiving 2015 Lyme literate care with Dr. Newman. With him, we would secure our sought after validation to disprove the mockery and denial Zach was subject to in Lyme diagnosis. In the hospitals, treatment centers, case manager meetings, physician appointments, and in the public eye, tick borne illness is a diagnosis too often ignored or full of skepticism. There had clearly been an unfortunate lack of evidence based education and training around the truths of tick borne illness diagnosis and patient treatment care that this community should embrace and employ, not unlike a familiar necessity within so many communities worldwide. Once we furthered our own personal Lyme learning curve chasing our son's wellness and recovery, we would better advocate this necessity. There would be tremendous value in educating the many ill-informed professional caregiving networks and professionals we had encountered on this harrowing health seeking journey. How many others would suffer unknowingly much like our Zach we would *always* wonder?

The E&T discharge strategy third time around included a Least Restrictive Alternative (LRA) agreement mandating that Zach abide by a minimum 90day commitment to medication adherence, outpatient appointments, and case management weekly sessions. The repeating cycle of hospitalizations would need to stop. Inaccurate diagnostics and treatments were expensive for everyone, but especially so for the life our son, Zach. This was costing him his life. Should he violate the LRA agreement, the court would send him to the state psychiatric hospital for a lengthy involuntary hospitalization which would include more extensive mental health treatment and evaluation, and a critical delay in treating his chronic Lyme. No one, especially Zach and his family, wanted this outcome. We would tiptoe around the shadows of this threat throughout next step protocol, haunted by this hovering possibility and taunted by Lyme's psychiatric presenting probability. Lyme treatment was mandatory in our eyes. If we could get a team to believe, we felt we could succeed. Here was the 90day yoke again! We were getting pretty skilled at 90day survival, three months at a time. So haunted are we, in the shadow of the three.

Our quieted Zach would return home. The medicines of mandate included 4mg of Risperdal twice daily for psychosis and mood stabilizing, 2 mg Lorazepam twice daily for anxiety or sleep, 2mg of Risperdal once daily for paranoia and agitation, and Prilosec for two more weeks to help the diagnosed gastritis. This was the designated daily menu. On discharge day, his father picked his weary son up and treated him to a favored meal on the Burgerville menu. Myself, therapy session four was on the menu, my favorite number and my appetizer to the remaining course of the day. December 31, 2014; a day of merry, a day of weary but definitely not wary, and once again, the beginning of no more contrary. Play that Lego song, add that happy to birthday, and bring on that promising new year of 2015. One more gift of the day was yet on its way. Into the doorway, twist, duck and glide, my beautiful son arrived. Zach handed me a simple birthday card with a picture of a sock

SONFLOWER

puppet holding a flower and a message written on the front of the card. I open it and the message takes me to so many occasions when a hug made the most impact.

> MOM ..... For all you are and all you do, On your birthday this hug's for you!
> I still love you and will always hug you, happy birthday, Zach.

Zach Moritz

YOU ARE WHAT YOU DO

WORKSHEET

I want to be ~~ACTIVE~~ Active

Act _pro-active_ by doing this:

1. Starting slow
2. building strength
3. Making gains / strides toward growth

I want to be ~~Independent~~ Independent

Act _Intelligently_ by doing this:

1. Getting healthy
2. Securing a place of independence
3. Having the motivation/finances to live Independently

I want to be ~~Healthy~~ Healthy

Act _Accordingly_ by doing this:

1. Playing along step by step
2. Taking the right meds
3. Seeing the right specialists

Name: **MORITZ, ZACHARY C.**
Medical Record
DOB: 06/06/1988   Age: 26
Date of Admission: 12/14/2014

57

Insert 29 •   2014, December. E&T document

Part Four

Awareness

Chapter 23: Bridge to Recovery Road

Bridge Over Troubled Water, Simon and Garfunkel

O-O-H Child, The Five Stair Steps

The Moritz family was finally prepared for and within sight of crossing the healing bridge over and into Lyme treatment recovery. In the new calendar year, we were certain that happy would be greeted on the other side of despicable. From January 2015 and beyond, there would be no more closed doors nor any psychiatric Lyme driven rage occurrences within our home. We all understood that the return of Zachary to our loving, nurturing home would continue to serve him both logically and logistically as his hometown haven for healing central. He would no longer argue or challenge that placement priority. The lockdown logistics of mental health hospitalization were behind us, and those unfortunate but ultimately timely stays served their stabilizing purpose during psychotically frightening cycles of our son's illness. We were now safe, together, and soon collaborating on accurately diagnosed care. The year 2015 we all hoped would launch a rebound to recovery promise, functional health and happy lives. We would rebuild trust while managing residual trauma, for we were ever so grateful to have survived trials and tribulations of such treachery. An optimistic season of LLMD practice and mandated LRA discipline was now in front of us. The Moritz team had to regroup, reorganize, and refocus. We would immediately manage the release and addition of a medical professional lead, the proper treatment and healing recovery path for persistent Lyme ills, and the steady search for wellness victories to celebrate throughout the ongoing exhaustive battle to defeat Zach's late discovered disease. Metaphorically speaking, we needed to kick some Lyme ass to replace the ass kicking it had been repeatedly giving us!

Zach would be training from two prospective positions, not unlike the athletic perspectives of previous coaching methods and philosophies experienced throughout the development of his 10year career playing basketball. He would work with mental health coaches to train for the familiar post position, the **L**east **R**estrictive **A**lternative coaching mandate, and he would work with physical health coaches to train for our preferred power forward position, the **L**yme **L**iterate **M**edical **D**octor coaching magnate. Zach would work with the specific skill sets of both position coaches, practicing their drills, learning their strategies, and applying their therapies of care treatment. He would honor each process to dedicate himself fully toward defeat of this crafty opponent from both positional perspectives, both mental health and physical health. Much like any of his struggling encounters within his athletic past, Zach would have to push beyond his relenting mix of mental and physical challenges. Yet, unlike anything he had ever faced, Zach would have to meet these challenges while extremely weak and unwell, both mentally and physically. His faculties were dramatically compromised. He would have to dig deep emotionally and spiritually, constantly seeking the personal strength and faith to trust in healing progress as promised and outcome value as hoped. His family and coaches would stand together with him as his primary fan base, actively acknowledging and tending his lingering ailments while steadfastly encouraging and saluting his exhaustive efforts.

We had successfully, albeit stressfully, maneuvered our way together through his mysterious duration of Lyme eruption and young adult life disruption in years 2013-2014. The LRA upon 3rd hospitalization discharge, the '**L**ess **R**estrictive **A**lternative' outpatient protocol mandate per court order, allowed him to return to his home court advantage with the understanding and signed agreement that he would honor the criteria set forth in legal contract. If in violation, he would be subject to longer term involuntary hospitalization at a state psychiatric hospital. For three months, that familiar 90day (yes, once again!) mental health handcuff would mandate outpatient supervised prescribed medication and weekly case management behavioral health counseling. In the hands of mental health recovery professionals, Zach would explore, seek, and practice recovery strategies for managing his mental health symptoms to achieve a returned quality of life. We were grateful for the LRA mandate, for we felt it would allow us the necessary time to institute and build greater allegiance to our recently prioritized Lyme treatment strategies. Hopefully, we could attain a sense of Lyme recovery promise beyond those mandated mental health drugs, for their negative side effects and possible short and long term implications frightened all of us. Our 2015 Moritz wellness team would attempt to post up and power forward. His collection of hospitalization diagnoses including Bi Polar Disorder, Anxiety/Panic Disorder, and Schizophrenia Disorder, indicate how Zach's psychiatric manifestations of Lyme brain had presented dramatically, cyclically, and in all manner of diagnostic form. The facts remained, however, that his ever present physical health symptoms and disease marker circular rash repeatedly eluded each medical professional's pool of knowledge and assessment tools, never receiving the accurate health care treatment as to the root of causation. Mental illness trumped physical illness, when in fact, the physical illness triggered mental illness. What would his mental health have looked like had the bacterial infection been treated properly in the beginning of medical care pursuit? How could we not wonder? Don't you think he now wondered?

John, Zach and I attempted to educate each of his LRA (mental health) caregiving teammates and coaches while our own rookie learning curve of educational knowledge about Lyme and tick borne disease developed and expanded. Not only had we shared the revelatory Lyme research found since our living room ah-hah moment of October 16, 2014, but we continued to share all that we learned from our nonstop search and discover. The assumption, of course, was that they wanted to know, wanted to learn, wanted to treat, wanted to do no harm. The public and medical professional gap toward Lyme disease awareness and credibility continued to mystify us, challenging our every effort. An ever present skepticism lingered amidst the LRA team about his psychotic presentations having any association to Lyme disease. Outdated and false negative tick borne illness lab diagnostics in the local medical clinics and hospitals delivered insufficient validating results for Zach, as did the initial guess and go test choice and round one outcome results from IGeneX. There continued to be repeated disassociation of Zach's glaring Lyme symptoms, his legitimate clinical diagnosis, his circular rash, and the spot on relevance to current scientific research on tick borne illness. The Moritz family was pitching a concept few medical professionals trusted buying into, regardless of science based evidence in the research provided them. The concept of a Lyme diagnosis eludes most mainstream physicians. This steady skepticism and doubt served to confuse and delay Zach's personal ongoing wellness campaign. The invalidating postures were in direct contrast to the credible and validating healthcare treatment we would pursue and secure through the local Lyme literate practitioner, the LLMD. Two separate teams, two separate coaching philosophies, yet ideally, their practices were both in pursuit of the same accomplishment; achieving Zach's wellness. None of us who participated in his care throughout Zach's sudden life eruption of 2014, including John and me, successfully discovered the tick borne illness association prior to a repeated encounter of elevated psychiatric symptoms, a consistent record of multiple physical symptoms, and our serendipitous living room ah-hah moment of awakening. These bizarre and brazen manifested psychiatric distractions led to a gross oversight in the recognition and remedying of his actual persistent and ever presenting Lyme symptoms. The immediate attention and support focused on the mental health arena to quiet the awakened and agitated giant. Finding and accepting immediate stabilizing support to the unfortunate escalations of mental health symptoms was essential. Once becoming conscious and awakened to Lyme, and working nonstop to validate the Lyme, our family searched and found credible Lyme treatment care. Alone. Not unlike Zach. Alone in his illness. Alone in his bacterial batty brain bursts. Alone in his chronic pain outcry. Alone. We straddled two divergent treatment camps regarding two legitimate cause and effect symptomology systems within the healthcare crisis encampment. Could they effectively coexist? At this point, we would strive to coexist and conquer this elusive enemy.

Welcome, Moritz family, to the plight of the Lyme patient and a caregiver team's framework to a bigger war than the patient's individual tick borne illness battle itself. Exhausting on another battleground warfront it all would be. All too often, advocating for accurate, integrative treatment and care was also humiliating and insulting, as to the acceptance of one's historic depth of knowledge about their loved one, one's intelligence capacity to assess holistically the presenting situation, and one's resolve to speak up against repetitive systems of denial and disrespect. While steadily in health decline then, a patient's motivational struggle to gain renewed hope emergence and recovery of health resurgence demands a resilience of fitful fortitude. We remained in support of Zach's LRA, our ticket and treatment for stabilization given his unfortunate circumstances of early misdiagnosis and thus further onset of disease penetration. Our acceptance and Zach's response to involuntary treatment eventually helped us access and adopt a more comprehensive care treatment strategy for attacking the discovered Lyme, the actual root of the problem. So, Zach played by the LRA contract rules of 2015. Never mind that this family began to question, as a result of our continued research, just what IV antibiotics might have successfully done to combat the early psychiatric features of Lyme presenting in our son, should any of the many hospital and medical encounters along this journey successfully identified Lyme as the culprit and treated it aggressively in its increasingly chronic state. Never mind that the medical records for Zach's 2014 year, *without* the credible and recorded validation of his Lyme clinical diagnosis and *without* the potential legitimacy of an infectious disease (ID) specialist's corroborated assessment and resulting treatment, would continue to bias all community health records toward mental health diagnosis following the early on, short lived, substance abuse defamation of a diagnosis. Never mind? Never on any of our distracted, wellness chasing minds in the crazed midst of saving his life, our family, his future, our future! Until we became awake, aware and awash in the heinous crime of Lyme lost time, we hadn't organized around the collection of injustices, we just experienced them and battled through. There were plenty of what ifs and why nots. Today and tomorrow would be our priority focus. We would continue to encourage and attempt pursuit of the ID referral as one more unexplored pathway of potential care and validated legitimacy in this post psychosis pocket of time, having lost the opportunity offered at year end in 2014. Meanwhile, we optimistically awaited our introductory intake appointment on January 7th with our newly acquired Lyme Literate Medical Doctor (LLMD), Dr. Daniel Newman. This new coach would offer a depth of experience and expertise, and ideally, we hoped he could validate our personal living room diagnosis beyond the CDC measurable markers and provide Zach with the long overdue proper path to healing.

As the new year and winter season transitioned, so did the continued responsibilities of daily living despite ongoing management of the aftermath of traumatized crisis. The day to day demands seldom pause in accommodation to seasons of setback. John resumed work travel to Arizona for the corporate annual meeting, having survived the 2014 threat of job loss and the 2015 impending proposal of a company restructure, thus a redefinition of all management positions. Gabrielle secured a marketing position with the Portland Alzheimer's Association, introducing herself to an arduous commute across the river, and a fuller engagement into her professional world. Beth resumed daily advocacy and home healthcare for Zach, continuing to balance primary home care responsibilities and support for the two career pursuing, paycheck renewing professionals of the household. Our cat Napoleon took turns tending to us all with his loyal pet love, often curled up safely now under the draped arm of his fellow recluse, Zach, or cradled into the rocking arms of our compassionate, pet loving daughter. Doors opened in the new year. From the moment Zach came home on my December birthday, our hugs resumed, and anger only presented occasionally during shared moments of expressed frustration for how difficult and bizarre this illness was. Even then, the expression was not violent, rage filled anger or uproar. Anger would now be expressed more so as disappointment for a healing progress that had repeatedly been so evasive and slow. Bedroom doors were closed only at night for sound reduction and sleep seduction, neither of which were guaranteed for him anymore, despite the steady access of prescribed medications to assist. We were very intentional to work at removing any triggers of the past year, and one of those was the closed door with its resulting isolation and a trend toward downward spiral. We had agreed that despite his frequent bed ridden daytime posture, the bedroom door would remain open or only partially closed when privacy was needed, thus implying an open commitment to working together, a receptivity reclaimed. Zach spoke openly to us about being afraid of his vulnerability to a fall back versus powering forward possibility. Equally, we managed this same fear, an apprehension we held unspoken to him. When his emotional and physical strength would rebuild in time, we would encourage him to embrace more outings and more engagement with the world, as would his case management team. This fear reflected the trauma.

This young man was exhausted, mystified, vulnerable and ever so hungry to rebuild a life worth living. Lyme treatment had not even yet begun. Symptoms continued to persist and side effects to the mental health drugs likely provided an assist. The cognitive deficits, language and mental acuity regression, the blank stare of a drug induced state accompanied lingering back, neck and joint pain, fatigue and malaise, stomach aches, light and sound sensitivity, and a host of cycling health symptom affectation confronting this formerly healthy and robust athlete. What was a result of the medication intake, and what was a result of the multiplying spirochete at stake? How would we know? How would we discern? Hair loss, bowel changes, urinary pains, tremors, appetite loss, nightmares and bouts of insomnia …. many of these symptoms he had been displaying and complaining about at various intakes throughout the previous year, but now we were openly talking about them, eager to lovingly tend them. Zach wanted and asked for our help in this post psychosis season. He welcomed and now frequently expressed appreciation for the family love and support. This refueled us all in the days, weeks, and months ahead chasing wellness. But he was still incredibly vulnerable and sick. In the handful of serendipitous moments throughout our 2year trial to expose and expel Zach's illness enemy, finding Dr.

Newman was among them. A successfully practicing Lyme literate MD was not an easily accessible find in 2014, nor is it yet today in the world of Lyme educated medical providers. Our best choices for practitioners at the time of Lyme discovery required us to travel south into the suburbs of Portland, Oregon, through ever increasing traffic delays, to travel north to a smaller community an hour away for a recommended naturopath, to travel north three hours on a good traffic day to Seattle for additional popular possibilities, or to work via telephone and long distance with California LLMD's offering a depth of experience in client care for treating tick borne illness. We were surprised to learn of the disease prevalence in California, especially in the Sierra Nevada mountains, but increasingly in pockets throughout the nature decorated, thus tick incarcerated Pacific Northwest which we called home.

There was demand for local Lyme care, and we were fortunate to find a knowledgeable physician a mere five minutes up the expeditious 99th Street road on into Hazel Dell. *The doctor in the Dell, the doctor in the Dell…. hi ho a cure we hope, the doctor in the Dell!* Humor, a medicine so crucial to anyone's wellness. Our popular local LLMD opened his 'closed to new client' door for Zach, endearing us to him and his treatment team, and building a hope allegiance within our Zach recovery dream. Again, doors opened. This doctor was a board certified internist and naturopath, a pain management and emergency medicine specialist, an acupuncturist, an instructor academically to his peers, a consultant to medical examiners and insurance systems, and an experienced physician in treating patients with tick borne illness, including those with psychiatric features. *Hi ho a cure we hope, the doctor in the Dell.* We could not believe our good fortune, and wished we could have understood our predicament long ago, securing him as our coach while in psychosis season. Post season would have to do. An obvious choice, he was, although there did exist a potential challenge in the longevity of our new relationship. This fated find was a ray of sunshine in our lives, yet still, a storm cloud hovered. Dr. Newman was battling stage four lung cancer as of fall 2014, a fact that lent itself to some worry and concern, no doubt. But the unfortunate life circumstance for him heightened our belief that, among all of his many accolades and accomplishments, this challenge he faced might influence the odds of an even more forthright, empathically dedicated warrior of a coach in treatment protocol and urgency of action. Our family wanted to stand in the doctor's corner as much as we wanted him in ours. We understood battle. *Hi ho, a cure for him, the doctor in the Dell.* We entered this new season of care believing in a championship outcome led by this dedicated and seasoned coach now leading our Lyme care team, trusting that he would refer us out if he could no longer care for himself or his patients. Our new man Newman had a loyal and dedicated following by measure of his staff and his patient's feedback. There was a community family feel to the look of the brick house exterior, the lobby shelves of holistic supplements and naturopathic readings and resources, and the buzz of neighborly folk steadily coming and going. The 5minute drive from our home meant that 6'10" Zach would not have to endure long, potentially traffic laden drives to and from any ongoing treatment and care, pushing and stressing his physical and mental fatiguing faculties of steady back, neck and joint pain aggravation, and cognitive acuity decline. Convenience was a privilege.

This coach, mentor, physician, humanitarian renewed my hope, our hope, in the medical profession from which we had been so wounded. Our work with him in direct care of Zach began the intake afternoon of January 7, 2015. Finally, someone was listening for more than madness, someone was responding to the actual truths of Zach's sadness. Did no harm. "Tell me about yourself, Zach. Your parents have given me some background, but I am most interested in your take, your story", the doctor began, seated in his weathered leather chair directly across from Zach, separated by a huge wooden desk and surrounded by walls of resource books and tools. His hospitality extended its silent yet graceful gesture in the form of an inviting bowl of plump cashews placed between the patient and physician on the desk corner, served by way of a hygienic spoon delivery system. "How can I help you in your wellness pursuit?" he questioned. Zach shifted ever so uncomfortably in the averaged sized chair, managing his oversized self and his supersized pain. "Would you mind if I lay on the floor?", he politely asked, tending to his immediate aches of discomfort, and then proceeding to answer the questions he had been practicing so often with medical professionals over the past year, in right mind and in lost mind, in honest clear delivery and in aggressive cloudy delivery. Today, he was in right mind with honest, direct delivery, and he summarized the crux of the matter.

"I believe I have Lyme disease, as evidenced by a series of sudden health outbreaks both physical and mental, as well as spiritual. It has gone undiagnosed and essentially has turned my life upside down", Zach speaks eloquently in a quiet yet clear voice while laying his large lumbering frame across the only open floor space in the cozy cocoon of care. I scoot my chair aside to accommodate. "It seems to have fully awakened and erupted while I was in Iowa. I desperately need to regain strength and clarity, to reclaim my life. My family has suffered alongside of me trying to understand what has happened, what is happening, and what to do. I need help." Zach's simplicity and truth was captivating. "Zach, what happened in Fairfield?" Newman inquired, intrigued possibly around the unique environment of the school and community as much as the mystery of the combined stressors that aggressively awakened a previously subtle bacterial spirochete reveal in his life prior to this Iowa breakout breakdown occurrence. The doctor had read the comprehensive notes provided in advance by Zach's parents, but he was wise enough to solicit the primary source. He seemed to wonder with great curiosity if there was something more that Zach wanted or needed to add to our shared perception of the Fairfield, Iowa story. With deeply saddened eyes, and a long, slow pause, Zach looked up at the doctor and simply responded, "I would rather not talk about it. It just saddens me so much. Some of it I understand, and most I do not. Talking about it doesn't change my situation." Zachary remained mum to MUM. Dr. Newman received and reacted to his patient's honesty with a reflective almost all knowing glance followed by an empathic and clear stance. "Let's move on into healing work, Zach."

I knew the familiar sorrow in Zach's voice, the lost vision protected in his response. Depression was as ever present in the daily battle of hope and recovery as we believed the spirochetes were to his tissue and organs. We were all ready to get on with healing. Prior to this initial Newman appointment, we were asked to complete a symptom checklist questionnaire. Previously, in October of 2014, we had retrieved a diagnostic online questionnaire resource written by Lyme researcher Dr. Burrascano and completed it at that time to initially assess Zach's Lyme symptoms. We shared this and he completed the assessment again at this intake. His current symptom status at Dr. Newman's had changed little from those October records, despite his December mental health hospitalization and the continued heavy antipsychotic medications for stabilization. Rage had been tamed to lame, but all else in the suffering game remained the same. He handed this completed assessment to Dr. Newman, and upon review of all the facts, the words we had longed to hear from a medical professional were finally spoken. "Zach, I believe you to be infected with Borrelia Burgdorferi, and I suspect there are co infections, which could explain the severity of the symptoms you have suffered with, and the necessity for psychiatric support. There are likely European strains of the bacteria to be considered given that you were bitten in Denmark. We must get the IGeneX results sent to this office, and I want to run the Western Blot. I will work alongside of your outpatient mental health team and their 3month mandate to medication. In the meantime, we will begin a holistic evaluation and treatment including graduated supplements, herbs and oils, nutritional guidance, various lab tests to rule in or out additional immune system health factors. We will discontinue the medications prescribed by the hospital for gastritis. I will want the results of your May 2014 brain MRI sent to me as well." Dr. Newman continued to speak with a sincere affectation delivering next a medicinal message specific to a reality commitment to long term care and recovery. "This is going to be at least a 1-2year difficult battle to stabilize your health, Zach, but stabilization and recovery are absolutely attainable. I have treated patients in your state of this disease, but we will have a tremendous amount of work to do. Zach, you *will* get better." He shared the affirmation we so needed to hear. No one had told us this. This was hope injection.

Dr. Newman spoke with rapid articulation and always delivered an extensive evaluation, thus note taking was of critical necessity. Mom micro managed the notes, while Zach micro managed the virtue of patience. *'Patience is a virtue'*; the tattoo on the back of his right arm messaged a truth, often preached by his mother and much more practiced by each family member when working with one another through these trying times. We all pledged to be virtuous patients of patience. Our appointments would be once a month, while we instituted a gradual introduction of the multiple pills, oils, powders, teas, drops, and procedures included within his Lyme treatment protocol. It was expensive, extensive, and intensive. Life is. Game on. We left that first appointment carrying home an array of bottles, jars, and lists, a binder of office and care information, lab packets for a stool profile GI panel, a Lactulose breath test exploring small intestine bacterial overgrowth, a Urinary Environmental Pollutants profile, and a toxic metals screen. We had a list of graduated supplement intake, a description of Herxing symptoms (a die off reaction to the dead toxic bacteria) along with a protocol for Herxheimer detoxification treatment, and an additional list of follow up to do's. We would not forget the doctor's most important prescription, that of validation. Validation, it was finally given in a dose that would treat those lingering open and aching wounds from missed diagnosis of infection for too long.

We would need plenty of refills prescribed for this particular medicinal drug, with no concern of overuse or unhealthy addiction.

Following the week after our Newman kickoff, Zach resumed outpatient care appointments with his mental health prescriber and began the new routine of required weekly therapeutic care and support with an assigned case manager from community health. Biweekly, he would work on the management of psychotropic meds and symptoms, while weekly we would host his case manager in the accommodating convenience of our home. She would work privately and solely with her adult client Zach, not at all working within his family, nor teaming with us in any case manager decisions, services, or assistance. Zach was an adult and they would treat him as such. The challenge in this was that his brain was cognitively infected, so record keeping and notes were critical. He would get out of the house for appointments, labs, and miscellaneous attempts at exercise or socialization, while his case manager would accommodate his health fatigue and emotional vulnerability by meeting in the safety and quiet of our home. A routine began to take shape. Her work with him was protected as private between the two of them, but her professional notes on record were found to be shared among her employer support team for collaborative analysis and decision making. None of her/their work or conversations or decisions were shared with us unless Zach chose to share. At 26 years of age, on Medicaid assistance, categorized as an independent adult despite total dependence on us for all life basics to survival, Zach's therapeutic treatment week after week was theirs to introduce, deliver, encourage and assist. The expanded team initially felt refreshingly liberating to John and me, after so much reliance upon ourselves to help him. Each engaging effort painted a promising picture of a more likely return to a healthier, functional Zach, encouraging his desired eventual return to independence and informing him of access pathways to community services for support. Their work together became a weekly exercise in redeveloping for Zach a healthier sense of self and purpose, a return toward vim and vigor, voice and vision, and possibly even revitalization of vocation. The ultimate victory would be his own validation of hope revitalized. What most interfered with any victory, however, would be the ongoing insidious impact of the spirochete on his brain and the ineffectiveness of rotating drug treatments tried. A cycling intake of differing mental health drugs were unsuccessful in attempts to quiet the nightmares, resolve the cognitive affectation, and help him break free from the multiple side effects of spirochete penetration. Frighteningly, these side effects frequently included suicidal ideation and severe depression. The graduated Lyme treatment protocol that Dr. Newman prescribed with careful consideration to an intentional measure and pace while coexisting with the LRA treatment priority, did at least provide relief to Zach's joint pain and the overall body aches of Lyme. However, the continued medications from the mandated mental health prescribing protocol, which were deemed necessary to stabilize the mentally disordered brain and ideally prevent recurring psychosis, had their own side effects forewarned within their prescription cautionary notes. Side effects were the tradeoff to controlling delusions, hallucinations, and rage. Which caused what, was always the question?

Month by month, it seemed impossible to discern what the antipsychotics and antidepressants were doing favorably versus unfavorably, while simultaneously seeking Lyme treatment results. Was it possible that intravenous antibiotics could instead best manage his psychiatric features? We wondered often. Dr. Newman was waiting to prescribe antibiotics until the 90day LRA expired and the IgeneX Western Blot results confirmed the clinically diagnosed Lyme. These early days and weeks in building this bridge to recovery road dragged on in monotony and confusion from the constant shifting of mental health prescription trials accompanied by unpredictable outcomes, new side effect challenges, and transition precautionary measures from dropping and adding the various ineffective remedying attempts. By the end of January, Zach and I showed up in the prescriber's office together questioning the Risperdal, the Lorazepam, the quantities and especially their affectation toward suicide ideation. He complained of vivid nightmares, the resulting insomnia, and ever present thoughts of death. His prescriber was vigilant in listening to him, making graduated changes as responsibly allowable, and working as required within the community health, government funded, prescribing constraints of a 'cheap drug prescribed first' pathway. Zach worked so hard, so dedicatedly, so diligently in the midst of a constantly weakened mind and body. This is the truth of the Lyme warrior, struggling to find relief, fighting for a functional life.

While in the ongoing work of exercising discipline and practice, the family would look for ways to lighten the days, lift the spirits, and liberate the recent past isolations. Each day offered a lot of time together for Zach and me, and each weekend or occasional weeknight for time with his father and sister. He was ever so hungry for engagement, for conversation about what all had happened to him and to us these past mysterious months, for ongoing research about mental health and Lyme, for attempts to reclaim something, anything, of resemblance to a former self. We each would make our way to his bedroom, to hang out with him, to play games of Boggle and cards with him, to share about current events and activities, and to encourage him. He was now so gentle, so vulnerable and tender, so frightened of what was and what might yet again be. None of us knew, and thus, Eckart Tolle became the mantra king again and again. At night, after a day of intermittent conversations that would reflect and ponder topics of past and or future, Zach and I would reflect together in the gift of the present, through excerpts from "*The Power of Now- A Guide to Spiritual Enlightenment*". I would read to him, as we would lay side by side in the kingdom king, Zach under bed cover with a heating pad and castor oil on his lower abdomen, and mom in the corner under an afghan, hoping to refuel both of us spiritually, while drowning out our own individual nighttime demons. Zach had been such an active reader, an avid writer, an animated sketch artist prior to this dramatic upheaval. All of this seemed so lost in the present. He could not keep his brain at task with any of those practices, and because of that he stopped trying.

On occasion, his sister would arrive home from wherever her travels led that day, come into his room and gently grab and massage his exposed toes popping out from under the bedcovers. She would pull and stretch those ginormous digits intending to crack and release the air pockets collected within the 3-4 inch monstrosities, and in so doing, offer a loving gesture of touch and care while checking in with him conversationally. Their life shifting separations continued to be complicated for the two of them, each admiring of the other, but one looking to launch her life, and one looking to save his. As parents, John and I were conscious of this juxtaposition, making ourselves available to both, but it was evident the current tipping of the sibling attention scales. Love and attention were easily dispersed, exercised in different measures within different moments of time, balanced by demand and intention. We felt we should reach out again to friends and family, encouraging their contact with Zachary again, and so we did. Zach made allowances for some company visits in the house, a first since April of 2014. As January came to a close, John offered up a buffet of homemade pizza creations for Super Bowl Sunday and suggested we invite his friends. Zach agreed to inviting his friends Blake, Torin and Josie, three friends he felt safe revealing and sharing his current vulnerable state. Blake had seen Zach in the fall, and Torin and Josie had recently reached out in email exchange to announce their engagement and upcoming wedding plans. We all hoped this small gathering would lift Zach's spirit and reconnect him gradually to an extended circle of support. Through and beyond these LRA restrictions and their ever intense, never relenting grip on his life reclamation, there must be pleasure to seek and people to be told, along with celebrations and gatherings to have and to hold. So in the here and now of championship playoffs, we would serve up a Super Bowl pizza party palooza, with football fandom of few family and friends to supplement the food and the fixings. Touch down.

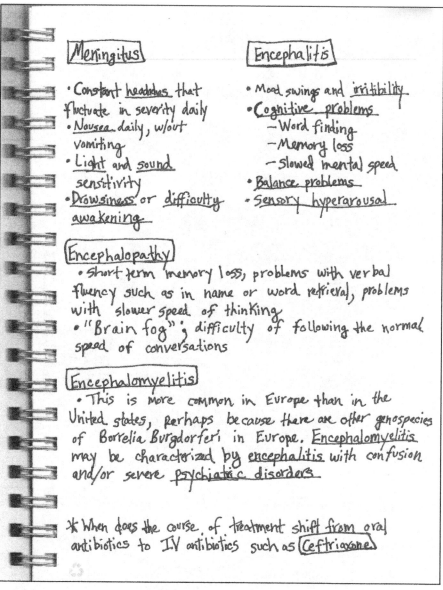

Meningitus

- Constant headaches that fluctuate in severity daily
- Nausea daily, w/out vomiting
- Light and sound sensitivity
- Drowsiness or difficulty awakening

Encephalitis

- Mood swings and irritibility
- Cognitive problems
  - Word finding
  - Memory loss
  - Slowed mental speed
- Balance problems
- Sensory hyperarousal

Encephalopathy

- Short term memory loss, problems with verbal fluency such as in name or word retrieval, problems with slower speed of thinking
- "Brain fog"; difficulty of following the normal speed of conversations

Encephalomyelitis

- This is more common in Europe than in the United states, perhaps because there are other genospecies of Borrelia Burgdorferi in Europe. Encephalomyelitis may be characterized by encephalitis with confusion and/or severe psychiatic disorders

* When does the course of treatment shift from oral antibiotics to IV antibiotics such as Ceftriaxone

Insert 29 • 2015 Lyme symptom notes

Insert 301 • **2015 January Super Bowl pizza**

Chapter 24: LRA: Lyme Routines of Adversity

Migraine, Twenty-One Pilots
Doctor, Truslow

By February, Zach had agreed to join our local athletic club and partake in yoga and pilates classes. While he still struggled with any success exercising his longed for meditative practices, he was open to resuming former to him, yet newer to me, practices of physical and mental health self-care. These were cautious initiations back into exercise, as balance was still challenging, and he had to overcome the interference possibilities of black outs, dizziness, and migraine pain. But once on the mat, and in the care of our tender voiced instructors, soothing music choices, and dimly lit studio spaces, it was a beautiful sight to witness his graceful outstretched limbs and still extremely coordinated athletic movements. Our peacefully orchestrated studio room early entries and gradual exits were accompanied by simple small talk with long hallways to walk, occasionally encountering old acquaintances and making new. Out and into the local community we finally were, and often even accompanied by his sister when her schedule permitted. Healing was happening in slow but certain shifts of effort and acceptance. And yet, the disease still manifested its internal damage, as tick bacteria, unseen to the human eye, hidden in the deep tissues and biofilm walls of its own bacterial cells, does so well. Zach's new routines of working to overcome this illness adversity became a series of weekly and monthly rhythms. He would take steps toward independent self-care, Lyme treatment integration, meds prescribing management, therapeutically driven goals and life activating supports. Eventually, he would add and subtract family events, friendship links, and activity alternatives as they presented, as they proceeded, as they prevailed and as they occasionally prevented. Everything was a trial and a consideration, while nothing held the guile of obligation. Well, nothing other than honoring the 90 day LRA contract expiring on March 31. By then, he will have fulfilled the medication and transcended the mindfulness of the required stabilizing drugs and therapeutic duty. This was the mental health yoke that allowed his Lyme treatment to initiate. SISU leftovers might be necessary to see us all through to this approaching date and then well beyond. Seriously.

The first week of February brought us back into Dr. Newman's office, gradually increasing treatment protocol, reviewing various lab results, and introducing among other healing agents, the aforementioned castor oil pack used in treatment for detoxification. Of all the many treatment additions Zach had in this wellness pursuit, none would have such shared intimacy for his family with him than the castor oil. The attending application became a nightly routine for the 45 minutes before he would attempt to sleep each evening. One or more of us would lay with him, read to him, play Boggle or the card game Go Fish, and speak of hopes and dreams, even of fears, attempting to reconnect with the young man we lovingly longed to see recover. A new man with the help of Newman. Castor oil treatment time was a wind down evening window of verbal and familial playfulness, when wit and wile were on display, and sometimes, the most tender and vulnerable of thoughts and feelings he would say. He was lonely, afraid, and weary so very much of the time. A smile was a treasure when it arrived, and laughter true gold. Tears from his eyes had dried up long ago in the tear duct reaction to meds or Lyme, but the emotion that typically drops them forth was ever present. He spoke of how he wished tears could fall, as if their cleansing would wash clear the stain and the pain he woke to every day. We would shed plenty of our own tears on his behalf, as would so many others. John and I inquired with Dr. Newman about Lyme support groups that might be available in the area and he was uncertain in the Vancouver vicinity. He had patients who travelled to Portland, Oregon, for a biweekly meeting, but he had heard from patients that the tendency was for these gatherings to become complaint sessions, understandably so, but not likely helpful for those new to the diagnosis, and newer to the truths of Lyme suffering depth. We chose not to share this interpretation with Zach, nor did we ever get to a support meeting to confirm. There would be plenty in the search for understanding tick borne illness that was negative, haunting, and lacking in hope.

Instead, Zach became engaged in local NAMI support groups, attending for almost two months, and allowing himself to step out into what seemed to be safe social circles where all involved were struggling with some type of setback. Lesson agendas were national in design while local in delivery. Gradually, and unfortunately, these circles fueled a deeper despair and discomfort for him, rather than firing and fueling his cylinders of recovery hope. No one he encountered in these NAMI groups had Lyme, or were aware if they did, and where he found commonality amongst them was only in the mental health diagnoses and his walk in that world. This only confused his healing beliefs and efforts, causing constant questioning and constant absence of answers. There seemed to be no one source of care or pathway that worked through the combined mental and physical health setbacks when one is in the lymelight. A dinner out with the NAMI director and her Lyme battling family member was our only face to face link to someone in the battle. One other Lyme link was our dentist's referral to an acquaintance who spoke to me at length on the phone about his long and arduous treatment pursuits over many years. While this kind volunteer insisted recovery is real and attainable, his ten plus years of never ending treatment options and efforts were not so convincing in our here and now. The only other link we made was with a friend's friend whose daughter continued to suffer severe seizures and other debilitating symptoms after years of seeking effective treatment. They needed and were desperately seeking a local LLMD referral as well. Seattle travel for care had become too difficult and expensive to continue for their family. More heartbreak. Lyme disease is lonely and isolating. Suffering is what the patient and family know best, with recovery a constant pursuit. We could understand that sufferers might gather in support groups simply to vent frustration, to be heard amongst each other and feel valued as a human being, to dignify their truth, to speak of the invisible and invincible bacteria robbing them of a quality life once lived. How could a medical system allow for such ignorance and denial amidst pervasive sickness and elusive healing? We would battle on.

Zach's LRA medical prescriber appointment records from January and February 2015 tracked her observations and own individual perceptions to include written notes such as, *'patient has complete denial of mental illness and believes it to be a result of a tick bite'* and *'patient has significant lack of insight to his mental illness'* and *'patient's theory of Lymes disease confirmed by his naturopath'*. Within these same notes, Zach's recorded quotes included his professed statement, *'I am trying to come off of Lorazepam but suicidal thoughts keep me on it'* and *'I feel pain, lethargy, and hopelessness'*. He expressed interest to his prescriber in reducing the Risperidone which he felt created too many negative side effects. Skepticism from this supposed support team was oozing like an infection itself, and was confirmed as actual truth in 2016 when records were eventually obtained. Sharing with his mental health prescriber the extensive list of Lyme treatment medications recently added to his daily regimen, the LRA team then discussed consideration of an Invega injectable as the antipsychotic replacement for Risperidone pills. The proposition was that the injectable would reduce the combined LRA and LLMD daily pill intake. Approximately 30-40 Lyme treatment pills were added initially to his Lyme protocol with an eventual increased intake of up to 60-70 pills daily. To have a once a month injection promised him fewer daily pills to take, less likelihood of him skipping or choosing not to take the meds, and for Zach, a longed for reduction in what he felt were Risperidone side effects. By the end of February, Invega was injected as the next trial of mental health treatment.

Weekly visits with his LRA case manager clinician began with work on safety contracts, goal setting, and appointment planning for infectious disease, primary care, and social service supports. By mid-February, he shared with this teammate that he hoped to have a job before summer, he wanted to explore educational and occupational pursuits toward new life goals, and he welcomed some assistance with creating an updated, credible resume. Together, they scheduled a Medicaid primary care appointment for late March, created an online referral for the Department of Social and Health Services Division of Vocational Rehabilitation, explored sample resumes, and discussed employment possibilities for those struggling with disability. They continued work on S.M.A.R.T. personal goals to successfully complete the ongoing LRA requirements and rebuild routines and activities that would support more feasible measures of acceptance for a successful life, adapting realistically to what might be permanent challenges. While this was all far better than the nothingness of a previously bedridden Lyme hidden cycle of uncertainty which we were living in, it was a far cry from the best of everything that Zach's colorful and thriving life pre-Lyme had offered. He was, however, a disciplined and trained student athlete of mind, body and soul work. He battled on.

Woven into the family fabric of his monthly caregiving quilt, offering threads of comfort and love healing, were outings, activities, and events initiated to ease mind, body and soul. Each of our family members would need tending to their individual scars from the aftermath of trauma, 2014. Zach and I had weekday outings when his energy would allow and his spirit would open to stepping out from his monotonous routine. We went to Japanese gardens, nature parks with walking trails, matinee movies, volunteer gardening trainings for restorative justice groups, a labyrinth walk, afternoon drives to bird and wildlife refuges and nature conservatories. Conversation was simple in content, volume, and context, while energy expenditure was always simply about conservation. Visual stimulus was the priority on the scale of sensory viability in choosing our outings. Colorful nature and quiet art would be the primary soul candy sweets we fed this starving artist. Occasionally, the deprivation doused requirement routines of what Zach referred to as 'living without luster' were overruled, altered, and even ignored. Luster would get lured. Food choice by Lyme rules were broken, liquid indulgence would be an occasional treasured token, and slipped treatments sometimes went unspoken. Monotony was seldom medicinal, even though the routines held honored necessity to critical recovery. We would only muster up some luster on few occasions. Music was desperately missed in the repertoire, as for years this family understood it to be life therapy and we had previously practiced expanding our knowledge base and variety of taste on a regular basis. Lyme sound sensitivity now turned off the music within our days, while the disease itself seemed to alter any familiar soundtrack to our lives. The lyric of Lyme was not found to be melodic. Art expression in any feasible form continued to be a healing pursuit, as long as Lyme sensitivities were not triggered into any torment.

The first movie outing escape from routine that Zach and I explored, we agreed to exit early and quickly if it was just too much to sit through emotionally or physically. The movie choice and valid concerns were oriented around Michael Keaton's chilling performance in *Birdman*, as well as the small theater seats which we knew to be uncomfortably sized for Zach's body frame and length. I had felt quite anxious, yet equally intrigued by the idea of observing a performance so recently familiar to the madness we witnessed and feared within our own home. The lead character was suicidal, and presented with schizophrenia. Throughout the story and plot, he was haunted by hallucinations and paranoia. When the 2015 Best Picture, Oscar award winning movie came to a startling finish, both of us remained silently glued to our seats. Zach eventually turned slowly toward me and said quite matter of fact, with first hand wisdom seemingly intact, "That…. is exactly what it is like, Mom. The voices, the control, the fear, the struggle and the dread. I remember it all and it was terrifying." Wow. Pause. Silence accompanying the pause. I recall slowly and sensitively responding with a subtle suggestion to Zach that when he felt stronger, healthier, more resilient emotionally as well as physically, perhaps we would consider telling his own story. He again slowly turned to look at me, and offered a noncommittal response, laced with doubt and apathy, and oozing with empty resolve. "Maybe." That idea sat and simmered for months.

Father and son mustered up some get away time together, full of luster, the first weekend in March, when they planned a 3day weekend to Astoria, Oregon, a destination accessible by a reasonable car drive north. The historic port city on the mouth of the Columbia River is full of monuments and attractions, good eats and beverage, with convenient hotel comfort for the weary among the leery. Zach felt a little unsure of his ability to muster, but he welcomed this alone time with his father as well as the trial of escaping his bed, his routine, his boredom, his lingering lack of luster. John was ecstatic to fly solo with his son, to help him set sights beyond that bedroom birdman nest, and to have the kind of available extended time together that Zach and I had the privilege to share every day. Gabrielle and I were able to then share a mother daughter outing of our own that weekend, shopping, dining, and taking in our own movie outing to see *The Skeleton Twins.* We both loved the hilarious actors Kristen Wiig and Bill Hader, and the promos seemed innocently relevant in that the lead characters were brother and sister, each reconnecting with one another under depressed circumstances, confronting various traumas and perceptions of their past. The movie was refreshingly entertaining, yet, once again, we found our way to extreme emotional vulnerability in a window of our lives where the relevancy moved beyond a simple brother/sister theme. Art was definitely imitating life. The movie themes and dramatic scenes included suicide attempts, deep depression, and siblings being present or not for one another, sometimes at the expense of each other's own life and living......it stirred some gut wrenching, tear drenching reaction for momma me amidst the fair share of comedic and soundtrack highlights. Once again, not unlike our Frank moment of 2014, and the Birdman flight of 2015, in the pursuit of theater art for anticipated entertainment and relaxation, we also found endorsement and explication. Needless to say, we were never far from a reality check moment or a fear swallowing torment.

Despite frequent doses of irony in our outings, we were still grateful for our reality checks and balances. We were alive and so trusting in life. Mixing up monotonous adverse routines seemed important to recovery, and so we sought these opportunities in the mix of our daily routines. The men returned exhausted but exhilarated that Sunday late afternoon, sharing stories of the Astoria Column climb, the Fort Stevens coastal view, the fresh seafood eats in town, and even the taste of a good craft beer, privileged especially for the gluten free, sugar free, alcohol free, Lyme diet practitioner, Zach. *Enjoy the moment.* And they had. This was another Zach tattoo of words and message inked to inspire, and spoken often in encouragement by his father to his son. We were making every effort to do so despite the Lyme pushback. John offered his son some moments of enjoyment, and certainly his father was a benefactor. As great as the getaway break from routine was, Lyme was still working its demons on Zach. He shared that he had a rough time sleeping, he felt panicked in public, and he continued to have nightmares and high anxiety. The day after he returned from Astoria, he wrote a list of ongoing symptoms to share with Dr. Newman. Paranoia, racing thoughts, loss of appetite, insomnia, apathy, anxiety, panic attacks, mental and physical fatigue, vivid dreams with inability to differentiate dream versus reality. What was Lyme driven and what was side effect to these mandated mental health drugs, he questioned, as did we? No one had answers. Dr. Newman agreed to begin antibiotic treatment in April. Zach's LRA would be finished, his priority to antipsychotic drugs lowered, and his IgeneX lab Western Blot results officially confirmed positive for Lyme. Hallelujah! Proof positive on 5 bands.

Zach saw his meds prescriber three times in March, to adjust quantity, to express worry that the Invega was ineffective, to share his struggle with emotions around lost identity, and then to drop in for a session of panic accompanied by me after finding him midmonth crying dry tears, fighting suicidal ideas, and cowering from intense nightmare fears. The Lorazepam that had been replaced by Cogentin was now substituted back to his meds mix in response. He complained that he would awaken from horrifically frightening dreams, experience insomnia following them, and then further awaken with the despair from researching his many diagnosed conditions, his many prescribed medications. It all would increase his many anxieties about his setbacks and his growing lack of faith toward recovery and healing. While the Less Restrictive Alternative was nearing an end, the Lyme Routines of Adversity were not. Even the eagerly awaited primary care provider (PCP) appointment held disappointment adversity in that the desired infectious disease (ID) referral attempt turned into a discouraging discovery that Zach would have to change his entire health insurance plan to obtain an appointment. Any ID treatment and insured coverage for local care would not occur without this change. Beginning in 2015, the clinic no longer accepted Medicaid clients and now required a different provider plan Zach was not enrolled in. We had missed our chance when they accepted his plan while in madness mayhem, November of 2014. Medical health care plan changes were not easily made, let alone easily understood or navigated. Zach would choose to not change his plan.

He had just secured a local psychology practice coverage approval on his current health provider plan, in pursuit of a full psychological evaluation. He wanted an expanded mental health team of weekly professional therapy support outside of his required and assigned community service outpatient case management team. This additional exploration and securement was something Zach worked diligently to obtain, believing he needed an outside team of support that was not biased to his mental health involuntary hospitalizations, and perhaps more open to the Lyme narrative and reality. This addition to his care Zach called 'his pursuit to peace of mind', referring to the constant back and forth diagnostic labeling about Lyme disease as separate from mental health disorder, versus Lyme disease presenting as mental illness symptoms. The ID specialist access would have to wait for now. And maybe that was a good thing, given the negative position ID specialists are known to have regarding chronic Lyme. Other than the discovered disappointment of not securing the ID appointment to at least explore additional possibility of further care, the PCP meeting was basically an orientation, a repeat series of lab work ups, an intake of Zach's current treatment protocol for bi-polar disorder and a conversation about his purported Lyme. Yes, this was the new PCP welcome posture all too familiar.

The nurse primary care practitioner did himself no favors in establishing new patient rapport with Zach or his mother when he spoke of Lyme as being trendy, what with celebrities Avril Lavigne and Yolanda Foster getting press and stirring this trend toward Lyme. TREND? WHAT? TOWARD? WHAT? EXCUSE ME? There is no toward movement other than to ward off shit like these comments! You are an asshole, I instinctively label and impulsively repulse, in my stunned silence. TRENDY???? These many months of despair and suffering have been anything but trendy, for Zach, for us, or for any celebrity or human being battling tick borne illness. Wake the fuck up!!!! Do no harm, mother fucker! Your rookie self has a primary care lesson to learn. This mom is on fire! Alicia lyrics inspire, Lyme ignorance is so tired. You…are…doing…harm. Here we go again……another medical professional who mocks the struggling patient credibility to their disease and symptoms, when in fact, they are quite possibly diverting from the likely reality that they know no accurate skill assessment of Lyme as a diagnosis other than a trusted false lab result, and would offer their patient nothing but a suggested insufficient referral in the way of treatment because they themselves know of nothing to offer their miserably suffering patient. If you play it off as trending, you don't have to work at the mending, leaving the patient and their family constantly defending. Get some informed and accurate training on Lyme, medical experts, and start tending your patients rather than trending the more readily diagnosed misdiagnoses, and the ongoing accompanying offenses. Clinics, hospitals, private practices, and all, make physician Lyme training trendy! For your patients need no additional harm.

The end of the month of March meant that Zach was inching closer to completing his required contract of meds and case management, and although he had no obligation to continue beyond the 90 days, he would personally choose to continue working with these teams. We felt tremendous relief that he had not fallen into the circumstance of a state mental health hospital diversion. But his choice to continue working with the mental health team might prolong the effectiveness challenges of working with the Lyme team. He was afraid to let go of the supports, for none of us knew what to expect. We understood that truth. When his 90day mandate came to official completion, Zach initiated a new additional relationship with an unbiased therapist at a nearby psych clinic on March 31, and also agreed to consider participating in a men's depression group screening through his case management network, beginning on April 1. No fooling. Both would prove to be expanded opportunities for him to get up out of his fatigue drenched bed just down our hallway, and into his fatiguing reality dread beyond our front door. Confronting the ongoing Lyme demons versus surrendering to them daily would be critical to survival. Twist, duck, and glide, he would add these additional calendared commitments to his minimal weekly appointment outings. But, upon return from each, he would disrobe back into his basketball sleeping shorts, climb under the comforting comforter covers and retreat to the quiet rest and hoped for remission from the relentless recovery routines of adversity.

Time of day	Medicine	Pill Qty	SUN	MON	TUES	WED	THUR	FRI	SAT
Wake	Doxycycline	2-100mg							
	Glutithion	2 caps							
Breakfast	Stevia	12 drops							
	Vital Detox	3 caps							
	R-Lipoic Acid	2 caps							
	Ultra E	1 cap							
	Glucanate	1 cap							
	Theralac	3 caps							
	Chinese Stomach Herb Tea	1-1/2 tsp							
	Vitamin D - Drops	3 drops							
	PSP (B6)	1 cap							
	Zithromax	1 cap							
	Hydrox Plaq	2 caps							
Mid Morning	Interfase Plus	2 caps							
	Lyme Plus	1 cap							
	Chinese Lightning Pearls	8 caps							
	Amino Acid Detox	1 TBS in H2O							
	Barberine	2 caps							
	Glutithion	2 caps							
	Candicyn	2 caps							
	Saccharomyces	1 cap							
Lunch	Chinese Stomach Herb Tea	1-1/2 tsp							
	Cod Liver Oil	7-1/2 mL							
	Stevia	12 drops							
	Vital Detox	3 caps							
	R-Lipoic Acid	2 caps							
	Glucanate	1 cap							
	Ultra E	1 cap							
	B-12	1ml Dropper							
	Folic Caps	2 caps							
MidAfternoon	Interfase Plus	2 caps							
	Lyme Plus	1 cap							
	Chinese Lightning Pearls	8 caps							
	Amino Acid Detox	1 TBS in H2O							
	Barberine	2 caps							
	Glutithion	2 caps							
	Candicyn	2 caps							
	Saccharomyces	1 cap							
Dinner	Chinese Stomach Herb Tea	1-1/2 tsp							
	Stevia	12 drops							
	Vital Detox	3 caps							
	Folic Caps	2 caps							
	B-12	1ml Dropper							
	Ultra E	1 cap							
	Glucanate	1 cap							
	Theralac	3 caps							
	PSP (B6)	1 cap							
Evening	Castor Oil Wrap	45 MIN							
	Candicyn	2 caps							
	Saccharomyces	1 cap							
	Doxycycline	2-100mg							
HerxProtocol	Charcoal Caps	8 caps							
	Potassium + 1 TBS Lemon	3 caps							

Insert 31 •   2015 Lyme medications spreadsheet list

Insert 32 •   2015 Lyme meds

Chapter 25: LLMD: Lyme Literate Mental Disturbances

They Know My Name, Big Little Lions

My Silver Lining, First Aid Kit

Easter holiday weekend delivered the gift of my sister's arrival on April 1. Less than a year ago, she had travelled to town, greeted by the surprise of Zach's first hospitalization, a choice we had enacted to help stabilize his madness. This 2015 trip, she was greeted by the guise of Zach's post LRA celebratory ink, a choice he enacted to uplift his sadness. Nephew Zach arrived home late that Auntie arrival evening, from what we expected was an afternoon of STRIVE classes at NAMI and his furthered personal strive in screening for a men's group addressing depression. At least these were appointments calendared for him on that April Fool's Day. It appeared we may have been the fools. '*Believe Succeed*', the tattoo read from pinky to wrist, right hand edge across to the left hand edge. His oversized and humbled hands came together in a namaskar gesture, now on display for us all in the entertainment room show and tell moment. Zach had skipped classes, sought out a tattoo artist, and stamped himself free of the formal LRA. He had believed, and he had succeeded.

Subjecting himself to an additional form of physical pain, the independent and seemingly impulsive choice of the afternoon initially confused and disturbed the untatted among us. His sister was perhaps the exception. Apparently, he had schemed about a tattoo such as this one well prior to the evening's ceremonial LRA closure, information he spoke of much later. His action stirred reflective concern for those of us in the family caregiving circle, for we could not fully grasp the layers of complexity to the choice. There was yet a continued fear as to whether Zach's decisions and actions were of clear mind or altered mind. We pondered. His father had an extreme dislike of tattoos, thus an implosion between the two of them the next evening upon John's arrival home. Arrival, eruption, commotion, emotion. Eventually, devotion. They would disagree, but eventually they would find where it was that they could agree. Both shared a devotion to each other and a respect for their individual beliefs. They could agree to disagree, and both were under great duress. Lyme owned each of us, for the disease was relentless, and the uncertainties added more stress. We were all walking on eggshells when it came to watching and caring for Zach, rebuilding trust with one another. Living through such dramatic upheaval, we had no guarantee that the Lyme disease was in fact healing, or if instead, another cycle was readying to erupt. The family kept working on the *believe*, we kept working to *succeed*. *Work a little harder, work another way*. The tattoos became prayers, chants, mantras, all symbolically demanding change. Or perhaps, more realistically, pleading for change. We needed money in the believability bank, fuel in the recovery tank.

Within the Easter holiday calendar window, the family journeyed out to Astoria again, seeking fresh air, nature, adventure, and connection. We found it in our midst, despite Zach's continued suffering of physical and emotional pain. He more frequently rallied, but severe fatigue crashes would follow. Our latest hope hoist was the anticipated antibiotic treatment expected to begin in April. The LLMD team would accelerate the treatment pace, and the LRA team would slow down the mandate chase. Surprisingly, but understandably, Zach made the decision that he was not emotionally confident enough to withdraw from the mental health medication nor the case management support despite meeting his LRA requirements. Deeply fearing a regression back into psychosis, we could promise no guarantees other than our love and our loyalty to his care. He also feared navigating the social services system alone without informed and assisted guidance, for he could not fight his bigger battle of reclaiming a life without back up supports. So, despite the successful completion of the 90 day LRA, the two systems of Lyme treatment and mental health treatment continued side by side, layering their various affectations onto each other such that it was difficult to discern which treatment modality was most healing and which might be harming. Our April meeting with Dr. Newman celebrated the review of Zach's positive Western Blot IgeneX results, saluted the LRA completion, and honored the long awaited prescriptions for antibiotic treatment. Doxycycline 100mg, Azithromycin 500mg, and Hydroxychlor 200mg were prescribed on a graduated basis. Herxing protocol was reviewed, and medication side effects and precautions were discussed. No fooling, we were finally on our way to hopeful antibiotic healing! Added to the daily barrage of capsules swallowed were probiotics to replenish his good bacteria. Herxing tools intended to relieve the discomforts resulting from bad toxins were another addition to the mix. Each month it was more. More medication, more management, more money. More wellness? The doctor's monthly treatment plan review, following his note taking check in and Q&A briefing with patient Zach, would always begin with a printout of what we should continue, what we should consider, and what we should anticipate. We were reminded of the longevity commitment to our recovery plan each visit, looking for even the smallest of celebrations to identify. April antibiotics were this month's celebration.

By mid-month April 2015, Zach's mental health prescriber and case manager would consistently note and record Zach's suicidal thoughts, pain, insomnia, nightmares, cognitive fog, paranoia, anxiety and depression. Again, we learned this information from records gathered in 2016. There was a constant back and forth of prescription attempts to offer him relief, and Lithium was the next rotational offering to aid the severe depression. The vulnerability of Zach's health and ever changing choices of prescribed medication demanded vigilant monitoring, for the constant starting and stopping required timed cycles to metabolize out the old and transition in the new. Zach chose to discontinue the Invega shot as he felt it contributed to the newer negative side effects within the last two treatment months. His prescriber worked with him to try and manage side effects, but how could they discern just where the side effects were coming from? We so hoped an antibiotic regimen would miraculously resolve it all, but then, herxing would add to the negative mix. Supposedly, the die off and detox would be a good thing, but more pain and suffering sounded intolerable. We were four months into our hustle to find relief, to assist Zach in his recovery, to build promise toward the idea that his life could be rebuilt. The LLMD had been carefully working alongside of the LRA and its mental health rotating prescription choices, while the mental health team had been noting and skeptically acknowledging Zach's work with Lyme treatment. The Moritz clan continued our own research for any and all updates on this duality approach of symptom treatment, this comorbidity cockroach of disease presentation. We found minimal information within evidence based research on psychiatric affectation resulting from Lyme that offered specific details within documented cases. Detailed examples and case descriptions to compare and contrast bacterial strains, geographical influences, and brain behavioral symptoms were not available. What we would find about psychiatric Lyme were generalized statements about patients with Lyme presenting symptoms of mental illness.

The mystery disease could present as Bi-Polar, Schizophrenia, Manic Depression, but what about psychosis? No one wrote about psychotic episodes. What would these presentations look like? We had no comparisons, so Zach relentlessly pursued a deeper understanding of Lyme and psychiatry. He secured a physician referral to complete a psychological evaluation, determined to sort out the confusion.

Working his way through this stretch of spring 2015, Zach pushed beyond the frequently occurring suicidal thoughts. He initiated participation in a men's support group, and he honored his medley of weekly appointments which included case management, prescribers, a vocational rehabilitation counselor, lab tests, therapy counseling, and prescription treatment adherence. The daily monotony of chasing wellness without results was discouraging. John and I invited and even implored extended family to correspond and reach out to Zach. We continued to initiate doable outings such as easy hikes and scenic drives. A May to June mother son attempt to regularly jog/walk/cycle at a local school track in hopes of a physical exercise rebound was short lived. Zach would try to honor the exercise of his sun salutations and simple daily meditations in his room, but the former yoga and pilates outings to the local gym by early April he left behind. His balance, his fatigue, his myriad of disease symptom and prescription consumption left him feeling too vulnerable, too afraid, too uncertain. Honoring Zach's trend and desire to embrace and practice meditative healing models, the two of us journeyed to a church in Portland in search of a labyrinth walk. His case manager had given him a visual diagram of a labyrinth mandala, and Zach found the design to be calming. He placed it on the wall of his bedroom directly across from his pill popping, pillow propping perch of a post. His Aunt Joanne had encouraged us to seek out a walking labyrinth to embrace the ancient spiritual practice of mindfully following a winding path that leads to a heart center and returns. The spiritual tradition is much like a private pilgrimage, or personalized quest for unification and wholeness in the design of one's life. Some consider the labyrinth design a mirror to the twists, turns and passages of our lives.

Zach's physical entry and exit design in life was one of twist, duck, and glide. Since the influence of Lyme infection, his spiritual entry had mostly found exit, in the twists, turns, and trials of the tick. For too long now, he could not find his spiritually centered mind, which left his once hungering soul lagging way behind. By design, tick bacteria seemed to twist, fuck with and hide. Returning to a search for spiritual wholeness together might help each of us assist, stick with and abide. The community labyrinth we sought and found was a painted replica from the Chartres Cathedral in France located on the backside concrete patio of an Oregon church exterior. A small circular birdbath fountain along the wall edge soothed with bubbling backdrop sound. Five stone sculptured birds were gathered at the birdbath edge, in pairings and alone, waiting and watching, perhaps symbolically readying their own pilgrimage or quest flight. The late April afternoon sky held intermittent, floral petal cloud shapes framed in rays of sunshine and sky blue, not unlike the cloud shaped heart center and the sky blue painted outline pattern of the labyrinth before us. Descriptive literature just inside the courtyard offered interpretive insight as to the ritual process and its meditative pathways of symbolic enlightenment.

Release/Purgation – with intention, make your way to the center and let go of the details of life, and surrender as you twist and turn and pass through.

Illumination – open yourself up to the grace and meditation of the center pause, allowing yourself to receive what is to come.

Return/Union –integrate that which has been illuminated or discovered upon the pathway out.

Zach and I each honored our own meditations and contemplations, and then quietly journeyed home, holding our gifts unknown to the other, but valued as sacred by one another. *Release, illuminate, return.* As we resumed the many nights of ongoing care under the spirit and intention of the labyrinth design visual on the bedroom wall, our afternoon outing would hold lingering resonance to reason. Let go, open up, and discover. What was at the heart, the spiritual center, with this discovery as we surrender into healing? What would we need to release? What more would illuminate?

Increasingly, throughout April and May of 2015, we discovered new articles and updated resources illuminating Lyme disease within various current media. Some evenings, I would read from these sources to inspire and encourage through discussion and logical analysis of his Lyme with mental health diagnosis. For Zach, a struggling, exhausted patient, invalidation of Lyme truths exacerbated his loneliness and fears. How could it be that no one we knew or worked with had knowledge or experience of this devastating disease other than a handful of people? How could this be so unknown? Let go, open up, and discover. We read from celebrated author Amy Tan's article titled, "*Slyme Disease: How a Speck Changed My Life Forever*", published in Humanthology, a social platform of 2014, about her ongoing battle with Lyme disease, getting diagnosis, seeking treatment, and struggling toward recovery. We read the Costco Connection article of May 2015 entitled, *"Targeting Lyme Disease"*, an article that summarized well the lessons that we personally had been educated about through our own misfortune. History, prevention, and awareness were themes. These themes validated some, but we longed to read of psychosis, of cures, of parallels to our own hurtful story. We might not feel so alone then, or distrusting of a recovery that promised healing even from the horrific psychiatric features of Zach's Lyme. Tick borne disease is excruciatingly lonely from so many strands of measure, and there are far too many strands of the bacteria to measure. Our search in late 2014 for organizations to draw support and guidance from frequently led us to conflicting philosophies and positions within the research and educational content of their websites. We noted that by 2015, various Lyme alliances, foundations, societies, research entities and regional organizations were either folding or merging. Some were even name changing and then reemerging. Mergers appeared to magnify greatly the renewed and combined efforts to battle this mysterious disease. An example was the April 2015 announcement of a merger between the Tick Borne Disease Alliance and the Lyme Research Alliance (ironically, another LRA). The newly acclaimed Global Lyme Alliance promised greater funding and furthered work toward research and education. While these findings meant little to Zach in the here and now of his suffering, it gave his caregiving parents material with which to educate and enlighten the medical naysay and the public hearsay. New tools of evidence based findings helped us build bridges toward collaborative care. We would continue to educate and enlighten, sometimes challenging professional postures or status quo.

For example, when Zach researched Major Depressive Disorder, in the Diagnostic Statistical Manual (DSM), code 296.34, his proposed diagnosis outcome result from the recently sought out psych evaluation, John and I instead researched Psychiatric Disorder due to Medical Disorder, code DSM 293.xx. Who dared to question the psych evaluation experts? Who among us would challenge the chosen codes for a more expansive scope? In Lyme world, one might want to, and one most likely will have to. Interpreting the DSM differently was a brilliant perspective of my cunningly compassionate and equally empathic listener of a therapist. She had been by my side professionally for six months now, advocating and advising alongside of her conflicted client with her exhaustive caregiving battles for Lyme credibility and illness care. My therapist, like most, was familiar with the medical practice limitations that can bias or misdirect diagnosis and treatment. With deliberate intention and skill, she anchored my vacillating back and forth vessel at sea, steering me through turbulent tides of uncharted waters, quieting the fear of drowning amidst unforeseen storms that deplete and defeat hope. She wisely navigated me and my family beyond the shark infested oceans of Lyme controversy. Together we had travelled far from the dark nights and hostile days of December 2014, my entry point to therapy, her entry point to my healing, and Zach's entry point to Lyme care. Our work would continue for months.

The 2015 days of May were in striking contrast to the mayhem madness of 2014, and yet, to Zach, he complained of little to no healing change, fearing intensely that he would never get well. Keeping Zach and our own spirits in the extended light of this spring arrival versus that lingering dark of winter departure, we enthusiastically made preparations for the onset of summer. John and I encouraged Zach to embrace upcoming social events, to continue the antibiotic care, and to increase his efforts to exercise and build stamina. A hike on Mother's Day and a restaurant dinner afterward were herculean efforts for Zach. The work would be followed by days in bed to recover from fatigue, ache, and agitation. Still, he rallied through the month with weekly dedication to his men's group, setting written personal goals about finding voice, building camaraderie, establishing accountability, and pursuing a sense of himself amidst so much management by others in his life. "I am not sure who I am anymore", he would be quoted as sharing to his new found group member confidants. Finding and trusting his own voice again would be an empowered display of growth and healing, we all agreed. Challenges to this goal included his ever dependent role in treatment protocols, and in trusted care from professionals presumed to be experts in his healing. Dependence and independence would require necessary balance for long term healing. His voice had been lost, but would be found. Zach needed some serious SISU, and some amazing grace, some miraculous juju and some healing space. After suffering the many voices from within and around him for months, confusing him, challenging him, denying him, robbing him of the authentic life he had previously been pursuing with such passion and devotion, our son was finding his own voice again. Zach let go, opened up and discovered new truths.

Yes, he had to believe to succeed, but what was it that he now believed? The answer would be much more difficult than a tattoo can be convincing. We who loved him, and there were many, believed fully in his ability to succeed, even against a challenge as complex as chronic Lyme proved to be. Just how penetratingly deep were his disturbances? None of his caregivers and practitioners would ever *feel* his pain physically, mentally, spiritually, or emotionally; we would only *hear* the pain when we listened close enough, when we stood by his side, with ears to his voice, and compassion for his soul. He had overcome early life challenges of much less magnitude and much less depressive and restrictive weight, always finding pathways, resources, and redirection through passage rites, meditative light, and even educational plight. But Tick Borne Disease would not be a comparable opponent to any K-12 dismay or collegiate athletic games at play. A warrior will get weary. The bleary truth became more disturbing with every tick tock and wearying worry of the daily dismal clock and its miserably lengthy Lyme illiterate days. Mental disturbance has its ways.

Insert 33 •   2015 Final Tattoo

Chapter 26: Three Weddings

Spirits, The Strumbellas

Seasons, Chris Cornell

For months in 2015, the family was eagerly evaluating the feasibility of attending three upcoming celebratory events for which we hoped Zach would get well enough to attend. The first invitation was for his Arizona cousin's wedding announced the previous year amidst our most difficult days. It seemed unfathomable that any of us would be able to attend looking out from the cloudy horizon at that time. But 2015 offered another perspective, a brighter day, an actual hoped for possibility of participation. Each month, we would measure the wellness factor, and Zach would consider and evaluate the how of it despite the ever present aches, pains, and mental health crazed games which he, more so than we, worried might interfere. We believed from the healing we had witnessed by early springtime, that he could succeed in attending and enjoying the celebration, so we would regularly encourage his own belief in these possibilities happening. Believe. Succeed. Zach expressed that he wanted to be able to attend each event, hoping to attend them with newfound confidence and ideally, with some kind of assurance that he could actually engage, participate, and feel some sense of joy while present. He wanted to feel normal, and this would truly be a new normal, without question. Just what would define normal from the here and now of this life altering disease management, we all wondered and felt uncertain. We just did not know. By late April, we made our reservations, while he cancelled his. We would stay at a vacation rental by owner (VRBO) around the corner from our Arizona family's residence, and we were committed to wedding event participation, while maintaining that Zach's care and our family's vulnerability would also be a priority for us. Everyone was excited at the idea that we would join in, thus allowing ourselves to be surrounded by the love of extended family in the name of this new found love. There was no Lyme credibility to confront or defend in this circle of care. We would rely on the four of us in our immediate family core to monitor each other's needs and care amidst the scheduled ceremonies and celebration gatherings. There was just so very much about our circumstances yet unknown by all of our extended family. The wedding was rightfully of priority and emphasis, and not the time nor the place to focus on the details of our struggle. Flights were booked, and arrangements were finalized. It was understood and embraced by family that we would have our own space to escape to if we needed, to rest and recuperate as needed, and to protect our privacy when needed. And it all would be needed.

Treatment protocols were prepared, packaged, and then packed up for out of town management and adherence. By June 13, the date of the wedding, Zach had been on antibiotics for two months, on and then off Lithium, moving toward a gradual reduction in quantity of Risperdal and Lorazepam. The collection of pills, powders, oils, and drops for Lyme treatment continued at a rate of up to nearly 70 daily pills, monitored by each of us on a John created spreadsheet to help everyone keep track. Those big hands of Zach's would hold upwards of 12 to 15 pills at a time, swallowed before meals, with meals, after meals, at bedtime, and always at the prescribed time. It amazed me the discipline around this daily practice that he exhibited for so long. He refrained from complain other than to validate the pain. A Lyme patient's countertop and or bedside table reveals an extensive display of personal intake discipline that serves and validates their pain management. Our family wedding weekend attendance had been a successful venture out into the world of Moritz family newfound normalcy, but especially so for Zach. Wedding photo proof of our presence and play, in addition to Zach's positive feedback he later shared with his medical teams after our stay, both affirmed a measure of success. The Arizona party participation parlayed groundwork forward toward anticipated success in managing the next two upcoming summer/fall weddings. He learned that he could rally and rise to the occasions of honor. One upcoming wedding honored his high school and beyond friend, Torin, and the other would honor his college hoops teammate/roommate and beyond friend, Paul. We were encouraged, particularly knowing that the Torin wedding involved an additional commitment by Zach to participate as groomsman and consider a bachelor party camping weekend among longtime friends. The stakes were now higher, of course, and we're not talking tents. The fears were not lower, of course, and we're now talking tense. Zach's readiness was no doubt, in question. But he would voice an assertive yes, with all coaches and teammates rallying support of his managed involvement.

In the meantime, Zach's LLMD team continued ongoing and additional protocol for Lyme treatment through June and July, adding follow up lab checks, dropping the Doxycycline antibiotic while adding Bicillin injections as an oral alternative, and suggesting the addition of Mepron for treatment of suspected Babesia co infection. His unrelenting ailments along with an increase in symptoms that had been previously milder in presentation, such as blackouts, severe digestive pain and cramping, vision blurring, and tinnitus, now motivated further prescription shifts, a recommended colon cleansing for detoxification relief, and an MRI referral to address the "brick in my head" sensation Zach spoke so often of. By early to mid-July, our son again found his voice and determinedly expressed it by suggesting his desire for reduction of all medications, mental health and Lyme. He had reached a point in the tedious treatment regime where he independently yet decisively voiced, 'ENOUGH!!!!!!' He was especially interested in taking a break from the antibiotics, from what he feared were the possible cause of the recent blackouts and severe stomach cramps. Zach hoped to negotiate a summer vacation in the form of a pill popping pause. So, he addressed an email letter to Dr. Newman, sending us a copy, and requesting time off from treatment. While Zach was weary of the prolonged protocol, John and I were wary of no protocol, so we wanted to make a phone call! But, Dr. Newman was in Germany participating in a month long cancer treatment study, and we felt it best for Zach to wait until the doctor returned and gave approval. We wrote a follow up note to the LLMD team expressing our concerns for both the necessity of continuing to follow the doctor's protocol yet also honor Zach's assertive plea for assumptive relief.

Privately, and between ourselves, John and I wondered if our son was simply determined to not be weighed down with all of these treatment procedures and symptom deterrents while planning and hoping to partake in his upcoming summer events. Or did he instead, choose to believe the recent psych evaluation results that suggested his true ailment was Major Depressive Disorder, not BiPolar, nor ADHD, nor Schizophrenia. There was suggestion of Lyme causation in the records, but the language was subtle and vague. Still, we were unclear whether his new treating therapist believed the Lyme diagnosis we had now legitimately obtained. Continuously, the insinuations were clear his case manager and mental health prescriber were still skeptics. Each coach and team wanted victory, but each had a different idea of the opponent. This discrepancy to a single minded approach remained challenging for focus and faith. By mid to late July, Zach would choose, with prescriber guidance, to discontinue his mental health drugs other than to continue taking the Celexa for depression. He would choose to get sloppy with and then even discontinue his Lyme treatments almost in full by the end of July, seeking permission around the antibiotics, but acting independently with the many other daily LLMD medications. Zach was tired. He complained to his mental health team, both prescriber and case manager, that he felt an increasing inability to manipulate his thoughts, that he felt so incompetent and unsure of himself, and that his memory was failing him along with a steady deterioration of his cognitive skills. The inability to markedly improve his health had taken its toll on him. The mental health team continued to emphasize vocational rehabilitation, now even suggesting disability application for determination of qualification. It was agreed among these care team members and Zach that he would apply for Social Security Disability Benefits, SSDI, so his case manager helped him understand and complete the application process. Acceptance of disability was a humbling experience for our previously vibrant and independence seeking son. It was one more lean in when he so wanted to step out and beyond these setbacks, leaning instead toward the intentional life he had once envisioned.

So, step out and beyond Zach would, on the last weekend of July, accompanying his friend Blake as a fellow future groomsman for Torin, and risking a social situation he would have found easy and quite doable when well. The two big men soul brothers drove up together to the Olympic National forest where the bachelor party celebration camp out would be held. All involved knew that Zach had been very sick for some time, and that Zach would be a slim shadow of his former self. They understood Zach would need comfortable inclusion and sensitive acceptance around his many adjustments and adaptations. None of them knew the full extent to his illness manifestation of past, nor the many expressions of recovery impact presently; none in the party other than Zach himself, that is. He would best look out for himself, understanding best his own limitations, but he so desired a normalization for comfortable participation. Zach was anxious to do this, he was eager to do this, and Zach prepared to do this. Much like the nature loving camper he was of days gone by, he created a camping list, he gathered supplies with Dad's help, and he packed up his preparations for the bachelor camp out, solo tent and extra-long sleeping bag included. He left behind the pills, powders, oils and drops, in anticipation of an attempt to enjoy a beer or two, and to engage playfully among friends he had once shared so many adolescent memories. Perhaps they would help awaken the sleeping giant they used to know through laughter, conversation, and camaraderie treasured.

John and I were enthusiastically energized by our son's welcome embrace of this courageously vulnerable weekend away, his first since 2014 without parents involved, his first since 2013 with friends involved. Zach had written the groom-to-be a deeply personal, almost confessional response to Torin's tenderly written, deeply personal, wedding processional request. Zach wanted to honor his friend with a devoted commitment to stand up for Torin and his wife to be, sweet Josie. He loved them both, and had witnessed their love as a couple during its early stages of bloom. And so, this agreeable groomsman's measurements were taken with details for delivery submitted online. How on earth would a 6'10" inseam bearing, size 15/16 shoe size wearing individual be fitted accurately online for wedding party attire, we all wondered? He could, he would, and sizing was actually accurately understood! A photograph for the parents should have been taken upon the wardrobe mail arrival and the subsequent try on trial. So enamored of the moment's significance and meaningfulness, the miss was sloppy and absentminded on my part. Ever so distracted anymore, I own this deeply regrettable error. Everything fit perfectly, and so handsome he was. Confident and assured, unbeknownst to any of us, he actually wasn't. He put on the face of foolery, as he masqueraded a convincing mastermind of morale for the upcoming marital merge. 'Fake it til you make it' was likely the mantra meme he masked.

Zach's bachelor weekend with his fellow bachelors offered a bonus of lingering date nights and late sleep in morns for John and me. Our son was presumed safe while away Friday through Sunday afternoon, and our daughter was house/pet sitting two weeks for another family friend. The freedom was invigorating. Worry was put on hold, and each other's priority to themselves and one another would casually and comfortably unfold. The weekend was an old familiar empty nest namesake, fueled by a reminiscent rest stop reprieve. We would turn the music back on for the entire window of time, exhale completely from the long, slow inhale of 2015 thus far, and intoxicate ourselves in the bottle of belief that life for each of us was finally turning a cathartic corner of cautionary care. That is, until Zach returned home late Sunday afternoon. Leaving his weekend gear in the garage upon drop off, he managed to twist, duck and hide his home entry and immediate down the hallway retreat. He had stripped down his camping clothes, taken a shower, and climbed right back into his bedroom boredom nest. It appeared he might have failed the 'fake it til you make it', outing amidst the peer group trial of normalcy measure. "How was your weekend with friends, Zach?", we both inquired as we stood bedside realizing his return and hoping for happiness not concern. "Did you enjoy being out in nature again, in the company of friends who love you? Did you come to realize you were among peers also seeking independent lives and adventure while facing their own complex definitions of personal adversity?" The loaded questions were stitched and sewn pretty tight in their darned dreams. Because Zach's life enjoyment and health adversity were yet unraveling at the seams. How could we dare compare their lives, and even try to normalize? The naïve and narrow minded attempt to do so was pathetic on our part. John and I made treason of the truth, standing in the shadow of Zach's sorrow, by the hallway of hope's hollow. We were trying to make right of what had been so very wrong. The lingering silence, and long slow delivery of response, was framed in ever so familiar pain, for the weekend had offered him no gain.

"It was just as I feared. I couldn't remember stories or events. I didn't initiate any conversation, there was no spontaneity from me, and I had no humor or logic to offer anyone. I was blank and shallow. Even a beer couldn't find its way to pleasure." Zach despaired from his deep within saddened soul, echoed by his spoken out loud perception of self. "I even went to my tent early. I hiked as best I could, but it was all just too difficult for me. I felt so incredibly incompetent," he finished. What to say in return? John and I listened carefully, attempting to comfort Zach without pity, without excuses, without lies, with love affirming. *Listen, Empathize, Accept, Partner.* LEAP. Our practiced leap skills in this fragile moment substituted accept for agree. Or maybe our leap should have been *Listen, Empathize, Attempt to Partner* in describing our momentary parental leap of love response. We would acknowledge acceptance, but deny agreement. To agree with him would deepen defeat, and we would not partner in that. While we both knew that Zach's affectation of engagement with others including ourselves had not yet progressed to successful conversation starts by him, he had at least been increasingly more engaging month by month. For we were watchful of improvements in brain process and engaged practice, reminding him of their occurrence and the significance in comparison to where we had been. Progress was happening, we truly believed, and we affirmed often with love and encouragement.

But it was also truth he still only engaged with others when prompted. The flat affectation and the lack of luster to engagement, we attributed to medications. We reminded him in good faith, that those presentations would change in time. The family and additional teams of support would claim as a clear and promising sign of significant healing progress in the brain the return of Zach's ability to start a conversation. His former refined skills of wit and wile, his humor and style, these had not returned in full form. Under the influence of too damn many drugs and too damn many spirochetes, he could respond with some of these skillsets but never did he initiate. Zach would firsthand experience this truth while in group gatherings or in the company of others. Group settings would stir his insecurity around this setback, but group settings, it seemed, would be necessary to redevelop and hone these skills. Maybe the mere mention of awareness would be a first step of intention to working specifically toward developing a return to self-initiated, enthusiastic engagement. We believed he would change over time with wellness progression. He questioned if he could change and if his wellness was even having progression. Zach was very hard on himself about this group experience and his expectations to adapt. John and I were always ready to partner with our son, but we did not always agree. If he had asked us what we thought about his weekend discovery, we would be guarded but gracious in our honest response. But he never initiated that question, either because he couldn't, or because he did not want to know our answer. We would accept his shared experience as his own truth, and attempt to comfort and lift his spirits through continued encouragement and loving care. A castor oil treatment, son? A game of Boggle? A reading from a book of your choice? What else can we do to ease your pain? How else can we show you your gains? The crime of healing Lyme just takes so much time, son. *Patience is a virtue. Believe Succeed.*

Insert 35•   Arizona Cousin's Wedding Sibling Photo

Chapter 27: A Farewell

I Think I'll Call It Morning, Gil Scott Heron
Keep Me in Your Heart, Warren Zevon

July came to an end fairly well while August initiated Zach's colon hydrotherapy appointments scheduled at a practice called, "All's Well That Ends Well". We purchased a six session pain treatment protocol, which Dr. Newman had been recommending as treatment for the more recent severe digestive and intestinal pain. The business name was clever, but the symbolism of the moniker was strangely foreboding within that first week of August 2015. Less than a week away from the Seattle travel with his sister to celebrate Torin and Josie's wedding, Zach appeared ready and willing to rally, moving beyond the bachelor party 'campfire backfire' of late July. Other than some concern about his self-selected summer vacation from the onslaught of too many layers of medication, John and I remained optimistic that our Lyme recovery road was slowly gaining traction. The second of three weddings was approaching, and wedding number three would follow in September. These events offered socialization opportunities for the Lyme impacted, socially retracted Zach, and he spoke of them as hopeful transitions for himself. Planning and preparation included early exit options if needed, and always the choice and support for declining attendance at any point should Zach's health and mindset warrant. He had been working diligently toward a wellness comfort measure to more peer engagement, but all had not yet been well. Instability was yet evident to us, but would not necessarily be evident to an outsider's observing eye. He looked striking physically, and appeared healthy and normal in his upright carriage and pleasing presentation. The psychotic thoughts and behaviors had been managed for seven months now, following the LRA and LLMD teamed approach that increasingly encouraged his social integration to further mental health improvement. All were grooming him to make continued adaptations while prioritizing physical health recovery. The Moritzs, much like old times prior to 2014, would do our part to socialize the family foursome. We enjoyed a dinner and movie date on Sunday night's summer eve of August 2. The men chose an adventure movie, '*Mission Impossible*', while the women chose a romantic comedy, "*Train Wreck*", two popular movie choices that satisfied each other's interests. Within three days of those current selections, one title would describe our search mission, the other our outcome. All would not end well this week.

Monday, Tuesday, and Wednesday held regular weekly calendared appointments intermixed with routines of mealtime, treatment protocols, errands, evening games, and our signature castor oil care. Tuesday, August 4, Zach and I drove east to an Oregon outlet mall for various errands and an excuse for an excursion. Always looking for engagement beyond the mundane routines and rhythms of his so called lusterless day to day, he willingly accompanied me. Our last stop returning home that afternoon involved some produce shopping at a nearby farm stand. While in the barn, I suggested Zach select a sunflower plant for us to bring home with the produce. For some time, I had hoped to further my garden plans at home to include a sunflower cluster once the proper location had been picked and prepped for growing success. Holding out two beautifully upright and intensely yellow sunflower plants, my Gemini sun sign returned with twins, two plants at the request of one. "Thank you! I love them! I'll locate a garden spot and get these beauties quickly in the ground." I acknowledge. He offered his own idea to share. "Mom, you should plant these along the shed. They'll remind you of me when they grow taller and reach up towering against the skyline," Zach casually encouraged me to consider. The suggestion seemed a spontaneous shared sentiment to a size identification, not a suspicious premonition. I thought nothing more of any alternate intention from this sunflower seed of thought other than his encouragement to enjoy a vibrantly dynamic flower species in shared association to Zach's sizeable height and physical charisma! People often pause and admire these willowy, mystical mammoth blooms of nature's creation, not unlike Zach's experience out in the world! The mighty sunflower growing up against the side of our property's outbuilding would call to mind our tall and mighty son, our charismatic bloom, our very own sonflower. I rather liked the idea and the imagery. So, we enthusiastically transported our plants and produce home that afternoon, with an impressionable sonflower seed of thought freshly planted.

That same afternoon, Zach decided to take a solo drive and walk following our return. I suspected at the time he was intentionally preparing himself for the physical demands of being up out of bed and interactive for longer stretches during the upcoming wedding weekend in Seattle. His fatigue and occasional blackouts were of concern to him, as were the psychological unknowns he might face. He continued to more recently express a desire for opportunities of independent expression, so we would encourage the solo outings to build endurance and exercise some independence. He left and returned. My early evening aquatics class would be my own solo outing, offering John and Zach a man date to dine and ping pong their way through the Tuesday evening together. I would complete the evening's end with castor oil treatment finale, fatigued and flat following my night of fitness and friendship frolic. Zach, however, was particularly playful that evening as he resonated an elevated energy and lightness of spirit, which we associated with the anticipated Seattle trip and wedding. Attending a peer's wedding was enough for him to be anxious and excited about, but to participate as a groomsman for a couple you deeply care about would justify added emotion. His family and caregivers were all eager for him to experience a satisfying outcome. He and his sister were prepared to leave Friday morning. A conveniently located hotel room had been reserved for both Friday and Saturday evening to accommodate extra spells of rest or escape as needed. This would provide necessary quiet retreat for privacy and recovery from the likely exhaustive events of ceremony and celebration. Our Arizona family wedding had prepared us to plan and protect accordingly, and so we made arrangements.

Attending this event with him, his sister would be accommodating all of us. Her commitment was an act of devotion, for she would agree to drive and navigate the entire wedding weekend with and for the cognitively impaired, Lyme laden traveler, her brother Zach. With sister caregiving subtlety, she would oversee his personal needs as necessary, and likely, they would be necessary in some form. Zach would have to recognize his own vulnerabilities within any unforeseen circumstance, trusting in her support to help make any necessary adaptations. All the while, they would join in the celebratory fun and festivity among friends and acquaintances who would know and understand so very little of their friend's challenges. For the most part, this group knew her as Zach's little sister, so this event was a social stretch for her own relaxation and enjoyment while on assignment. She would accommodate the unexpected, serve the nuances of the situation, and honor the celebration all the while managing and respecting her own personal reservations and valued needs within the mix. Her commitment would be a gift to her brother and the marrying couple, but also, to John and me. No question, there had been tremendous sacrifice Gabrielle had quietly and willingly provided for us all. John and I hoped this trip would also prove to be a gift to herself. Sacred sibling time spent together had become a valued commodity, increasingly more limited between the two, for she had become consumed by work and personal commitments, and her brother had continued to be consumed with ongoing battles and personal disappointments. We trusted that this Seattle social circle would surround both of them with love and support, patience and understanding. There would be no regrets for the yes of this destination decision, made with sentimental intention from within each of our remaining faith, hope and love reserves. Our love, it was a bottomless well of resource reserve to tap. The faith and hope were works in progress.

Those works in progress were put to the test within an unexpected 24hour shift of circumstances on Wednesday, August 5, 2015. The familiar, now quite comfortable daily routine shifted suddenly into an unfamiliar, increasingly uncomfortable evening scene. Zach's early afternoon case manager appointment in the kitchen of our home that day gave no indication of an altered plan unfolding. Our Lyme warrior, presumed to be preparing as a wedding weekend traveler, was in actuality preempting this presumption to prepare instead as a cosmic traveler. Zach left for another 'drive and walk' before the weekend getaway. Within two hours of his case manager session without any confession routine appointment, John and I trusted his drive and walk's perceived intention. It may as well have been April 1 on August 5. Zach's departure that day from the home, from all that he had ever known, was preceded by a "Goodbye, Dad!" shout out toward his father's downstairs office space from the top of the stairway. His father was once again hustling to get out the door and on the road to work appointments, cell phone and laptop in tow, without reason or suspicion to otherwise know. Our kind hearted son had earlier that afternoon delivered, to an unsuspecting father, a heated cup of his favorite tea with honey. Zach's silent, loving gesture of lasting memory for his father was a servant salute, likely to soften the painful memory soon to be delivered. "Love ya, Mom!", was his gift deliverance to me in kitchen care central, followed by a sacred hug so long and tender, sadly unsuspecting in its there and then render. There had been no reason to question, no reason to suspect, but our sonflower would soon bolt and go to seed. Zach would twist, duck and glide out the door one final time, an oblivious exit to us, made more obvious not long after. John travelled for work south into Oregon overnight, and I finished the day in my pilates class, Namaste. As usual and customary in the all too familiar weekday evenings of Lyme recovery routine, Zach and I were to share dinner alone that evening, for his sister and father had obligations elsewhere. But when the dinner hour arrived, and Zach had not returned home from his drive and walk, the extended time away was unusual and out of character. My old familiar, sick in the intuitive gut feeling waved an unwelcome greeting of hello after a long sabbatical in 2015. Repeatedly, I texted my son by 6pm, by 7pm, then 8pm, for he had left at 3:30pm. I inquired about dinner, I inquired if he was with a friend, I inquired if he was in trouble, and I inquired if I could be of help. Where are you, Zach? Please text me back, Zach!

Practical judgement and eventual necessity warranted our son's acceptance finally to use and carry a cell phone these past few months. I could message him and he would message me back. It became an essential tool for our teamed care. I vividly remembered the Portland appointment outing from August of 2014 when he adamantly resisted the use of a cell phone by choice. I had not been able to call him when he appeared to be missing or lost at the time while in an actively Lyme stirred mind. Instead, crazy had come calling, and the resulting Lyme rage had been shockingly appalling. Zach had stormed into the house that particular evening only to explode into a freakish and initially quite intimidating meltdown. We were now so distanced from those unpredictable days of rage and Lyme crazed haze. But, still, we all wondered if we were never far from one step backward into any unpredictable or unforeseen disordered behavior presentation. I hibernated this particular evening in our back office den upstairs, not unlike the aforementioned scenario a year ago. Suddenly, I heard the front door open. Was this déjà vu? Would he storm in again? I hoped it to be Zach, but I was greeted instead by Gab. The voice and exuberant spirit of our bubbly, blooming daughter was all aglow from good news to share. She oozed with contagious enthusiasm, infectious in a healthy way. "Mom, I just got back from meeting with Uncle Rob and Aunt Marta, and we've arranged for me to occupy their empty house in Portland while they ready it to sell!" she eagerly relayed. "It is only 5-10 minutes from my work, so my marathon commute days will finally be over!" Bright eyed and spirit fired from the flame of her glowing sparkle she was. "Excellent!", I respond sincerely in return, expressing simultaneously my genuine Gab cheer and my facial frown Zach fear. I so love this beautiful, young, dynamic woman, but I am so frightened for our beautiful, beloved young man. She pauses in hesitation, apparently seeing through my disguise, and after telling of her plans, she intuitively inquires. "I'm going downstairs to gather some clothes for my interview tomorrow, and then I'll head back to the house. Is everything ok?" With one more evening of care for our friend's home and pet, she had an important interview scheduled all afternoon the next day following her morning work hours. She would then finish her house/pet sitting commitment with transportation home for our friends from the airport tomorrow night. The Portland homestay would begin the following week and we would help her make that move then. What do I dare tell her in my fear filled moment of escalating doubt and uncertainty? What should I say, or not, for what did I actually know, on the spot?

Finally, our daughter's life began to offer her a return of independence and freedom, a return to joy and jubilation. Since college graduation, she had postponed opportunities for personal bloom and flight, remaining nearby in the recovery corner of her brother and family's crisis. Perhaps now, roadways would expand and pathways would present for her. I respond honestly, and expect nothing in return but empathic understanding which she lovingly delivers. "Well, I am actually a bit concerned that Zach has not returned home from a drive and a walk since 4 hours ago. Dad is in Corvalis, and I keep texting your brother. It's so out of character for him with his regular routines these days, so I am actually pretty anxious." My grown up daughter gives me a comforting hug, offers herself as a sounding board for later in the evening by phone if I need it, and heads downstairs to gather clothing. Shortly, she is out the front door, buoyed by an adoring mother's grateful thank you and genuine good luck wish for tomorrow. We mutually exchanged an 'I love you' and 'good night', in an evening forevermore traced to an 'I love you' and 'good bye' send off. A next day discovery of unsuspected family farewell expression would leave a permanent family farewell impression. In just two days, Gabrielle anticipated a great wedding weekend away in Seattle with her brother and friends, trusting in that shared time together with no reason to fear or doubt otherwise. Focused on her personal pursuits and responsibilities, her innocence and perseverance would prevail while I would momentarily resume going pale.

By 11 pm of this tortured Wednesday evening, fear and anxiety sickeningly gripped me. John and I spoke on the phone long distance. "What should I do? Should I call the police? Should I try to find him in the dark? What if someone hurt him or took advantage of him? Where is he?", I rapid fire ramble at him in near hysterics, while John responsibly reasons back with logic and optimism. "Try to sleep, and trust that he is ok. I will come home in the morning after one critical business call that must be made," he offers, even though we both know I will not sleep, nor likely will he. The circumstance isn't simple for traveler John, away long distance, chasing the almighty dollar to provide, when son, wife and daughter are quite possibly within heightened proximity to another abysmally dark place that once again might harken. Regardless, John proposes the light and promise of a new day's break, the possibility of both at daybreak. To push aside the scars and traumatization of recent past experiences and trust that a reasonable resolution might surface were the ultimate faith and hope challenges of this threatening evening. For John, the father, the husband, the man of conviction, but also the employee, the coworker, and seeming target of corporate attrition, the balance of faith amidst the fear was the juggernaut of the juggle. The immediate concern for his son and his family's safety and stability, but also the ongoing pressure of an employer's earned distrust and twisted torment; they were both weighted burdens unbearably insecure. What was continuing to happen to our once stable, predictable, and reliable life? Unravelling even more, we feared. How do we help each other discover, discern, and disclose next steps of appropriate action in light of this uncertain but increasingly apparent disappearance? John sensed his priorities to balance, as did his family. Zach evidently had his own. Was this a fleeting moment of failed faith on my part, to not trust in a positive outcome? What might that positive outcome be? For we had guarded closely and monitored carefully for so very long, working in good faith to protect, provide, and procure. Could this evening of unexplained absence simply be a protest, a proclamation, or an act of outraged expression from our exhausted Zach? Had he chosen to stay out all night to express a longed for freedom, so lost and forlorn?

I imagine all kind of emotion Zach might feel as he anticipates witnessing his marrying peers in celebration of life anew together, while his own life had been so set back and imprisoned. Was this possible all-nighter a rebellious act of severance expression, or an act of drastic defiance to Lyme's continued restrictions and relentless sufferings? I imagine possibilities all night long as I toss and turn, staring at the tick tock of my alarm, all too aware of the tick that tracks our alarm. When do we set off an alarm? Will an alarm go off? And where the heck would that promised Shepherd be while I fervently prayed as

SONFLOWER

His lost sheep throughout this dark and lonely night, on into the empty early morn? I cried out to all the gods and guardian angels for protection, for guidance, for assistance, for assurance. I had been doing so for such a very long time. Surely, the measure of my life, our family's life, had proven to be that of faithful followers and humble servants? Our prayers would be answered as promised, wouldn't they? Such a weary lost soul, either of us. This young man had tried to expand his own spiritual pursuits, working devotedly toward developing an emergent adult vision of purposeful life direction well beyond his childhood youthful acts of discretion. The tick borne illness came knocking, and then all else became shocking. Surely, he/we would be deserving and worthy of the Shepherd's rescue? Aren't we all God's children in that holy family flock of care? Yes, we are all sheep, we are all worthy, and we are all lost at some point within the murky meadows of living life. How would this missing sheep be found? What about the lost one? Faith alone? Confusing cluster flock, all of it was, as my mind raced around questions, end of life fears, realistic possibilities, and holy contradictions. Faith had been fearfully fading and frantically flailing, yet still it fluttered with desperate gasps and grasps for some type of breathable, touchable life affirmation as to our son's status in these wee hours of disappearance despair. Oh ye of little faith, Beth. Searching but not finding, calling out but not hearing answer. Where were those footprints in the sand, of the Man, to carry Zach, to carry ME, to carry US? I needed to find those trusted footprints. Footprints would in fact be found, but not by the symbolic sainthood of poetic safety net ground. My head spun, my heart hurt, and my thoughts were twisted. Mourning would come and the day would actually break.

Arrival came in the sun's early light of the wee morning hour. Departure followed. I hope for afterlife sake, that an arrival came after departure. *Sonflower* unfolds as forewarned, and the farewell chapter completes. Zach made the decision to leave, to retreat, to retire, to expire. ENOUGH, he expressed when he sought Lyme treatment's July summer vacation. ENOUGH, he expressed louder through his soon to be revealed August act of sedation. A six pack of Total Domination IPA, a bottle full of Ativan, and a final bullet had all three bases covered for his horrific home run hit. I did not find his footprints, but I searched and scoured within the vicinity. He was found by his own intentional footprint, for the trail he left to be discovered was the Ford Transit parked blocking a restricted access zone directly across the street from his wooded roadside resting place. The bustling sand company was just up the roadway hosting huge mountains of sand awaiting sale and distribution. The early morning delivery truck drivers would demand that that Transit truck be transitioned. Zachary Charles Moritz. License plate CO9112B. Once lost, now found, he left amazing trace. Zach made sure he would be found. My early morning desperate momma search by car was within a mile or two of this farewell find, but I had been mystically protected, perhaps through prayer, or simply by instinct, to turn around and search in another direction. Maybe it was me whom He carried from the sand. Zach's farewell footprint was found early that morn by the property and sand company owner, a merciful man of guided grace, a faithful follower with a respectful instinct to pray for our dead son upon his disturbing discovery. When I meet the sandman, I will hold him in deep gratitude for that parting gift of love and light, for his fatherly parent protective insight.

Before we knew Zach had been found, John phoned me that August 6th morning around 8am. I was once again near hysteria, for I had searched everywhere the past two hours of daylight looking for our missing son. Driving around town exploring mom and son's favorite walking spots, nature spots, waterfront spots, I shouted prayers and begged for guidance from any spirit or guardian of the promised land. I was desperately seeking Zachary, tear blinded at the wheel, actively on the hunt since the early summer day's sunrise arrival. '*Ask and ye shall receive*', I chose to believe, while pleading frantically in prayer. '*Knock and the door shall be opened*'. Scripture confused me in these harrowing moments, the carefully conditioned messages of trusted promise from my faithfully practiced Protestant upbringing. I had been specific in my asking, and I had been repeated in my knocking. Doors were supposed to open. This turn of events and feared outcome could not possibly be 'God's plan' for my son, for our daughter, for our family. Would this be His answer to my asking and my knocking? Back and forth my thoughts swayed, not unlike the foreboding days, hours and multiple months of continued confusion throughout these past two years of mystery now my story. What the hell is happening here? I heard in my head a taunting lyrical tease of Dylan's '*Knockin on Heaven's Door*', a murmur of melodic moan, possibly a premonition in this maddening moment of potential mourn. Haunted by conflicting personal beliefs and values with themed messages circulating in my mind of possible relevance to this closing in crisis of confrontation, the assurances I was desperately seeking, appeared to be sunk. Back and forth my car hunted, driving fiercely forward in hope of not drifting despairingly backward in doubt.

John, my Dylan diehard devotee, an exhausted, knocked down parent like me, reached out in that 8 am phone call. He heard my fear and offered a comforting ear, while I would question and confront decisions now drawing near. "Should I call the police, should I cancel my therapy, when will you come home, what should I tell Gabby, WHAT SHOULD I DO?" The frantic questions bombarded him, feverishly flowing nonstop from my frenetically frenzied frontal globe of my Lyme infected life. In return, John offered me a steady, calming delivery of optimistic opinion, his wisdom centered omnism, a spiritual quieting. Not unlike the previous evening, my husband assured me he was on his way home. We would work out a plan together once he arrived, for he was peacefully confident that Zach was ok. The encouragement and confidence quieted my hysteria, released a long overdue exhale, centered a peaceful place in my own psyche, and granted a personal permission slip to pause from the search of Zach's trail. Tenderly and lovingly, John had experienced some form of a momentary spiritual connection that he paid forward. "Beth, I had a clear vision this morning that Zach will be ok, he's going to be alright, he IS alright. It was a calm sense, an assurance of sorts, and I want you to hold that thought just as I am. Go ahead to your scheduled therapy appointment, and I will be home shortly after. We will find him and he will be ok. I love you, and I'll see you shortly." This man was my rock of ages, and I had been known to be his. We would rock a bye the bawling Beth baby cry, back and forth, with hush a bye, lullaby, calming intention. Our phones and our hopes were cradled in substitute for one another, assuring ourselves with the belief that somehow we would catch Zach and cradle his fall. Lullaby lyrics, childhood music, fleeting flashbacks, songs meant to soothe anticipated sorrow. He is just lost, by chance, just maybe. He will be found, by grace, won't he?

After John's comforting conversation, I drove directly to my appointment with the other rock of reliable measure, my gemstone therapist of healing energy and wisdom truth. Together, she and I proceeded to professionally tend that morning's exhaustive torment of traumatizing tease. Together, she and I blanketed my fears while I collapsed into her reliable chair of care with ease. We challenged and confronted the realism versus idealism of the possibilities within a grown child's choice versus the desperate desires within a mother's rescuing voice. We reviewed that which I could control, and that which I could not. We shared the painful truths in the realization of this mother's life or death moment, and she comforted the pained falsehood of the idealization of a mother's savior complex. Donna knew how feverishly hard our family had worked throughout 2014 and 2015 to piece the broken parts back together, searching for wellness, redefining roles, and fueling credible hope for healing and recovery. Like many Lyme infected individuals and families, we had been and continued to be traumatized by cycling pain, steady suffering, looming loss, confused medical care, public scrutiny steadily fueling doubt, threat of recurring illness behavior and body breakdown, and ever present faith challenges to trust in a healing recovery. She knew all of it, and momentarily, she would again know all. When the cell phone rang at the close of the therapy appointment on that exhaustive, elusive morning, I naively still held hope in the ideal possibility that it was my son calling. Innocence was yet pure and hope hung on a thread as its promising allure. But we had to be prepared for other possibility. You are never prepared for farewell finality. 'He did it', were the clarifying words spoken. Your hope disintegrates into a hollow hole, an empty echo chamber, replaced with a lonely longing for life extended. Here we were, the two of us in this shared physical space together sitting with this sudden sorrowful news facing each other. My treasured therapist and soul guardian, a compass rose throughout and beyond this unimaginable life twist of fate, shared the ultimate intimate vulnerability within the present intersection of my appointment for therapeutic care and my disappointment phone call so rare.

From my December 2014 therapeutic entry point of deep depression and family crisis to my grown child's exit point of diseased suicidal license, she sat with me face to face, heart to heart, woman to woman, mother to mother, but above all, therapist to client. She was a compassionate human being who understood our individual roles and thus she maintained composure so as to carefully focus on me. In this day breaking moment of my mourning mom's wear and my paralyzed parent's blank stare, my therapist gathered her professional self and protectively guided my way. I listened and lamented, vulnerably dazed from my own Lyme induced, death produced, cognitive loss from brain fog moss. We agreed I would call a friend and we agreed I would wait for John with this friend at our home. Together, the three of us from home would then safely engage in the next steps of death response protocol. I agreed to call Donna if I needed her, and we explored how John and I would share this shocking revelation of deep loss and sorrow with our daughter. Beautiful, innocent, unaware Gabby. There would be no easy or best way to deliver something so unfathomable, so permanent, so heartbreaking, so life altering. Your brother, your best friend, he ended his life. I am sorry. I love you. The delivery will not be that simple, but the words of this truth are truly that simple. Zach is dead.

Who would be prepared to serve up this truth platter to the hungry souls of caring companions while the depleted parent belly is so starved from the devastating death of their child? Gone too young, too soon, unexpectedly, departed in an actionable, intentional manner such as suicide, done with a degree of clarity, purpose, and planned readiness, all the while happening on your watch; I ask, who would be prepared? NO ONE! EVER! But you must and you do respond, to each person in their time, and some more quickly than others. Vulnerable becomes your new first name, for a very long time, and Able is not the shortened nickname for any relevant reference. One must learn when and how to safely lean in, and with whom you might trust any details of this precious cargo. Then lean in and deliver. A dear friend, whom I was to walk with the day of my son's departure, learned of my Zach worry early that Thursday morning when I cancelled our scheduled walk so that I could search for him. She offered to accompany me but I declined. I did let her know I would keep her informed. Our sons had become friends early in life as preschoolers, circumstantially bringing the adults into a friendship that lasted well beyond the kid's school days. I leaned in and Terri rushed to our house when I shared the heartbreaking outcome. She wanted to search for him, and instead she would rescue us. Search and rescue, mission impossible, train wreck, all did not end well after all. Our friend Terri became our confidante, our chauffeur, our first friend on the frontline, and our circumstantial stabilizing source of love and resilience. Like my therapist, she shared an unfathomable intimacy within the day's unfolding to such shocking reveal of our family loss that day, our son's intentional death. She was amazing, another gem. I would be forever endeared to my many women friends and loved ones who stood by, held hands, expressed love, gave grace, face to face.

Our immediate priorities with Terri at the wheel, would be to drive to the police station, confirm details of Zach's death, collect his belongings, become advised of funeral options, retrieve his car from impound, take note of and handle any other required procedural steps. Basically, we had to pick up the scattered remnants of this surreal shitstorm. He chose to surrender, and now we must face our own surrender. Business, not as usual. We made the decision to not interfere with our daughter's afternoon interview that day, but rather we would meet her afterwards at our friend's home where she was to complete the housesitting job that evening. We would privately share with her the sorrow drenched truth, seeking any comfort and relief we might possibly share together in the torture of this tragedy. There would be no perfect guide to right choices and decisions in the bombshell bursting moments of this crushing new reality. Shrapnel is everywhere and some may even become deeply embedded. Following our intimate time with our daughter, we would respectfully share responsible duties together in notifying family, the bride and groom, friends, medical caregivers. All details would play out, get out, spill out, spread out, and we would then fall further down and out. Grief does not wait; it slaps you in the face, stabs you in the heart, and then remains a bruising pain during every breathe, following every breathe, and beyond every breathe. We would learn to live with it.

The police station conference room visit was a first, having managed to raise two children without an incident of trouble with the law, other than an adolescent moment of mischief and a teenage time of token warning, as in some teenage toke followed by some woke ass warning. The three of us sat around the boardroom sized table, with two officers seated directly across from us. We were informed where our son's body had been found early that morning, and we recognized the site description as a sentimental hangout destination for Zach and friends of high school yore, not much further beyond my frantic morning search. The questions continued as we were asked if there would be any reason for the officers to investigate homicide, we were asked if there were any clues, messages, or indications of suicide found in our home, and we were then advised to refrain from viewing our sons remains. We could choose to view, for certainly it was our right, but really, it would be wrong. Zach, John and I had spent much time together within clear view of each other in the past 24 hours. We had conversations, meals, games, medicinal treatments, and shared many an expression of healthy familial love. These touchpoints would stay forever fresh, forever gold, forever our final view. His sister, however, had not seen him since our family night on Sunday, four days ago, during our meal and movie night out. Her anticipated sibling time alone together on the upcoming trip would now be denied. Her future with her brother would now be denied. Any physical living view of her brother would also now be denied. John, Gabby, and I each held our own recent image and interaction with Zachary to carry forward in memory. But to be denied because of this sudden death, the opportunity to physically touch, laugh, converse, emote, and engage together again here on earth, these would be our deepest losses. The gift of his earthly presence would never be unwrapped and opened up again, nor would that of his future. We would be denied plenty. Pictures and memorabilia would offer a reminded visual, a recollection, a resurrected treasure, but the thriving viewpoints, the differing outlooks, and those purposeful actions and interactions of his would keep us longing and lonely throughout our remaining lives. Possibility had prevailed then. Honor whatever here and now of together time alive with loved ones available to you, for that is what creates lasting treasure in the sudden unexpected face of farewell. Unpredictability of our time together is a universal truth too often taken for granted. Savor that gift called the present. Clean your closets of conditioned constraints. Open your closed doors. A farewell might be final. Maybe we meet again in the afterlife. Savor the time and the talks and the treasures together in this gifted life.

In those immediate moments of accepting the news of Zach's death, it was excruciatingly painful to dare wonder what might have been his perspective in the impending final moments of self-directed death? We can only speculate from our own perspective, our own suspicions, our own ammunitions, and ammunition was perspective enough to not view his remains. When considering and valuing the officer recommendation to refrain from viewing our deceased son, my personal pain pulsed palpably at the mere thought of him alone at dusk, determined and directed toward enacting the death choice he felt he must carry out. Such deep despair and hopeless sorrow for no faith in a better tomorrow. The driven action to end his life stirred indescribable maternal ache permanently scarring my mournful motherly soul. Whether he had been in an altered state influenced by a combination of medications, side effects, and vacillating Lyme induced psychotic thoughts, or whether he had been clear as a whistle, blowing it loud and shrill as his defiance and life ending domination of the Lyme and symptoms, to leave life by choice had been initially quite unthinkable to me. The Zach I knew would not choose this, I firmly believe. But the Zach we had come to know post chronic Lyme and its incurable manifestations within him could and did. I couldn't believe it. I could believe it. Zach must have believed he could finally defeat those ticks in his head, leaning on the liquid courage and the 'at a man' Ativan to carry out this perceived act of freedom for himself. No one else could help us rid the bacteria from his brain and stop the constant thievery. He had no faith in it ever happening. Death was his middle finger held up to the disease. He stopped believing in the promise that someone or something could catch this sneaky thief and solve this credible crime. My rumbling, tumbling, ever so humbling self-absorbed sorrow finally surged up and spilled over, pouring forth the long preserved self-pity. I had restrained myself from revealing much of it while standing stoic beside my living son in search of effective weapons to employ in the tenacious tick borne illness battle. Self-pity oozed now, overflowing upon death's impact, previously silenced in battle by a fierce mother's hope shield but now confronted with a grown child's plummeting faith bullet. Love endured, but it was not enough to block that bullet's pierce. We had optimistically leaned into teaming with the LRA and the LLMD to ideally reclaim a life of freedom for our adult son. Exhibiting pity during those flaming faith and hope fires burning would only have extinguished valuable energy fueled up for the duration of our wellness pursuit. My personal pity party would now officially begin in the aftermath of my son's Lyme dosed death. Where does a Lyme patient find a legitimate longstanding recovery and cure? How many have to suffer before this is validated as a critical concern, rather than just cautionary conversations that all too often cultivate ignorance, oversight, and absence of medical ethics in such epic proportion? What will it take to commit accessible resources and provide credible promise and care to prevent these types of hopelessly driven personal choices by frustrated fighting warriors within this relentless battle of infectious disease? I am so weary from our fight, but my thoughts are not. From self-pity, to indignant outcry, to frustrating fury and yet all of it right now, for me, would motivate action and advocacy in no immediate hurry. I am/we are exhausted. I am/we are discouraged. My body and soul's grief pain recovery would take time before action responds to an advocacy driven mind. The wounded would need time to heal.

In response to the officer inquiries, John and I looked up from our hanging heads in that stark expanse of space. Through tear stained eyes, we were ever so tired of too many pathetic medical lies. We spoke clearly to the officers about Zach's legitimate enemy, his murderer as we saw it, the rhyme and reason for this beautiful young man to express ENOUGH, only to seek his own self-directed relief of personal pain exit design. "You do not need to investigate homicide, officer. Zach has been battling Lyme disease for two intense years. It has manifested in his brain in very frightening ways as well as throughout his body in equally destructive ways. He has been struggling with suicidal thoughts frequently throughout this mysterious battle. Some of his thoughts were possibly attributed to the disease working its destruction and thus there existed an accompanying sense of hopelessness to ever getting well. Some of these thoughts were attributed to the medicinal treatment side effects, well known to generate suicidal thoughts as symptomatic. Or perhaps it is a combination of these truths. We just don't know." We preached the Lyme story we had sadly come to know. We validated and spread the truth seeds we now willingly chose to sow. "It is an elusive disease, and treatment is challenging. At this stage of diagnosis and recovery work, we thought we had come to a fairly stabilized mental health point in treatment care. We knew the disease was taxing him, but John and I were caught off guard with this tragic outcome. There was no clue or indication at home." The two of us continued to explain through our blinding tears and quivering voices. We taught the Lyme story we had sadly come to know. We further validated and spread the truth seeds we now tragically must sow. But preach and teach were not fully necessary in this atypical review of the what and why to our son's farewell, following the how and where of the officer's investigation. A rare and sensitively timed intimate personal response to our lifeless loss and Lyme awareness lesson was received in return. This police officer's heart had been touched, and not just emotionally by our circumstances defined. John and I would never forget the kindness and the validation gifted to us, when upon listening, hearing and believing our shared message, the officer slowly, with a deliberately soft spoken delivery, offered up personal acknowledgment and affirmative response in return. "I am so sorry. I have a friend who suffers with Lyme and I understand it is so debilitating." That simple, honest, tender, straight forward, compassionate, two sentence response to us was not found in a single medical office other than with our devoted LLMD, Dr. Newman. We may have fought Lyme credibility throughout the short but intense life of this disease's affectation to our son's body and mind, but in death, we found Lyme brotherhood. Brotherhood had been something our son craved and missed for far too long in the neglected neighborhood of Lyme. Thank you, officer, for gifting it at his death's closing door. How blessed that your suffering friend has you in his or her or their corner, offering genuine compassion and credibility. Please help us fight this battle and redeem the dignity of so many who have been struggling far longer than our dear Zach. Please do not forget the story of our Zach. Let it power you further into lifting up the important, not to be neglected story of your own suffering friend, of the all too many 'Lyme trends' that our society chooses to defend, among the absurd denials that medical systems of power must begin to amend. Our newfound Lyme awake officer of tick borne brotherhood speaks up with another thoughtful intention. He plants the seed for an even greater *Sonflower* gift than the treasured validation moment, when he manages to explore a possibility we would never have thought of in that dour hour. "We have your son's cell phone here. Is it possible he would have left something for you on his phone? Perhaps a message or some other information? Do you happen to know his pass code?", he asks. "I do! I have been with him every day in treatment, and I can visually see him entering those four digits.", I animatedly share. The officer enters the digits, looks up, and responds to our hungered look of longing for more of our Zach. "There is an indication of an unread message.", he affirms. John immediately spoke up and looked directly at our friend Terri and the officers, requesting a private moment alone for the two of us. Zach's phone quite possibly hosts an unwrapped gift, ours alone to treasure and tell. Perhaps some light of greater understanding would be shed upon this darkness so withstanding. All oblige. John and I hold hands as we open up Zach's phone message to discover a family message left with Zach purpose and intention, his last rite of passage prayer. Emotions tremble between us before any words are read, before any message is received. Zach is alive in this final moment of family farewell.

Thank you, I love you, forgive me, I'm sorry.

Dad, you're the hardest working man I know. I respect your uniqueness and will miss our friendship. Thanks for everything!

Mom, forever my champion. Thank you for your everlasting love. I will miss your strength and spirit. Please forgive my lack of faith.

Gabby, remember the good times we shared. I've cherished our laughs and adventures. They are timeless. You were my best friend and I will deeply miss our bond.

I am sorry for the pain I've caused but all things will heal in time. Life has just become too painful and empty for me to continue faking it. I refuse to live a life void of luster. Too many rules to abide by too soon.

Please cremate my body and scatter my remains somewhere meaningful. Give my belongings to friends and family and remember the happy go lucky Zach of yore.

I love you all beyond compare. Your love will carry me into the cosmos. I love you!

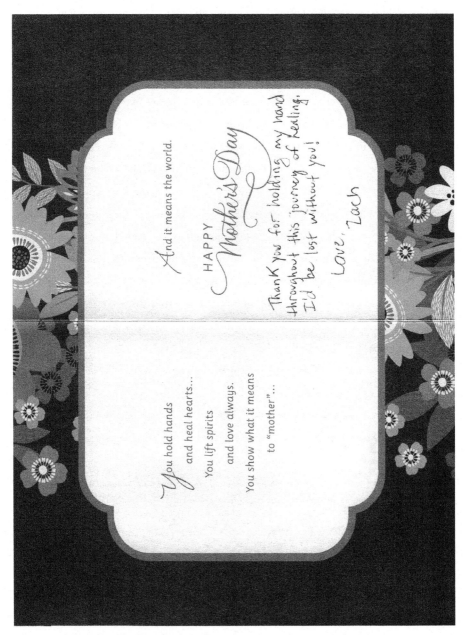

You hold hands
and heal hearts...
You lift spirits
and love always.
You show what it means
to "mother"...

And it means the world.

HAPPY
Mother's Day

Thank you for holding my hand
throughout this journey of healing.
I'd be lost without you!

Love, Zach

Insert 34 •   2015 Final Mother's Day message

Epilogue

Sunflower, The Weepies
Sunflower, Post Malone & Swae Lee

Five years have passed since our son Zachary took his life while in a Lyme/tick borne disease (TBD) battle. Our family faced an unfortunate life circumstance, confronted with trials unforeseen, illness never imagined, and a resulting grief from loss that now coexists in sorrowful symmetry. The loyal love and caregiving compassion consistently provided were not enough to conquer the infectious disease and its multiple complexities of lasting impact. We long for Zachary's presence and the abundance of his endearing attributes in our lives every day. Telling this story somehow keeps him alive as a beacon of caution, a bastion of strength, and a boost to the ever present cause. His young adult developing intentions were to serve a community, to find belonging, to help others heal. Thus, we grant him these graces.

Sonflower is a story told to honor a loved one lost, to advocate for individuals and families in circumstances familiar, to educate further about awareness of Lyme and tick borne disease, especially psychiatric Lyme, and to ideally inspire greater compassion and comforting inclusive care for the chronically ill. Following our loss, we memorialized Zach, we nurtured our souls, we worked on grief recovery, we rebuilt connections, we engaged in advocacy, we walked among our TBD peers, we stood among the suffering, we searched for suicide understanding, and we survived. Some of this work was done together as family, and much was done individually. Work, play, and rest were sought in balance for optimal long term healing measure. John, Gabby, and I continue to hone recovery practice and wellness balance, each of us with our own preference and priority. We mend deep wounds, rebuild family dynamics, nurture soul hunger, and welcome serendipitous grace amidst our surroundings, among our friends and family, and within our various communities. Laughter and music, fellowship and outreach, and even some spiritual peace find embrace again. We remain alert to Zach's presence among the living, keeping Zach very much alive within us. Blessed we were to have and to hold our precious son for 27 amazing years. From his day of farewell forward, he resides forevermore in our longing hearts and souls.

It is my sincere hope that as you read my story, you awaken to or further establish a personal commitment of practicing careful and cautionary preventative steps to avoid this complex disease. The bite of a bacteria transmitting tick can subject anyone to a neglectfully attended, underemphasized, and often misleadingly minimized risk of penetrating infection likely accompanied by long term illness complication. Unfortunately, the unexpected can happen, and consequences can be dramatically out of one's control. Especially, then, we must be compassionate and clear about guided care. The chronically ill often share a similarly shamed or silenced sickness of suffering and isolation. *Sonflower's* caregiving model of steadfast support and research readiness intends to include acknowledgement of these community health pockets of pain as well. My story, however, speaks its lived truth particularly on behalf of the Lyme/TBD community, most specifically in the transparent and telling details of psychiatric presentation. My message encourages an emphasis on attentive action toward the vulnerable core of the chronically ill, toward the valued care of someone's illness credibility too often challenged, and toward a viable pathway to comfort and cure from that unpredictable, unsuspecting health crisis that suddenly surfaces amidst or among any one of us.

Sonflower's initial draft included additional chapters that explored and addressed outcomes and experiences beyond our son's death, some of which are mentioned above. Honoring personal instinct and professional recommendation, these additional chapters were separated into a simpler sequel body of work nearing completion. This separation allowed the *Sonflower* book to offer its own seed germination, its own memorializing impact of influence. *Sonflower Harvest,* the sequel book, thus serves to bridge the palliative gall of the memoir ending to an eventual peaceful acceptance of such painful past. A purposeful present holds promise, and a foundation for the future is again foreseeable. While *Sonflower* delivers its narrative truth through various themes such as belonging and inclusion vs. loneliness and isolation, and purposeful, intentional living vs. relentless struggle to deter dying, *Sonflower Harvest* delivers from the perspective of the forest for the trees. The sequel tills the bigger picture of outcome influence and meaningful significance.

What happened beyond Zach's death? How would our family heal? What healing tools and resources proved invaluable? How and why would we choose to champion and what might that entail? What harvest would we reap from the story of *Sonflower* to plant thoughtfully forward in rebound and restitution from such loss? The sequel following death addresses many questions, while the rebirth of our lives beyond the death address reveals most answers. I encourage you to share *Sonflower's* narrative, harvesting conversations, considerations, and a developed constitution of humbled humanity toward such heartbreaking tick borne disease healthcare hindrance. May the story seed greater wisdom, expectation, and action. Please, tell the vital stories of the living and the dying; share the varied struggles of the healing and the trying. For each story's seed is a precious start and each message matters. Let the seeds be planted. Help our knowledge garden grow.

Appendix A: Chapter Inserts

Chapter 2: Hoop Dreams

- 2006 June high school poem "Don't Stare at the Tall People"
- 2006 High school graduation note to parents
- 2007 BSU basketball
- 2008 Family holiday card
- 2007 Modest Mouse tattooed lyric
- 2009 'The Buff Mob' poem
- 2010 Father's birthday message
- 2011 BSU basketball
- 2011 Mother's Day message
- 2011 College graduation with parents at BSU

Chapter 3: ADHD

- 2010 Idaho summer on the dock
- 2011 Vancouver Volcano IBL summer season
- 2011 Father's Day and birthday message with ADHD poem

Chapter 4: Z in Zamora

- 2011 Zamora Zach in uniform
- 2011 Mother's birthday message
- 2012 'The Burning House' by Zach Moritz

Chapter 5: Hello TM, Farewell MM

- 2012 Personal list of dreams and goals
- 2012 Bubba grandmother tribute

Chapter 7: SISU Season One

- 2012 Copenhagen Zach in uniform

Chapter 8: Pink Martini

- 2012 Mother's birthday card message

Chapter 10: Quest for Purpose

- 2013 Father's Day card message

Chapter 12: SISU Season Two

- 2013 Copenhagen basketball

Chapter 13: Bound for a Rebound

- 2013 Mother's birthday card message

Chapter 16: Rescue Mission, Iowa

- 2014 Easter Sunday PDX return

Chapter 18: Bi-Polar Blip

- 2014, June, E&T document

Chapter 19: Kundalini or Spiritual Emergency?

- 2014 Zach with Baby T

Chapter 20: Fall Back Panic Attack

- 2014, October, E&T document

Chapter 21: Bull's Eye!

- 2014, October, Lyme checklist Pages 1 & 2

Chapter 22: Holiday Hostage

- 2014, December. E&T document

Chapter 23: Bridge to Recovery Road

- 2015 Lyme symptom notes
- 2015 January Super Bowl pizza

Chapter 24: LRA: Lyme Routines of Adversity

- 2015 Lyme medications spreadsheet list
- 2015 Lyme meds

Chapter 25: LLMD: Lyme Literate Mental Disturbances

- 2015 Final Tattoo

Chapter 26: Three Weddings

- 2015 Siblings at Arizona wedding

Chapter 27: A Farewell

- 2015 Final Mother's Day message

Appendix B: Chapter Song List

Part One: Action

Chapter 1: Tick Tock, Therapy Shock

- *Knockin' on Heaven's Door*, Bob Dylan
- *Mercy Mercy Me*, Marvin Gaye

Part Two: Adolescence

Chapter 2: Hoop Dreams

- *Empire State Human*, Human League
- *Move On Up*, Curtis Mayfield

Chapter 3: ADHD

- *ADHD*, Truslow
- *Teach Your Children Well*, Crosby, Stills, Nash & Young

Chapter 4: Z in Zamora

- *Spanish Caravan*, The Doors
- *Alive and Well*, Big Little Lions

Chapter 5: Hello TM, Farewell MM

- *Transcendental Highway*, Colin Hay
- *Let It Be*, The Beatles

Chapter 6: Why-oming?

- *Nature Boy*, Nat King Cole
- *On the Road Again*, Willie Nelson

Chapter 7: SISU Season One

- *Copenhagen*, Tina Dickow
- *Find Your Tribe*, Big Little Lions

Chapter 8: Pink Martini

- *Happy Birthday*, Altered Images
- *Splendor in the Grass*, Pink Martini

Chapter 27: A Farewell

- *I Think I'll Call It Morning*, Gil Scott Heron
- *Keep Me in Your Heart*, Warren Zevon

Epilogue

- *Sunflower*, The Weepies
- *Sunflower*, Post Malone & Swae Le

Bibliography

Chapter 1: Tick Tock, Therapy Shock

- Tolle, Eckhart. The Power of Now: A Guide to Spiritual Enlightenment. Vancouver, B.C. Namaste Publishing. 1999.

Chapter 3: ADHD

- Hallowell, Edward M., and John J. Ratey. Delivered from Distraction: Getting the Most Out of Life with Attention Deficit Disorder. New York. Ballantine Books. 2005.

Chapter 5: Hello TM, Farewell MM

- Rosenthal, Norman E. Transcendence: Healing and Transformation through Transcendental Meditation. Penguin Group (USA) Inc. New York. 2011.

Chapter 10: Quest for Purpose

- The School of Lost Borders. Big Pine, CA. 2013. http://www.schooloflostborders.org/term/youth-programs.

Chapter 14: MUM's the Word

- Malloy, Ed, and Candace Badgett. *"Rush Hour in Fairfield, Iowa"*. Interview with Oprah Winfrey, Oprah's Next Chapter. OWN. Fairfield, Iowa. March 27, 2012. https://www.oprah.com/own-oprahs-next-chapter/rush-hour-in-fairfield-iowa-video.

Chapter 15: Reawakening in Iowa

- Williams, Pharrell. *"On Writing Happy"*. Interview by Oprah Winfrey on Oprah Prime. April 13, 2014. https://www.oprah.com/own-oprahprime/pharrell-williams-on-writing-happy-video.

Chapter 16: Rescue Mission, Iowa

- Perlmutter, David, with Kristin Loberg. Grain Brain. New York. Little, Brown and Company of Hatchette Book Group. 2013.

Chapter 17: Home Front Hellth

- Bolles, Richard N. What Color is Your Parachute? A Practical Manual for Job-Hunters & Career Changes. Berkeley, California. Ten Speed Press. 2014 edition.

Chapter 18: Bi-Polar Blip?

- Family Medical Leave Act of 1993 (FMLA). H.R. 1. 103rd Cong. https://www.dolgov/agencies/whd/fmla.

- National Alliance on Mental Illness (NAMI). https://www.nami.org.

- Patient Protection and Affordable Care Act (ACA). H.R.3590. 111th Cong. https://www.obamacareusa.org/affordable-care.

- Thomson Reuters Westlaw. Washington Civil Jury Instructions. *"WPI360.12 Gravely Disabled-Mental Illness-Definition"*. https://govt.westlaw.com. 2014.

Chapter 19: Kundalini or Spiritual Emergency?

- Amador, Xavier. I AM NOT SICK: I Don't Need Help. New York. Vida Press. 2010.

- Cornwall, Michael. *"What is Madness"*. https://michaelcornwall.com.

- Grof, Stanislav, and Christina Grof. Spiritual Emergency: When Personal Transformation Becomes a Crisis. New York. Penguin Putnam. 1989.

- Sannella, Lee. The Kundalini Experience. California. Integral Publishing. 1987.

Chapter 20: Fall Back, Panic Attack

- Indy Bay Media. Icarus Project SF. May 2013. https://www.indybay.org/newsitems/2013/05/22/18737245.php.

- Total Health Institute. Bay Area Mandala Project. 1987. https://www.bayareamandalaproject.org.

Chapter 21: Bull's Eye!

- Bain, Julie. *"Scary Superbugs in the News-Are You at Risk?"*. **AARP** The Magazine. October/November 2014.

- Burrascano, Joseph J. Jr. *"Advanced Topics in Lyme Disease: Diagnostic Hints and Treatment Guidelines for Lyme and Other Tick Borne Illnesses"*. October, 2008. 16th Edition. https://www.lymenet.org/BurrGuide200810.pdf.

- Center for Disease Control and Prevention (CDC). Division of Vector-Borne Diseases. *"Two-Tiered Testing for Lyme Disease"*. November, 2011. https://www.cdc.gov/lyme/healthcare/clinician_twotier.html.

- Dubrey SW, Bhatia A, Woodham S et al. *"Lyme Disease in the United Kingdom"*. Postgraduate Medical Journal, 2014. 90:33-42. https://www.pubmed.ncbi.nlm.nih.gov.

- Edelstein, Ludwig. The **Hippocratic Oath**: Text, Translation, and Interpretation. Baltimore. The John Hopkins Press. 1943.

- Holtorf, Kent. *"Lyme Disease and Psychiatric Disorders"*. Holtorf Medical Group. March 21, 2013. https://www.holtorfmed.com/lymedisease-psychiatricdisorders.

- Infectious Diseases Society of America (IDSA). https://www.idsociety.org.

- International Lyme and Associated Diseases Society (ILADS). https://www.ilads.org.

- Strasheim, Connie. Insights into Lyme Disease Treatment. CA. BioMed Publishing Group. 2009.

- *'Under Our Skin'* documentary. Wilson, Andy Abrahams. Blumenthal R, Burgdorfer W, Goozner M, Hughes M, Hughes S, Walsh D. IMDbPro. June 19, 2009.

- Weintraub, Pamela. Cure Unknown: Inside the Lyme Epidemic. New York. St. Martin's Griffin. 2013 Revised Edition.

- Yerges, Karen and Rita Stanley. Confronting Lyme Disease: What Patients Stories Teach Us. Oregon. 2005.

Chapter 22: Holiday Hostage

- IGeneX. Medical Testing Laboratory. California. https://igenex.com.

Chapter 23: Bridge to Recovery Road

- Burrascano, Joseph J. Jr. *"Advanced Topics in Lyme Disease"*. Pgs.9-10. https://www.lymenet.org/BurrGuide200810.pdf.

Chapter 25: LLMD: Lyme Literate Mental Disturbances

- Doucet, J. *"Targeting Lyme Disease"*. The Costco Connection. May/June 2015. Pg 43.

- Tan, Amy. *"Slyme Disease: How a Speck Changed My Life Forever"*. Humanthology. September 9, 2014. https://www.humanthology.com/lyme-disease/2014/9/15.

Made in the USA
Monee, IL
05 December 2020

50947544R00203